INTRODUCTION	ELIMINATION

ΠI

$$\varphi(\beta)$$
$$\therefore \; \prod_\alpha \varphi(\alpha)$$

Where β does not occur free in any premise or undischarged assumption, and where $\varphi(\beta)$ is like $\varphi(\alpha)$ except for containing free occurrences of β where, and only where, $\varphi(\alpha)$ contains free occurrences of α.

ΠE

$$\prod_\alpha \varphi(\alpha)$$
$$\therefore \; \varphi(\beta)$$

Where $\varphi(\beta)$ is like $\varphi(\alpha)$ except for containing free occurrences of β wherever $\varphi(\alpha)$ contains free occurrences of α.

ΣI

$$\varphi(\beta)$$
$$\therefore \; \sum_\alpha \varphi(\alpha)$$

Where $\varphi(\beta)$ is like $\varphi(\alpha)$ except for containing free occurrences of β wherever $\varphi(\alpha)$ contains free occurrences of α.

ΣE

$$\sum_\alpha \varphi(\alpha)$$
$$\varphi(\beta)$$
$$\vdots$$
$$\psi$$
$$\therefore \; \psi$$

Where there is no free β in ψ; where β does not occur free in any premise or undischarged assumption; and where $\varphi(\beta)$ is like $\varphi(\alpha)$ except for containing free occurrences of β where, and only where, $\varphi(\alpha)$ contains free occurrences of α.

NATURAL

DEDUCTION

Date Due

MAR 4 1965		
JAN 1 9 1968		
DEC 1 3 1968		
JAN 1 7 1969		
DEC 8 0 1974		

NATURAL

DEDUCTION

The Logical Basis of Axiom Systems

John M. Anderson

and

Henry W. Johnstone, Jr.

The Pennsylvania State University

WADSWORTH PUBLISHING COMPANY, INC.

Belmont, California

L.C. Cat. Card No.: 62–11239
Printed in the United States of America

PREFACE

This book is based upon Gentzen's techniques of natural deduction. The propositional and quantificational rules on which the exposition pivots are stated essentially as Gentzen stated them, and even the names used for them are free translations of his names. Gentzen's techniques constitute a very natural approach to the study of the proofs occurring in axiom systems as well as a sound basis for the analysis of the properties of formal systems as such.

The book is divided into two main parts. In Part One various rules and sets of rules for deduction are presented. Part Two is largely concerned with the metatheoretical analysis of deductions based upon these rules.

Part One begins with a chapter in which a simple set of axioms (those for simple order) is presented and attention is called to the use of logical rules in the deduction of theorems from these axioms. In Chapter Two all the standard propositional rules are given. Here one of the great merits of Gentzen's formulation is obvious: it permits the analysis of proof in an axiom system without presupposing another axiom system—namely, that of the logic itself. The power of this formulation is revealed in the early use of conditional proof, here introduced, of course, as a primitive rule. The analysis of negation into four rules reveals something of its nature and facilitates transition in a later chapter to the intuitionistic logic.

Chapter Three temporarily sets aside the basic exposition of the nature of deduction in an axiom system in order to introduce truth tables and normal forms. This material not only serves the science student interested in computers, but also lays the ground for later metatheoretical discussions. Chapter Four is intended to suggest that the problem of what constitutes a deduction is by no means closed, for alternative logical systems such as those of three-valued logic, intuitionistic logic, and modal logics are available and may be used.

Chapter Five is occupied with the explicit development of monadic predicate logic. The rigorous statement of the rules of predicate logic in a form in which they lead, in Chapter Six, to a final justification for the steps in deductions within first order axiom systems returns the reader to the fundamental problem of axiomatic proof. Chapter Seven introduces the concepts of identity and description, thus completing a standard first course in modern logic.

Part Two is concerned with the properties of deductions in axiom systems. In Chapter Eight the problems of metatheory are introduced on the basis of a distinction between the traditional axiom system of geometry regarded as a description of space and modern abstract axiom systems. This distinction makes clear the need for tests of consistency and completeness not dependent on the literal truth of the theorems. The use of models in such tests is described, and it is pointed out that this use establishes consistency relative to the model. The student is thus led to see the need for metatheoretical methods capable of establishing absolute consistency.

In Chapter Nine the concept of a formal system is developed and meta-theoretical proofs of the absolute consistency and completeness of the propositional rules are presented. Techniques used here are applied in Chapter Ten to monadic predicate logic, for which several decision procedures are also sketched. Chapter Eleven contains a further application of metatheoretical techniques to general predicate logic. Henkin's completeness proof is given in this chapter.

The difficult problems and apparent limitations of the axiomatic method are introduced through the contradictions and paradoxes of set theory. Chapter Twelve is an elementary account of the operations on sets and the relation of set theory to logic and to mathematics. The reader already acquainted with the rudiments of set theory might skip this chapter. In Chapter Thirteen some of the contradictions and paradoxes of set theory are presented, and various attempts to deal with the problems raised are discussed: Zermelo's axiomatization, Russell's theory of types, Brouwer's intuitionism, and Hilbert's formalism.

This book can be used in logic courses in many ways. Used in its entirety it serves as the text of a year's course in intermediate logic, or of an intensive semester's course for students with mathematical background. Part One alone constitutes the basis for a course in the techniques of deduction. Many teachers giving such a course, however, will probably prefer to omit some sections or chapters in Part One and include some of the metatheoretical material of Part Two. Perhaps the clearest way to indicate what selections are possible is to say that Chapter Six presupposes Chapter Five, which in turn presupposes Chapter Two; and that chapter Eleven presupposes Chapter Ten, which in turn presupposes Chapter Nine, but all the other chapters can be read more or less independently by a student having some familiarity with logic since only fundamental concepts are presupposed in them.

The authors wish to acknowledge with gratitude the help of a number of anonymous publishers' readers whose criticism has been most constructive. Among those critics that they can name they would like to thank Professor Haskell B. Curry whose work on Gentzen's systems is well known; Professor Edward J. Cogan, who has read several drafts of the manuscript and has made valuable suggestions; and Dr. Robert Price, who has also given us considerable help, partly as a consequence of having used the manuscript as a textbook in a course in logic. To Mr. William J. Coe and Mr. John Kozy, Jr., we are indebted for much work on the exercises and for correcting a number of drafts of the manuscript. The index was prepared by Miss Margaret A. Mitchell. Messrs. Laurie W. Cameron, Gerald E. Rubin, James C. Morrison, and Bernard M. Goldsmith have given substantial help with proofreading. Miss Joan Lee has performed with distinction the difficult and arduous task of typing the manuscript. For financial assistance at all stages of our work on this book we are grateful to the Central Fund for Research of The Pennsylvania State University.

J. M. A.
H. W. J., Jr.

University Park, Pennsylvania

CONTENTS

Part One

Introduction to Logic

Part Two

Introduction to Metatheory

Part One

Introduction to Logic

Chapter 1

Proof and Rules of Inference

1.1 Introduction

One way of beginning the study of logic is to consider the role it plays in proof. In general, we *prove* an assertion when we show that it is the consequence of other assertions that have already been either explicitly accepted or implicitly assumed. Thus, if Brown is asked to prove that he is an American citizen, he may produce a birth certificate showing that he was born in Narberth, Pennsylvania. This proof involves many assumptions, some of which might be expressed as follows:

Anyone born in the U.S.A. who has not renounced his American citizenship is an American citizen.

Anyone born in Narberth, Pennsylvania, was born in the U.S.A.

Anyone possessing a duly witnessed birth certificate certifying that he was born in a certain place was born in that place.

Brown possesses a duly witnessed birth certificate certifying that he was born in Narberth, Pennsylvania.

Brown has not renounced his American citizenship.

The statement that Brown is an American citizen is a consequence of all these statements at least. Of course, one might wish to question some or all of these assumptions. It might be pointed out, for example, that forged birth certificates are possible. When the assumptions upon which a proof rests are questioned, the status of the proof itself is brought into question. In any event, we cannot prove everything. Fortunately, we do not always need to. For there are areas of knowledge in which it is just not to the point to question the assumptions involved in proof. Axiomatic systems are an example. Aristotle long ago pointed out that those who question the assumptions of geometry are not engaged in geometry, but in some other inquiry.* One reason why mathematical proofs can be rigorous is that the question of the truth or falsity of the assumptions on which they rest usually does not arise, and when it does arise, it falls outside the scope of the axiom systems themselves. Thus, although proofs and alleged proofs do in fact occur in many areas, it is perhaps with the axiom systems of mathematics that the idea of proof is most commonly associated. A mathematical assertion is proved by exhibiting it as the consequence of assumptions. Thus if we assume that $x(y + z) = xy + xz$, we can prove that $x[(y + z) + w] = (xy + xz) + xw$; for

$$x[(y + z) + w] = x(y + z) + xw, \text{ by our assumption}$$
$$= (xy + xz) + xw, \text{ using the assumption again.}$$

Mathematical assumptions are often called *axioms* or *postulates*. As they were originally used, these words had distinct meanings. An axiom was a truth regarded as common to several areas of enquiry, whereas a postulate was an assumption peculiar to a single area, such as geometry. But this distinction is no longer made, and we shall follow modern practice in using the words "axiom" and "postulate" interchangeably, with emphasis on the former.

Common as the conception of a proof from axioms is in mathematics, it is important to remember that this idea had to be discovered and developed. Even geometry has not always been axiomatized. The geometry of the Egyptians and Babylonians consisted of little more than assertions based upon the empirical observation of spatial relationships; *e.g.*, that a right triangle can be constructed of ropes which are 3, 4, and 5 units long respectively. After several thousand years, this body of practical information came to the attention of the Greeks, who, in about the seventh century B.C., began to formulate sets of related geometrical assertions in such a way that some of the assertions were exhibited as consequences of others, and thus no longer needed to be confirmed by observation. Pythagoras' proof of the famous theorem named after him is one of the most striking achievements of this period. (*One* of the particular consequences of this theorem is that ropes 3, 4, and 5 units long form a right triangle.) It was not until the fourth century B.C., however, that Euclid was able to organize the entire body of geometrical information then available into a system comprising chains of consequences deduced from a small set of more or less clearly stated axioms. A similar account could also be given of the development of axiom systems

---

* *Physics* 184^b 25–185^a 4

in other areas of mathematics or, for that matter, in the theoretical sciences such as physics. Such systematization is usually a relatively late development in the history of a field.

Although the technique of axiomatizing an area of mathematics was discovered by Euclid early in Western intellectual history, this technique was not extended to arithmetic and analysis, for example, until the end of the nineteenth century. Indeed, modern intellectual history is even more influenced by the idea of an axiom system than was the Greek age of Euclid and Aristotle. Today axiomatization is a method used in all parts of mathematics, in the natural sciences and, more astonishingly, in biology, economics, and sociology as well.* What is the appeal of an achievement such as Euclid's? No doubt we are struck by the power and beauty of such a synoptic vision of geometrical relationships. But perhaps what most attracts the mathematician is the fact that a completely axiomatized geometry minimizes the need for geometrical intuition. A relatively small number of assumptions can be made to carry the weight of all the theorems which can be deduced from them, and the steps of these deductions can be made very simple and extremely clear. The result is a geometry that can be taught easily, since anyone can check every step. These advantages hold not alone for geometry, but for any area that can be axiomatized. As soon as we use this technique, we are able to state in the briefest possible form the needed fundamental assumptions (the axioms) and to offer proof of statements (the theorems) that follow from these axioms. Further, we are able to present proofs of these theorems in terms of finite series of simple steps rendering the acceptability of these theorems beyond ordinary questioning.

The advantages of axiomatization are great enough to warrant the enthusiasm of its ancient and modern advocates, but those advantages demand a close study. We must be sure that we understand such a powerful method lest the hope of coherent organization, clarity, ease of communication, and rigor in all areas of knowledge blind us to the problems and difficulties inherent in its use. One purpose of this book is to introduce the reader to the study of the axiomatic method, a method he is sure to use at many points in his professional and intellectual career. We begin this study in Part One not with the nature of undefined terms and axioms but with the ways in which proofs can be analyzed into a finite number of deductive steps and with the rules of inference that justify these steps. Certainly one of the most interesting and important characteristics of axiom systems is the way in which theorems are proved. In Part Two we shall discuss the nature of undefined terms and axioms, and consider the properties of axiom systems as a whole.

---

* See J. H. Woodger, *The Technique of Theory Construction* (Chicago: University of Chicago Press, 1939).

1.2   An Example of an Axiom System: Simple Order

If we formulate an area of knowledge in terms of postulates or axioms, we can rigorously prove the other statements that follow from these axioms. In fact, we can exhibit any such proof as a series of steps, each of which is justified by a rule of inference. Take for example the ordering relation of the natural numbers or that of any other set of entities a, b, c, ... such that a is less than b, b is less than c, and so on. Intuitively, we know a great deal about such order. If we like, though, we can state certain axioms for this ordering and exhibit the knowledge we have as a body of consequences of our assumptions.

The axioms that are ordinarily used to articulate this order are the following:

Ax. 1   If a and b are distinct, then $a < b$ or $b < a$.

Ax. 2   If $a < b$, then a and b are distinct.

Ax. 3   If $a < b$ and $b < c$, then $a < c$.

Here $<$ symbolizes the familiar relation *is less than*.

On the basis of these axioms, we can readily prove the theorem

> *1.1*   It cannot be the case that $a < a$.

For if we substitute a for b throughout Ax. 2, we obtain

> If $a < a$, then a and a are distinct.

But to say that a and a are distinct is clearly absurd; so it follows that $a < a$ cannot be true.

Logic is involved in the proof of this theorem in two ways. In the first place, it is what authorizes the substitution of a for b throughout Ax. 2. Any reader acquainted with mathematics knows how frequently such substitutions are essential to proofs. Oddly enough, the precise formulation of the logical principle in question requires considerable sophistication. We shall not be able to formulate it before we reach Chapter Five.* It is best to leave the matter for the present, and focus attention on a second logical principle used here which is, fortunately, much more readily stated. This is the principle that authorizes the move from the premises:

> If $a < a$, then a and a are distinct

and

> To say that a and a are distinct is absurd

to the conclusion

> It cannot be the case that $a < a$.

Notice in the first place that we are using somewhat more flamboyant

---

* This principle is not to be confused with a Rule of Substitution to be stated in Section 2.7.

language than we need to when we characterize "*a* and *a* are distinct" as an *absurd* statement. It would certainly be sufficient to characterize it as *false*, for the falsity of $a < a$ would still follow. It would follow in precisely the same way as would each of these conclusions:

> If it is before eleven o'clock, the library is open.
> The library is not open.
>
> *Conclusion*: It is not before eleven o'clock.

> If the earth is flat, it has an edge.
> The earth has no edge.
>
> *Conclusion*: The earth is not flat.

All three arguments have exactly the same pattern, which can be expressed

> If A, then B.
> Not B.
>
> *Conclusion*: not A.

Here for A and B one could substitute sentences like "It is before eleven o'clock", "The earth is flat", $a < a$, and so on.

The pattern we have just exhibited illustrates a fundamental logical rule which is frequently appealed to in all domains in which arguments and proofs occur. This rule is generally identified by the Latin phrase *Modus Tollens*.* We shall use the abbreviation MT. Now, using some symbols that are almost self-explanatory, we can write

MT $A \supset B$
Instance† $\sim B$
                $\therefore \sim A$

Obviously, $A \supset B$ must mean "If A, then B". Any statement of this form is said to be a *conditional statement*, or, more simply, a *conditional*. In a conditional, the statement to the left of the $\supset$ is called the *antecedent*; that to the right is called the *consequent*. MT is the rule that when you add to a conditional premise the further premise that the consequent of the conditional is not the case, you can obtain the conclusion that the antecedent of the conditional is not the case.

The *converse* of a conditional is the result of interchanging the antecedent and consequent. Thus the converse of $A \supset B$ is $B \supset A$.

---

* The full name of this pattern is *modus tollendo tollens*; *i.e.*, argument that denies by denying. This refers to the fact that in this argument we obtain a conclusion that is a denial by using a second premise that is a denial. But this is a point in traditional logic that is really irrelevant to this book.

† The qualifying word "Instance" is used here because, as we shall see when we reach Section Two of Chapter Two, the rule stated above is not MT in its fullest generality, but only an instance of it.

As to ∼B, this means "not B", "it is not the case that B", or "B is false", or words to this effect. Thus ∼(a < a) means "a is not less than a", or "it cannot be the case that (a < a)" or "(a < a) cannot be true". The statement ∼(A ⊃ B) means "it is not the case that A ⊃ B". The student should resist the temptation to "multiply through" by ∼: ∼(A ⊃ B) is not equivalent with ∼A ⊃ B, or even with A ⊃ ∼B. On the other hand, ∼B ⊃ ∼A, which is called the *contrapositive* of A ⊃ B, is equivalent with A ⊃ B. The contrapositive of any conditional is a second conditional having as its antecedent the denial of the consequent of the first and having as its consequent the denial of the antecedent of the first.

Returning to our theorem, we can write

1. (a < a) ⊃ (a and a are distinct)

2. ∼(a and a are distinct)

3. ∼(a < a)   1, 2, MT

We write "1, 2, MT" next to the conclusion to indicate that this conclusion is reached as a result of lines 1 and 2 and the logical rule MT.

It is customary to represent the distinctness of *a* and *b* by saying that $a \neq b$; *i.e.*, *a* is not identical with *b*. Using our new notation, we can also write this as ∼(a = b). Accordingly, we can now refine the step in the theorem we are now examining by writing

1. (a < a) ⊃ ∼(a = a)

2. ∼∼(a = a)

3. ∼(a < a)   1, 2, MT

The repeated ∼ draws our attention to line 2. This line evidently means the same as a = a, for there is clearly a logical principle to the effect that whatever statement A may be, A is equivalent with ∼∼A. This is called the *Law of Double Negation*. In this book we shall find it convenient to break this law down into two rules:

∼∼I	A
Instance	∴ ∼∼A
∼∼E	∼∼A
Instance	∴ A

Here ∼∼I means *Double Negation Introduction*; *i.e.*, the rule that permits us to move from a premise to the double negative of that premise. Similarly, ∼∼E means *Double Negation Elimination*. ∼∼I and ∼∼E are rules on exactly the same footing as MT.

Perhaps, then, the most natural way to think of ∼∼(a = a) is as a conclusion reached by applying ∼∼I to the premise a = a. But what of the premise itself? Although it does not appear among the axioms so far listed, it is surely one of the assumptions upon which this proof rests. Accordingly, we must add it to the list of axioms:

Ax. 4 $a = a$

In listing Ax. 4 we go beyond customary mathematical practice. We do this only because, for the moment, we are being far more rigorous about the steps involved in mathematical reasoning than the mathematician himself usually is. But it is precisely this rigor that brings logic into focus.

Let us now restate the proof of Th. 1.1:

1. $(a < b) \supset \sim(a = b)$ Ax. 2
2. $(a < a) \supset \sim(a = a)$ From Ax. 2 by substitution
3. $a = a$ Ax. 4
4. $\sim\sim(a = a)$ 3, $\sim\sim$I
5. $\sim(a < a)$ 2, 4, MT

Notice how each line is justified either by indicating its status as an axiom or by showing how it is derived from previous lines by a rule of inference.

We now turn to the proof of a second theorem.

1.2 $(a < b) \supset \sim(b < a)$

The proof of Th. 1.2 rests on the fact that if we assume $a < b$ and assume $b < a$, this leads, by Ax. 3, to $a < a$, which we have just demonstrated to be false. Therefore *if* we assume $a < b$ we can *not* at the same time assume $b < a$; i.e., if $a < b$, then $b < a$ is *false*.

Let us look at the logical structure of this proof all at once, and afterwards discuss the steps one by one:

1. $[(a < b)\ \&\ (b < c)] \supset (a < c)$ Ax. 3
2. $[(a < b)\ \&\ (b < a)] \supset (a < a)$ From Ax. 3 by substitution of a for c

First assumption —— 3. $a < b$
Second assumption — 4. $b < a$
5. $(a < b)\ \&\ (b < a)$ 3, 4, &I
6. $a < a$ 2, 5, $\supset$E
7. $\sim(a < a)$ Th. 1.1
8. $(a < a)\ \&\ \sim(a < a)$ 6, 7, &I

9. $\sim(b < a)$ 4-8, $\sim$I

10. $(a < b) \supset \sim(b < a)$ 3-9, $\supset$I

There are many new rules and procedures to be noted here. Indeed, the only logical principle that is now familiar is the one giving rise to line 2, which we are not going to discuss until Chapter Five. Notice the use of the symbol & in lines 1 and 2. Obviously, this means "and". It also occurs in lines 5 and 8.

Lines 3 and 4 contain the assumptions we make in the order in which we make them. First we assume that $a < b$, and then we see whether at the same time we can assume $b < a$. But line 8 tells us that if, having assumed $a < b$, we also try to assume $b < a$, we run into a contradiction, so that $b < a$ must be false, as we are told in line 9. The outer path, leading from the left of line 3 to below line 9, indicates that having assumed $a < b$, we must conclude $\sim(b < a)$. The inner path, leading from the left of line 4 to below line 8, shows why this is so; for it says that having assumed $b < a$ in the face of the first assumption that $a < b$, we must conclude $(a < a)$ & $\sim(a < a)$, which is a contradiction; *i.e.*, we could *not* assume $b < a$; *i.e.*, $b < a$ must be false if we have already assumed $a < b$.

Now for some details. Line 5 uses the logical rule of &I, or *And-Introduction* to form $(a < b)$ & $(b < a)$ from the two constituents $a < b$ and $b < a$. In general, where A and B are statements, we have

&I	A
Instance	B
	$\therefore$ A & B

The compound statement A & B is called a *conjunction*, and its constituents— the A and the B—are called *conjuncts*. Notice that the antecedent of line 1 and the antecedent of line 2 are both conjunctions. It does not seem necessary to dwell further upon &I. Another example of it is provided by line 8.

Look now at line 6. This is the consequent of line 2. We have derived it by being in a position to assert the antecedent of line 2. Generalizing, we may say that whenever a conditional and its antecedent can both be asserted, the consequent of the conditional follows as a conclusion. This is the rule of $\supset$ E, or *Conditional Elimination.** Thus:

$\supset$ **E**	A $\supset$ B
Instance	A
	$\therefore$ B

Another use would be in

It is before eleven o'clock $\supset$ the library is open.

It is before eleven o'clock.

$\therefore$ The library is open.

---

* The traditional name for this rule was *modus ponens*—more precisely *modus ponendo ponens*, an argument that asserts by asserting.

This is one of the most fundamental rules governing argument and proof. Its name arises from the fact that the $\supset$ in one premise does not appear in the conclusion. (Of course, $\supset$ E is not the only way in which a conditional can be eliminated; MT, for instance, is also a way.)

Line 7 simply recalls Th. 1.1. Line 8 uses &I to combine that with line 6 to form the self-contradictory statement $(a < a)$ & $\sim(a < a)$.

Look now at line 9. This results from an application of one of the most powerful techniques of mathematical proof; *i.e.*, the technique of *reductio ad absurdum*, or *indirect proof*. The guiding principle of this technique is the rule that whatever assumption gives rise to a self-contradictory statement is false. This is the rule of *Negation-Introduction*, $\sim$I:

$\sim$I
Instance

$$\boxed{\quad\text{Assumption}\!-\!\text{A} \\ \vdots \\ \text{B \& } \sim\text{B}\quad}$$

$$\therefore \sim\text{A}$$

Notice the assumption involved here to the effect that every self-contradictory statement might be expressed in the form B & $\sim$B. Later we shall see what justification there is for this assumption.

This brings us to the final line. The rule of $\supset$I appealed to here is that whenever, having assumed A, we must conclude B, we can write A $\supset$ B.

$\supset$I
Instance

$$\boxed{\quad\text{Assumption}\!-\!\text{A} \\ \vdots \\ \text{B}\quad}$$

$$\therefore \text{A} \supset \text{B}$$

In practice, we use the rule of $\supset$I so instinctively that a formal statement of it seems irritatingly trivial. In point of fact, $\supset$I is no more trivial than any of the other rules. Indeed, in some logical systems proofs of it are given.

We use $\supset$ I, then, to proceed from the observation that *having assumed $a < b$ we must conclude* $\sim(b < a)$ to the new conclusion $(a < b) \supset \sim(b < a)$.

We shall turn now to one further theorem:

1.3 $$(a = b) \equiv [\sim(a < b) \,\&\, \sim(b < a)]$$

This theorem is in the form of a *biconditional statement*, or, more simply, a *biconditional*. In general, the biconditional statement A $\equiv$ B means $(A \supset B)$ & $(B \supset A)$. It may be read as "A if and only if B". Biconditionals express necessary and sufficient conditions. Thus, Th. 1.3 expresses a necessary and sufficient condition for identity in a simply ordered set.

The proof of Th. 1.3 involves the establishment of the two conditionals:

> **I.** $(a = b) \supset [\sim(a < b) \;\&\; \sim(b < a)]$

and

> **II.** $[\sim(a < b) \;\&\; \sim(b < a)] \supset (a = b)$

Roughly, I depends on Ax. 2 and II depends on Ax. 1. Turning first to I, we see that $(a = b) \supset \sim(a < b)$ and $(b = a) \supset \sim(b < a)$ both follow directly from Ax. 2. Obviously, $(a = b) \supset (b = a)$, so $(a = b)$ implies both $\sim(a < b)$ and $\sim(b < a)$.

"Obviously"? If we are being scrupulous in recording our assumptions, we shall have to admit that $(a = b) \supset (b = a)$ does not appear anywhere among our axioms. Nor can it be deduced from them. Accordingly, we must begin by giving it explicit recognition as an axiom:

Ax. 5 $(a = b) \supset (b = a)$

We can now state the proof of I as follows:

1. $(a < b) \supset \sim(a = b)$	Ax. 2
2. $(b < a) \supset \sim(b = a)$	From 1, by substitution
3. $(a = b) \supset (b = a)$	Ax. 5
Assumption —— **4.** $(a = b)$	
5. $\sim\sim(a = b)$	4, $\sim\sim$I
6. $\sim(a < b)$	1, 5, MT
7. $(b = a)$	3, 4, $\supset$E
8. $\sim\sim(b = a)$	7, $\sim\sim$I
9. $\sim(b < a)$	2, 8, MT
10. $\sim(a < b) \;\&\; \sim(b < a)$	6, 9, &I
11. $(a = b) \supset [\sim(a < b) \;\&\; \sim(b < a)]$	4-10, $\supset$I

None of the steps so far make use of unfamiliar rules. No further commentary, therefore, seems necessary at this point.

In working out the proof of II, we shall find it convenient first to symbolize Ax. 1:

$$\sim(a = b) \supset [(a < b) \;\mathbf{v}\; (b < a)]$$

The consequent of this conditional can be explained as follows. When A and B are statements, A **v** B, which is read "A or B", is called an *alternative statement*, or a *disjunction*. The statements that flank the **v** are called *disjuncts*. Notice that "or" is used here in an *inclusive* sense: A **v** B means "A or B or possibly both". In the case of the consequent of Ax. 1, of course, $(a < b)$ and $(b < a)$ are not compatible, so that the inclusive sense of "or" here tends to coalesce with an exclusive sense in which the word is sometimes used.

The proof of II is

12. $\sim(a = b) \supset [(a < b) \mathbf{v} (b < a)]$ Ax. 1
Assumption——13. $\sim(a < b) \& \sim(b < a)$
14. $\sim[(a < b) \mathbf{v} (b < a)]$ 13, DM
15. $\sim\sim(a = b)$ 12, 14, MT
16. $(a = b)$ 15, $\sim\sim$E

17. $[\sim(a < b) \& \sim(b < a)] \supset (a = b)$ 13–16, $\supset$I

Only line 14 seems to require comment. DM stands for *DeMorgan's Rule*— actually a set of four rules named after a nineteenth-century English logician who was among the first to state them. These rules are the following:

DM	(a)	(b)	(c)	(d)
Instance	$\sim(A \& B)$	$\sim A \mathbf{v} \sim B$	$\sim(A \mathbf{v} B)$	$\sim A \& \sim B$
	$\therefore \sim A \mathbf{v} \sim B$	$\therefore \sim(A \& B)$	$\therefore \sim A \& \sim B$	$\therefore \sim(A \mathbf{v} B)$

It is evidently version (d) to which we appeal in line 14. To see the validity of (d), note that both the premise and the conclusion are ways of expressing "neither A nor B"; *i.e.*, "not A *and* not B" and "not either A *or* B".

We now use the rules of &I and ≡I to combine lines 11 and 17. ≡I, or *Biconditional Introduction*, is the following:

≡I $(A \supset B) \& (B \supset A)$

Instance $\therefore A \equiv B$

This is clearly just a restatement of the meaning of $A \equiv B$. We have, then,

18. $\{(a = b) \supset [\sim(a < b) \& \sim(b < a)]\} \&$
    $\{[\sim(a < b) \& \sim(b < a)] \supset (a = b)\}$ 11, 17, &I
19. $(a = b) \equiv [\sim(a < b) \& \sim(b < a)]$ 18, ≡I

This completes the proof of Th. 1.3.

The proofs of these three theorems illustrate the role of some logical rules in proof. Proofs require assumptions—in this case, axioms—but without the rules of logic we could not express in detail the steps from the assumptions to the consequences we wish to prove.

EXERCISE 1.2

I. Prove the following theorems on the basis of the axiom set of Table 1.1 below, plus Theorems 1.1, 1.2, and 1.3, the additional axiom

$$[(a = b) \& (b = c)] \supset (a = c),$$

the rules of Table 1.2 below, and any other rules you may think it proper to introduce.

1. Th. 1.4 $\sim(a = b) \supset \sim(b = a)$

2. Th. 1.4a $\sim(a = b) \equiv \sim(b = a)$

3. Th. 1.5 $[(a = b) \& \sim(b = c)] \supset \sim(a = c)$

4. Th. 1.6 $(a < b) \supset [\sim(a = b) \& \sim(b < a)]$

5. Th. 1.7 $\sim(a < b) \supset [(a = b) \vee (b < a)]$

6. Th. 1.8 $[(a < b) \& (b = c)] \supset (a < c)$

7. Th. 1.9 $[\sim(a < b) \& \sim(b < c)] \supset \sim(a < c)$

II. Each of the following proofs or arguments depends on a rule of inference not listed in Table 1.2. In each case state the rule, using the style of Table 1.2.

1. Since $\sim(2 < \sqrt{4}) \& \sim(\sqrt{4} < 2)$, therefore $\sim(2 < \sqrt{4})$.

2. If $2 = \sqrt{4}$, then $\sim(2 < \sqrt{4})$. If $\sim(2 < \sqrt{4})$, then $2 = \sqrt{4} \vee \sqrt{4} < 2$. Hence, if $2 = \sqrt{4}$, then $2 = \sqrt{4} \vee \sqrt{4} < 2$.

3. If the switch is closed, current flows. If the switch is open, current flows. The switch is either open or closed. Hence, current flows.

4. $\sim[(\sqrt[3]{3} < 1) \& (1 < \sqrt[3]{3})]$. But in point of fact, $1 < \sqrt[3]{3}$. Hence, $\sim(\sqrt[3]{3} < 1)$.

5. Smith is 42 years old and Smith is not 42 years old. Hence, pigs have wings.

6. Either $\pi < 3\frac{1}{7}$ or $3\frac{1}{7} < \pi$. However, $\sim(3\frac{1}{7} < \pi)$. Therefore, $\pi < 3\frac{1}{7}$.

7. Jones will come today. Thus, Jones will come today or tomorrow.

8. Roses are red and violets are blue. Therefore, violets are blue and roses are red.

III. The axioms of a simplified Projective Geometry are stated in Carmichael, *The Logic of Discovery*, Ch. III, and in Cohen and Nagel, *An Introduction to Logic and Scientific Method* (New York, 1957), Ch. VII. Each of these texts exhibits the proofs of several theorems on the basis of these axioms. Analyze each of these proofs carefully, mentioning every rule of inference involved.

1.3 Recapitulation

The use of the axiomatic method in mathematics and as a tool for systematizing other areas of human knowledge has become so widespread and has

TABLE 1.1

THE AXIOMS FOR SIMPLE ORDER

Ax. 1 $\sim(a = b) \supset [(a < b) \vee (b < a)]$

Ax. 2 $(a < b) \supset \sim(a = b)$

Ax. 3 $[(a < b) \ \& \ (b < c)] \supset (a < c)$

Ax. 4 $a = a$

Ax. 5 $(a = b) \supset (b = a)$

TABLE 1.2

INSTANCES OF RULES USED IN THIS CHAPTER

&I

$$A$$
$$B$$
$$\therefore \ A \ \& \ B$$

⊃I ⌐—Assumption — A

⋮

B

$$\therefore \ A \supset B$$

~I ⌐—Assumption— A

⋮

B & ~B

$$\therefore \ \sim A$$

⊃E

$$A \supset B$$
$$A$$
$$\therefore \ B$$

~~I

$$A$$
$$\therefore \ \sim\sim A$$

~~E

$$\sim\sim A$$
$$\therefore \ A$$

≡I $(A \supset B) \ \& \ (B \supset A)$
$$\therefore \ A \equiv B$$

MT

$$A \supset B$$
$$\sim B$$
$$\therefore \ \sim A$$

DM

(a)	(b)	(c)	(d)
$\sim(A \ \& \ B)$	$\sim A \vee \sim B$	$\sim(A \vee B)$	$\sim A \ \& \sim B$
$\therefore \ \sim A \vee \sim B$	$\therefore \ \sim(A \ \& \ B)$	$\therefore \ \sim A \ \& \sim B$	$\therefore \ \sim(A \vee B)$

We have also used the rule that authorizes the move from Ax. 2 to $(a < a) \supset \sim(a = a)$, etc. This rule will be given in Chapter Five.

proved to be so important as to demand an introduction to the problems and possibilities which it occasions. The possibilities of a deductive conceptual apparatus for human knowledge have always interested thinkers, and the advantages of clarity, rigor, ease of communication, and systematization are evident enough to attract scientists in all fields. One approach to knowledge of the axiomatic method is by way of the rules of inference used in the analysis of proof; that is, used for justifying the steps of the deductions leading to the theorems. It is this approach we shall follow in the next chapters, leaving until Part Two the examination of problems and limitations to which the use of axiom systems is subject.

Tables 1.1 and 1.2 are given for easy reference in connection with working the exercises and, in the case of Table 1.2, to anticipate the set of rules to be developed in Chapter Two.

SUGGESTED READINGS

1. E. T. Bell, *Mathematics, Queen and Servant of Science* (New York: McGraw-Hill, 1951), pp. 20–44.

2. R. D. Carmichael, *The Logic of Discovery* (Chicago: The Open Court Pub. Co., 1930).

3. E. Nagel, "The Formation of Modern Conceptions of Formal Logic in the Development of Geometry," *Osiris*, Vol. 7 (1939), pp. 142–222.

4. H. Poincaré, *The Foundations of Science* (New York: The Science Press, 1913), pp. 55–91.

5. M. Richardson, *Fundamentals of Mathematics*, rev. ed. (New York: The Macmillan Co., 1958), Ch. XVI.

6. R. L. Wilder, *Introduction to the Foundations of Mathematics* (New York: John Wiley & Sons, 1952), Ch. I & II.

Chapter 2

The Propositional Rules

2.1 Introduction

In the last chapter we pointed out the use of rules of inference to justify each step taken in proving a theorem. Thus, if we begin with the axiom that if *a* is less than *b*, then *a* and *b* are distinct, we can use a rule to conclude that if *a* is less than *a*, then *a* and *a* are distinct. But, since it is also an axiom that *a* and *a* are *not* distinct, we can use an additional rule to reach the conclusion that *a* is *not* less than *a*. This gave us Th. 1.1.

In the present chapter we undertake a survey of logical rules of a certain elementary kind. The first kind of rules in which we are interested is illustrated by the second of the two steps taken in the proof of Th. 1.1, which we may distinguish from the first step. What is the difference between these two steps? In the first of them, we have

(1) If *a* is less than *b*, then *a* and *b* are distinct. Therefore, if *a* is less than *a*, then *a* and *a* are distinct.

In Chapter One we did not name the rule authorizing this step, and deferred its statement to Chapter Five. We observe now that the conclusion is formed from the premise by substituting *a* for *b* throughout the premise. Note that *a* and *b* function as nouns or pronouns in the premise and conclusion. The second step is different.

(2) If *a* is less than *a*, then *a* and *a* are distinct.
     But *a* and *a* are not distinct.
     Therefore, *a* is not less than *a*.

This inference does not involve substitution. And the nouns or pronouns in the conclusion are exactly those in the if-clause (antecedent) of the first premise. The conclusion as a whole is the denial of the entire antecedent. The structure is

If A, then B

Not B

Therefore, not A.

Here, A and B can be arbitrarily chosen statements, regardless of what nouns or pronouns might be contained in them. But clearly, the sentences involved in (1) could not be arbitrarily chosen. The structure of (1) is not exemplified by

Today is Tuesday.

Therefore, if a is less than a,

then a and a are distinct.

The difference, then, is that between steps which, like (1), cannot be justified by appealing to a structure involving arbitrarily chosen statements and those which, like (2), can be so justified.

Rules like the one authorizing step (2) we shall discuss first in this chapter. We shall call them *propositional rules*. The phrase *Propositional Logic*, abbreviated PL, refers to the systematic treatment of the propositional rules. There is considerable precedent for the use of the word "propositional" in this context, although some authors prefer "sentential".

EXERCISE 2.1

Which of the following inferences are propositional?

1. He'll marry her, for he's a fool, and being a fool implies that he'll marry her.

2. Socrates is a man and all men are mortal, so Socrates is mortal.

3. No misers are happy, for they live in continual fear, and people cannot be happy if they are afraid.

4. Either I wore my hat or I left it at home. It isn't here, so I must not have worn it. It must be at home, then.

5. Some fools are truthful, and to be truthful is to be good. Furthermore, whoever is good should be admired, so it follows that we should admire some fools.

6. $x^2 - 1 = (x + 1)(x - 1)$. Therefore, $6^2 - 1 = (6 + 1)(6 - 1)$.

7. $\sqrt{2} < 2$, and if $\sqrt{2} < 2$, then $\sqrt{3} < 3$. Hence $\sqrt{3} < 3$.

8. If $\sqrt{x} < x$, then $\sqrt{x + 1} < (x + 1)$. If $\sqrt{x + 1} < (x + 1)$, then $\sqrt{x + 1} < (x + 2)$. Therefore, if $\sqrt{x} < x$, then $\sqrt{x + 1} < (x + 2)$.

We could equally well argue

      ────**1.** N & T
          2. T   1, &E

In general, then, &E governs any specific deduction that is an instance of either

&E $p \& q$ or $p \& q$
                    ∴ p ∴ q

There is a symmetrical relation between &I and &E. Having used one of these rules to justify a step, we can always use the other to return to the initial line. Thus

      ────**1.** p
      ────**2.** q
          3. $p \& q$ 1, 2, &I
          4. q 3, &E
          5. p 3, &E

Whenever we have $p \& q$ we might equally well have had $q \& p$; for as line 6 of the above argument we could write

          6. $q \& p$ 4, 5, &I

Thus any conjunction *commutes*, or *obeys* the *commutative law*. The reference, of course, is to algebraic commutative laws according to which, for example, $x + y = y + x$ and $xy = yx$.

The deduction carried out in lines 1–6 above is expressed in schematic terms; *i.e.*, in terms of p and q, not A and B. It represents many specific deductions and we call it a *deduction schema*. Because a deduction schema represents all instances of a kind of deduction, there is a specific deduction of this kind holding for A and B, for C and D and all other pairs of statements. Thus, we can write as a *derived rule* the schema

CM $p \& q$
                    ∴ $q \& p$

The designation CM stands for *Commutative Law*.

We have shown by informal substitution of statements in the deduction schema that it is possible to deduce the conjunction of one pair of statements from the conjunction of the commuted pair. Because this is so, we introduce the derived rule CM into a deduction as an abbreviation for any of these specific deductions. As a rule, CM represents all of these specific deductions and justifies them all. When we use CM to justify a step in a deduction, it states that there is a deduction which could be added at this point, thus shortening the whole deduction by the number of omitted steps. Having established CM, we can write the last deduction schema with four steps instead of six:

$$
\begin{array}{ll}
\text{1. } p & \\
\text{2. } q & \\
\text{3. } p \,\&\, q & \text{1, 2, \&I} \\
\text{4. } q \,\&\, p & \text{3, CM}
\end{array}
$$

The next two rules have been discussed briefly in Chapter One. These rules involve the introduction and elimination of "If . . . then . . ." in the lines of a deduction. Any statement of the form "If p, then q", symbolized $p \supset q$, is called a *conditional,* and here p is the *antecedent* and q is the *consequent.* The *contrapositive* of $p \supset q$ is $\sim q \supset \sim p$. The *converse* of $p \supset q$ is $q \supset p$.

THE RULE OF $\supset$ I

An "If . . . then . . ." relationship between statements may be introduced at a line of a proof when the consequent is deducible from the antecedent. Thus, since B follows from A & B, we may write (A & B) $\supset$ B. This deduction can be expressed

$$
\begin{array}{ll}
\text{1. A \& B} & \\
\text{2. B} & \text{1, \&E} \\
\text{3. (A \& B) } \supset \text{ B} & \text{1-2, } \supset \text{I}
\end{array}
$$

The line below line 2 is intended to suggest that line 3 is a consequence of the entire deduction from 1 to 2, not of the separate ingredients of this deduction. This fact is also suggested by writing "1–2" instead of "1,2" to the right of line 3. In practice we shall add a vertical line thus:

$$
\begin{array}{ll}
\text{1. A \& B} & \\
\text{2. B} & \text{1, \&E} \\
\text{3. (A \& B) } \supset \text{ B} & \text{1-2, } \supset \text{I}
\end{array}
$$

A more complicated case of $\supset$ I is the following:

$$
\begin{array}{ll}
\text{1. (A \& B) \& C} & \\
\text{2. A \& B} & \text{1, \&E} \\
\text{3. C} & \text{1, \&E} \\
\text{4. A} & \text{2, \&E} \\
\text{5. B} & \text{2, \&E} \\
\text{6. B \& C} & \text{5, 3, \&I} \\
\text{7. A \& (B \& C)} & \text{4, 6, \&I} \\
\text{8. [(A \& B) \& C] } \supset \text{ [A \& (B \& C)]} & \text{1-7, } \supset \text{I}
\end{array}
$$

Here line 1 is called the *assumption* of the deduction. Lines 1 through 7, in which consequences of the assumption are stated, make up what is called the *scope* of the assumption. In line 8 we say we *discharge* the assumption, *i.e.*, the lines in the deduction beginning with the line discharging the assumption are not dependent upon the truth of the assumption.

The rule schema is

⊃I

$$
\begin{array}{l}
\boxed{\begin{array}{l} p \\ \vdots \\ q \end{array}} \\
\therefore p \supset q
\end{array}
$$

The specific deduction ending with line 8 above can be restated as a deduction schema in terms of *p*, *q*, and *r*, as can a similar deduction yielding the converse of line 8. As so restated they represent all specific deductions of this kind and hence serve as evidence for another derived rule known as the *Associative Law*. Like the commutative law, the associative law is a derived rule and an abbreviation for the specific deductions which it represents. We write it

Assoc
$$
\begin{array}{ll}
p \,\&\, (q \,\&\, r) & (p \,\&\, q) \,\&\, r \\
\therefore (p \,\&\, q) \,\&\, r & \therefore p \,\&\, (q \,\&\, r)
\end{array}
$$

The existence of the specific deductions represented by this law makes it possible to obtain proofs by shifting parentheses. Indeed, now that we know these deductions exist, we can shorten our proofs by appealing to the law or, more radically, by dropping all parentheses serving to group conjunctions which are themselves conjuncts. Hereafter we shall write simply A & B & C.

Nothing prevents the occurrence of scopes within scopes. For example:

1. A		
2. B		
3. A & B	1, 2, &I	
4. B ⊃ (A & B)	2–3, ⊃I	
5. A ⊃ [B ⊃ (A & B)]	1–4, ⊃I	

Beginning with line 4, in which the assumption B is discharged, the deduction proceeds relative to the assumption A only. Line 5 states an assertion which is not relative to any assumptions.

We need not have discharged the initial assumption of the last argument. If we had not, the result would have been

1. A	
2. B	
3. A & B	1, 2, &I
4. B ⊃ (A & B)	2–3, ⊃I

We standardize our vocabulary by referring, in a deduction, to undischarged assumptions as *premises* and to discharged assumptions as, simply, *assumptions*. In practice, premises are introduced from information sources external to the deduction; from physics, for instance, or mathematics, or engineering, or in some cases logic itself. The axioms used as premises in Chapter One are a good example. We introduce such premises because we wish to know what they imply, what conclusions may be based upon them. An assumption which is discharged, on the other hand, is merely a part of our deductive machinery. We introduce assumptions in mathematical arguments when, in a proof by *reductio ad absurdum*, we assume the contradictory of what is to be proved; in arguments based on a consideration of alternative cases; or in arguments where we accept the hypothesis of a theorem in order to deduce a conclusion. An example of this last instance is found in the proof that if *a* is less than *b*, then *b* is not less than *a*, given in Th. 1.2. Here the assumption serves as a step toward a conclusion. It is introduced, as we sometimes say, for the sake of the argument.

A useful distinction is one between conclusions reached on the basis of premises and conclusions reached without premises (those reached when all assumptions, if any, have been discharged). We shall designate conclusions of this latter type as *Zero-Premise Conclusions*, and we shall abbreviate zero-premise conclusion as ZPC. The conclusions of those deductions of the present section in which all assumptions are discharged are illustrations. For example:

1. A & B		
2. B	1, &E	
3. (A & B) ⊃ B	1–2, ⊃I (a zero-premise conclusion)	

and

1. A		
2. B		
3. A & B	1, 2, &I	
4. B ⊃ (A & B)	2–3, ⊃I	
5. A ⊃ [B ⊃ (A & B)]	1–4, ⊃I (a zero-premise conclusion)	

On the other hand, the following deduction does not have a zero-premise conclusion:

1. A		
2. B		
3. A & B	1, 2, &I	
4. B ⊃ (A & B)	2–3, ⊃I (not a zero-premise conclusion)	

THE RULE OF ⊃E

The following two independent assertions might be made:

1. If the key is pressed, the solenoid in the next room is actuated.

2. The key is now being pressed.

The first could be verified only by observing antecedent-consequent relations in an electrical circuit, whereas the second has nothing to do with any circuit, but is instead the assertion of a physical event. Either sentence might be true independently of the other.

From the two sentences just cited, although not from either one alone, it is possible to infer

3. The solenoid in the next room is now being actuated.

The deduction here is

    ——— **1.** K ⊃ S
    ——— **2.** K
       3. S   1, 2, ⊃E

The rule justifying step 3 is called ⊃-Elimination because its effect is to dissolve the conditional premise, thus eliminating the ⊃. The conclusion tells us not merely that the solenoid is actuated *if* the key is pressed, but that the solenoid is in fact actuated. The rule is

⊃E

$$p \supset q$$
$$p$$
$$\therefore q$$

The two rules of ⊃I and ⊃E are symmetrical in the following way:

    ——— **1.** A ⊃ B
    ⌐ **2.** A
    | **3.** B   1, 2, ⊃E
      4. A ⊃ B   2–3, ⊃I

Thus if we begin with a conditional premise we can recover the conditional by using ⊃I.

The following deductions are further illustrations of the uses of ⊃E and its relationship to ⊃I:

I		II	
——— **1.** (A & B) ⊃ C		——— **1.** A ⊃ (B ⊃ C)	
⌐ **2.** A		⌐ **2.** A & B	
⌐ **3.** B		**3.** A	2, &E
4. A & B	2, 3, &I	**4.** B ⊃ C	1, 3, ⊃E
5. C	1, 4, ⊃E	**5.** B	2, &E
6. B ⊃ C	3–5, ⊃I	**6.** C	4, 5, ⊃E
7. A ⊃ (B ⊃ C)	2–6, ⊃I	**7.** (A & B) ⊃ C	2–6, ⊃I

The specific deductions given in I and II above can be restated as deduction schemata. We can see that specific deductions are available for any statements and that we have here the basis for derived rules. These derived rules are

Exp $(p \mathbin{\&} q) \supset r$ **Imp** $p \supset (q \supset r)$
$\therefore p \supset (q \supset r)$ $\therefore (p \mathbin{\&} q) \supset r$

The designations Exp and Imp refer to the *Law of Exportation* and the *Law of Importation*, respectively.

The next two rules we consider involve the word "or". In Chapter One we called *p* or *q* an *alternation* or *disjunction*, and the *p* and the *q* were called the *disjuncts*. We shall use $p \vee q$ to symbolize *p* or *q*, bearing in mind that "or" is used in its inclusive sense. Thus "Jones is an executive v Jones is a stamp collector" leaves open the possibility that he is both.

THE RULE OF vI

If it is true that today is Wednesday, then it follows that today is Wednesday or Thursday. This argument can be justified by the rule of **vI** (v-Introduction).

　　　　　——1. W
　　　　　2. W v T   1, vI

From the same premise, for that matter, we might have concluded today is Wednesday or roses are red—or today is Wednesday or *p*, where *p* represents any statement whatever.

The rule is

vI p or q
$\therefore p \vee q$ $\therefore p \vee q$

Note that **vI**, like &E, has two forms, guaranteeing the commutativity of **v**.

THE RULE OF vE

The rule of elimination for **v** is like $\supset$ I in that it discharges assumptions. This point is clearest in the instance of mathematical proof by cases. For example, if we wish to prove that the area of a triangle is half the product of the base by the altitude, we may consider as an assumption the case in which the altitude falls within the triangle and then as an assumption the case where it falls outside. We discharge these assumptions by showing that from each we can deduce the same formula for the area. Then, on the premise that either one or the other case must hold, we can prove the formula freed from our assumptions.

An example of a logical form of this kind is

    ——1. (A & B) v (C & B)
      —2. A & B
         3. B   2, &E
      —4. C & B
         5. B   4, &E
         6. B   1, 2–3, 4–5, vE

We indicate the discharge of the assumptions A & B and C & B by the usual lines. Here we discharge *two* assumptions to reach the conclusion B. This kind of discharge, found in vE, differs in this respect from that in ⊃ I, where only one assumption is discharged and the conclusion incorporates ⊃.

The inference we make here involves three things: (1) the disjunction of two statements, $p \mathbin{v} q$, (2) a deduction of r by any rules from p, and (3) a deduction of r by any rules from q. Given these three conditions we may infer r. The rule can be expressed

vE

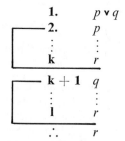

There is a standard argument form in classical logic which is easily confused with the rule of vE. This is the *Constructive Dilemma*. However, we are here regarding vE as more fundamental than the dilemma, which may be considered as a derived rule. The dilemma in its simplest form has the schema

CD I

$$p \mathbin{v} q$$
$$p \supset r$$
$$q \supset r$$
$$\therefore \; r$$

The derivation of this rule is based upon the deduction schema

    ——1. $p \mathbin{v} q$
    ——2. $p \supset r$
    ——3. $q \supset r$
      —4. p
         5. r 2, 4, ⊃ E
      —6. q
         7. r 3, 6, ⊃ E
         8. r 1, 4–5, 6–7, vE

Another form of the Constructive Dilemma is also derivable using **v**E; this is

CD II $p \vee q$
                                             $p \supset r$
                                             $q \supset s$
                                        $\therefore r \vee s$

Its derivation is based on the deduction schema

$\quad$ 1. $p \vee q$
$\quad$ 2. $p \supset r$
$\quad$ 3. $q \supset s$
$\quad$ 4. p
$\qquad$ 5. r $\qquad$ 2, 4, $\supset$E
$\qquad$ 6. $r \vee s$ $\qquad$ 5, **v**I

$\quad$ 7. q
$\qquad$ 8. s $\qquad$ 3, 7, $\supset$E
$\qquad$ 9. $r \vee s$ $\qquad$ 8, **v**I

$\qquad$ 10. $r \vee s$ $\qquad$ 1, 4–6, 7–9, **v**E

The derived rules CD I and CD II permit the analysis of many arguments such as the following.

> Suppose I am driving to a destination on the other side of a large city. When I reach the point at which the bypass leads off from the road through the city, I read a sign stating that there are several detours along the bypass. Clearly I must take the city road or the bypass. Being a logician, I stop and consider the implications of this sign. If I take the city road I shall be late (because of the traffic). On the other hand, if I take the bypass, I shall be late (because of the detours). In either case I conclude, I shall be late.

This argument may be symbolized as

$\quad$ 1. B $\vee$ C
$\quad$ 2. B $\supset$ L
$\quad$ 3. C $\supset$ L
$\quad$ 4. L $\qquad$ 1, 2, 3, CD I

THE RULES OF $\equiv$I AND $\equiv$E

In mathematical arguments and those in other areas there are many cases in which we say "... if and only if ..."; that is, (A $\supset$ B) & (B $\supset$ A); so that the abbreviation of this expansion as A $\equiv$ B is of great convenience. In Th. 1.3, for example, we used $(a = b) \equiv [\sim(a < b)\ \&\ \sim(b < q)]$ as an abbreviation for the conjunction of two lengthy conditionals. The expression $p \equiv q$ is called a *biconditional*, and may be read "*p* is equivalent to *q*".*

---

* In mathematical contexts the biconditional is often expressed as "iff".

Biconditionals may be introduced into and eliminated from deductions according to the rules of *Biconditional-Introduction* and *Biconditional-Elimination* which we now state.

$$\equiv\!\mathbf{I} \quad (p \supset q) \,\&\, (q \supset p) \qquad\qquad \equiv\!\mathbf{E} \quad p \equiv q$$
$$\therefore\ p \equiv q \qquad\qquad\qquad\qquad \therefore\ (p \supset q) \,\&\, (q \supset p)$$

In this section we have discussed eight underived rules—&I, &E, $\supset$I, $\supset$E, vI, vE, $\equiv$I, and $\equiv$E. Some of these were used in Chapter One. Other rules used in Chapter One have not yet been discussed in the present chapter. Some of these are derivable from the underived rules so far given. Others, governing the introduction and elimination of negation, are formulated in the next section.

EXERCISE 2.2

Examine the following inferences, citing all the propositional rules so far stated which are used. In case a rule is used that has not so far been stated, state the rule.

1. A, therefore A **v** B.

2. A & B, therefore A.

3. [A & B] **v** [(C $\supset$ B) & C], therefore B.

4. A, B, therefore A & B.

5. A & B, therefore B.

6. A $\supset$ B, E $\supset$ B, A **v** E, therefore B.

7.

> ──A & B
> B

    (A & B) $\supset$ B.

8. A $\supset$ C, A, therefore C.

9.

> ──(A $\supset$ B) & (B $\supset$ C)
> (A $\supset$ B)
> (B $\supset$ C)
> > ──A
> > B
> > C
>
> A $\supset$ C

    [(A $\supset$ B) & (B $\supset$ C)] $\supset$ (A $\supset$ C).

10.

> ──A & (A $\supset$ B)
> A
> A $\supset$ B
> B

    [A & (A $\supset$ B)] $\supset$ B.

11. ┌─A & B
     │ A
     │ A v C
     │ B
     │ B v C
     │ (A v C) & (B v C)
     └─────────────
        (A & B) ⊃ [(A v C) & (B v C)]

12. ┌─A & A
     │ A
     └─────
        A & A ⊃ A.

13. ┌─A
     │ A v B
     └─────
        A ⊃ (A v B).

14. ┌─A
     │ A
     │ A & A
     └─────
        A ⊃ (A & A).

15. ┌─A & ∼B
     │ A
     │ A v B
     └─────
        (A & ∼B) ⊃ (A v B)

16. From A ⊃ (B ⊃ C), derive B ⊃ (A ⊃ C).

17. From A ⊃ B and A ⊃ C, derive A ⊃ (B & C).

18. From A ⊃ B, derive (A & C) ⊃ B.

19. From A ⊃ B, derive (A & C) ⊃ (B v D).

20. From A v B, (A v C) ⊃ D, and (B v E) ⊃ D, derive D.

21. From (A & B) ⊃ (C & D), derive A ⊃ (B ⊃ C).

22. From A ⊃ B and C ⊃ D, derive (A & C) ⊃ (B & D).

23. From A v (A & C), derive A v B.

24. From (A & B) v (C & D), derive B v C.

25. From A ⊃ (B ⊃ C), A v (B ⊃ C), and B, derive C.

26. From A ≡ B and A, derive B.

27. From A ≡ B and B, derive A.

28. From A ≡ (A & B), derive A ⊃ B

29. From A $\supset$ B, derive A $\equiv$ (A & B)

30. It's raining; therefore, it's raining or it isn't.

31. The temperature is 25°F and it's snowing; therefore, the temperature is 25°F.

32. Either the snow isn't melting and the temperature is less than 30°F or both the temperature is less than 30° in order that the snow not be melting and the snow isn't melting; therefore, the temperature is less than 30°F.

33. Today is July 4th. There is going to be a fireworks display. So today is July 4th and there is going to be a fireworks display.

34. The trees are shedding their leaves and the squirrels are gathering acorns; therefore, it follows that the squirrels are gathering acorns, and it also follows that the trees are shedding their leaves.

35. If a rocket orbits the moon, we will get pictures of the other side. A rocket will not only orbit the moon, it will orbit both the moon and the earth. So we will get pictures of the moon's other side.

36. The President flew to Moscow; therefore, either the President flew to Moscow or the Secretary of State did.

37. If a radioactive substance has a long life, it has medical value. Uranium isotopes are long-lived radioactive substances; consequently, they have medical value.

38. Aristotle was born in Stagira, and he was tutor to Alexander the Great. Now if he was born in Stagira, he was a Macedonian by birth; so he was a Macedonian.

39. Let us assume that Plato gives us an accurate account of the life and doctrines of Socrates. If so, Socrates was a poor father and also advocated that people pursue the good. So if Plato's account of Socrates is accurate, Socrates was a poor father.

40. T. S. Eliot is both a Christian and a conservative. If he is a Christian, his poems will praise religious experience, and if he is a conservative, his poems will criticize modern cultural trends. It is obvious then that Eliot's poems praise religious experience and criticize modern cultural trends.

41. I forgive you if and only if you apologize; therefore, if I forgive you, you apologize.

42. I forgive you if and only if you apologize; therefore, if you apologize, I forgive you.

43. "Smith speaks" is equivalent to "Smith exaggerates". Therefore, "Smith speaks and Brown listens" is equivalent to "Smith exaggerates and Brown listens".

2.3 Negation Rules

When p is any statement, not p, which we write as $\sim p$, is said to be the denial of p. The denial of p is a *negation statement*. A negation statement is sometimes called *a negation*.

Negations can occur in the lines of a deduction without having been introduced there as a part of the deduction. Thus "If the switch is not closed, the current will be zero" might be the premise of an argument. Using obvious symbols, we might write the deduction:

$$
\begin{array}{lll}
\text{——} & 1. & \sim C \supset Z \\
\text{——} & 2. & \sim C \\
& 3. & Z & 1, 2, \supset E
\end{array}
$$

Here negation occurs incidentally, because instead of $\sim C$ we might have written O, to stand for "The switch is open".

Of course, conditionals, conjunctions, and alternations can likewise occur in the lines of a deduction without having been introduced there as part of the deduction. Consider an argument involving the premise "If the switch is open, then either the current is zero or there is a short circuit":

$$
\begin{array}{lll}
\text{——} & 1. & O \supset (Z \vee S) \\
\text{——} & 2. & O \\
& 3. & Z \vee S & 1, 2, \supset E
\end{array}
$$

Here alternation occurs only incidentally. To introduce alternation as an essential part of a deduction, the use of $\vee$I or some derived rule specifically requiring an alternative conclusion is required.

THE RULE OF $\sim$I

A deduction in which negation occurs as an essential part is

$$
\begin{array}{lll}
\text{——} & 1. & A \mathbin{\&} \sim B \\
& 2. & A \supset B \\
& 3. & A & 1, \mathbin{\&}E \\
& 4. & B & 2, 3, \supset E \\
& 5. & \sim B & 1, \mathbin{\&}E \\
& 6. & B \mathbin{\&} \sim B & 4, 5, \mathbin{\&}I \\
\hline
& 7. & \sim(A \supset B) & 2\text{–}6, \sim I
\end{array}
$$

Notice that $\sim B$ occurs in lines 1 and 5 inessentially. The fact that we are concerned with $\sim B$ rather than with some positive statement—say D—has no effect on the use of &E to obtain 5 from 1. In line 6, however, negation is an essential part of the deduction. $B \mathbin{\&} \sim B$ is a *contradiction*, whereas B & D would not have been. Whatever implies a contradiction must be false, but we can make no corresponding assertion about whatever implies B & D. Thus we infer line 7. The $\sim$ in line 7 is introduced into the argument; it did not appear before. For this reason the rule that justifies line 7 is called $\sim$I, or *Negation Introduction*. The rule is

$\sim$I

$$
\begin{array}{l}
\quad p \\
\quad \vdots \\
\quad q \ \& \sim q \\
\hline
\therefore \sim p
\end{array}
$$

As in the case of $\supset$I and $\vee$E, the use of $\sim$I involves the discharge of an assumption. In our notation this is made evident by the dots in the rule schema and the customary lines for discharge in the rule and specific deductions.

The rule of $\sim$I can be used to derive the important rule *Modus Tollens*, which we shall abbreviate MT.

MT
$$
\begin{array}{l}
p \supset q \\
\sim q \\
\therefore \sim p
\end{array}
$$

For given the premises $p \supset q$ and $\sim q$ we can give the proof schema

$$
\begin{array}{lll}
1. & p \supset q & \\
2. & \sim q & \\
3. & p & \\
4. & q & 1, 3, \supset E \\
5. & q \ \& \sim q & 4, 2, \&I \\
\hline
6. & \sim p & 3\text{--}5, \sim I
\end{array}
$$

The rule of $\sim$I is used in *reductio ad absurdum* proofs. A celebrated example is Euclid's proof that there is no greatest prime number. Assume that P is the greatest prime number. Then form the number

$$\text{P}' = (2 \times 3 \times 5 \times 7 \times 11 \times \ldots \times \text{P}) + 1,$$

where the product in the parentheses comprises every prime number up to and including P. P′ will be a prime number (since every attempt to divide it by a prime factor will have a remainder of 1), and P′ will be greater than P. But this contradicts the hypothesis that P is the greatest prime number.

If we take P to mean "P is the greatest prime number", we can write the deduction in the form

$$
\begin{array}{lll}
1. & \text{P} \supset \sim\text{P} & \\
2. & \text{P} & \\
3. & \sim\text{P} & 1, 2, \supset E \\
4. & \text{P} \ \& \sim\text{P} & 2, 3, \&I \\
\hline
5. & \sim\text{P} & 2\text{--}4, \sim I
\end{array}
$$

Other examples of such deductions include many proofs of crucial theorems in geometry and algebra. Some of these examples are used in the exercises at the end of this section.

THE RULE OF ∼E

Like **vI**, the rule of ∼E is primarily of technical utility. Like **vI** again, ∼E sanctions the introduction of an arbitrary statement q into a deduction. It justifies writing q (any statement we please) as a line succeeding any contradiction derived in the course of the proof. Thus

$$
\begin{array}{ll}
\underline{}\;\;1.\;A & \\
\underline{}\;\;2.\;{\sim}A & \\
3.\;A\,\&\,{\sim}A & 1,\,2,\,\&I \\
4.\;B & 3,\,{\sim}E \\
\end{array}
$$

The rule is

∼E
$$p\,\&\,{\sim}p$$
$$\therefore q$$

In practice, this rule is not used except within the scope of an assumption, so that p and $\sim p$ occur relative to assumptions, and not as initial premises. To see how ∼E is used, let us derive the important rule of the *Disjunctive Syllogism*.

DS
$$
\begin{array}{ccc}
p \lor q & \text{or} & p \lor q \\
{\sim}p & & {\sim}q \\
\therefore q & & \therefore p \\
\end{array}
$$

We set up the deduction schema

$$
\begin{array}{ll}
\underline{}\;\;1.\;p \lor q & \\
\underline{}\;\;2.\;{\sim}p & \\
3.\;p & \\
4.\;p\,\&\,{\sim}p & 3,\,2,\,\&I \\
5.\;q & 4,\,{\sim}E \\
\\
6.\;q & \\
7.\;q & 6,\,\text{Repeat} \\
8.\;q & 1,\,3\text{--}5,\,6\text{--}7,\,\textbf{v}E \\
\end{array}
$$

The use of "Repeat" as a justification for a line in which a previous line is written down again will be discussed shortly in connection with the rule of ∼∼E.

The operators &, ⊃, v, ≡, and ∼ are called *connectives*. Further connectives will be introduced in Chapter Three, but these five are the ones most commonly used, and the only ones that we shall discuss in the present chapter.

THE RULE OF $\sim\sim$I

Not all of the ten rules for introducing and eliminating logical connectives discussed so far are, strictly speaking, independent. We could have constructed deduction schemata to show how some of them can be derived from the others. Such constructions, however, would have been fairly complex. They are best carried out only after the use of the rules has become familiar. Yet one instance of an introduction rule that can be derived without difficulty is the first of the final pair that we shall consider as basic. This is *Double-Negation-Introduction*, $\sim\sim$I:

$\sim\sim$I
$$p$$
$$\therefore \sim\sim p$$

The rule is established by this deduction schema

$$
\begin{array}{ll}
\text{1. } p & \\
\text{2. } \sim p & \\
\text{3. } p \ \& \sim p & 1, 2, \&I \\
\text{4. } \sim\sim p & 2\text{-}3, \sim I
\end{array}
$$

THE RULE OF $\sim\sim$E

Finally, we shall need a rule permitting us to eliminate—"cancel out"—pairs of iterated negation symbols. In Section 2.5 we state in detail the conditions under which such cancellation is possible. It is important to do this because the negation sign in logic does not in general behave like the minus sign in algebra. Thus $\sim(\sim A \vee \sim B)$ does *not* reduce to $A \vee B$. For the moment, we shall simply state the rule on which such cancellations as are permitted depend:

$\sim\sim$E
$$\sim\sim p$$
$$\therefore p$$

The use of $\sim\sim$E is illustrated by the following schematic derivation of the *Law of the Excluded Middle*, for centuries regarded as one of the ultimate axioms of logic but appearing here as derivative.

$$
\begin{array}{ll}
\text{1. } \sim(p \vee \sim p) & \\
\text{2. } p & \\
\text{3. } p \vee \sim p & 2, \vee I \\
\text{4. } (p \vee \sim p) \ \& \sim(p \vee \sim p) & 3, 1, \&I \\
\text{5. } \sim p & 2\text{-}4, \sim I \\
\text{6. } p \vee \sim p & 5, \vee I \\
\text{7. } (p \vee \sim p) \ \& \sim(p \vee \sim p) & 6, 1, \&I \\
\text{8. } \sim\sim(p \vee \sim p) & 1\text{-}7, \sim I \\
\text{9. } p \vee \sim p & 8, \sim\sim E
\end{array}
$$

Thus, a statement is either true or false; there is no middle ground.

In the derivation of the rule DS, we repeated a line in the schema. Such repetition seems justified, but we may now introduce the rule of Repeat as a derived rule. The schema establishing this rule begins with any statement p and shows that it may be reintroduced later.

$$
\begin{array}{lll}
\text{1.} & p & \\
\text{2.} & \sim p & \\
\text{3.} & p \mathbin{\&} \sim p & 1, 2, \&I \\
\text{4.} & \sim\sim p & 2\text{–}3, \sim I \\
\text{5.} & p & 4, \sim\sim E
\end{array}
$$

Although it may not be immediately obvious from this schema, a line may be repeated only from broader scopes to narrower ones, that is, only within the scope of an assumption in which it initially occurs. Thus we state the rule with a restriction

Repeat p

        $\therefore p$ within the scope of the assumption in which p initially occurs.

The restriction on Repeat is but a special case of a more general warning: premises are not to be chosen from within the scopes of assumptions once these assumptions have been discharged. The following "deduction", for example, is in error.

$$
\begin{array}{lll}
\text{1.} & A \mathbin{\&} B & \\
\text{2.} & A & 1, \&E \\
\text{3.} & (A \mathbin{\&} B) \supset A & 1\text{–}2, \supset I \\
\text{4.} & A & 3, 1, \supset E \text{ (Erroneous)}
\end{array}
$$

We may illustrate the use of the rule of Repeat by observing that there is a symmetry between the rule of vI and the rule of vE introduced in the last section, so that if we begin with any statement p and apply vI to it we can always recover p by using vE. Thus

$$
\begin{array}{lll}
\text{1.} & p & \\
\text{2.} & p \mathbin{v} q & 1, vI \\
\text{3.} & p & \\
\text{4.} & p & 1, \text{Repeat} \\
\text{5.} & q & \\
\text{6.} & p & 1, \text{Repeat} \\
\text{7.} & p & 1, 3\text{–}4, 5\text{–}6, vE
\end{array}
$$

EXERCISE 2.3

I. Which, if any, of the following are *reductio* proofs? Exhibit the logical form of each such proof you find.

1. Assume that there are two different integers, I_1 and I_2, such that

$$(1) \quad I_1 + a = a$$
$$(2) \quad I_2 + a = a$$

Then by (1), $I_1 + I_2 = I_2$, and by (2) $I_2 + I_1 = I_1$. But by the commutative law, $I_1 + I_2 = I_2 + I_1$. Hence, $I_1 = I_2$.

2. Assume $a = b$. Now $a + c = a + c$. Hence, $a + c = b + c$. Thus if $a = b$, then $a + c = b + c$.

3. Assume $\sqrt{2} = m/n$. Cancel out common factors in numerator and denominator, leaving $\sqrt{2} = k/l$. Square both sides, obtaining $2 = k^2/l^2$. But this is possible only if k and l have at least one factor in common. Hence, $\sqrt{2} \neq m/n$.

4. Assume that $\pi = 3$. Then the area of a circle with radius $2''$ is 12. With a mechanical integrator, however, we find that the area of this circle with radius $2''$ is 12.57. Hence, $\pi \neq 3$.

5. There can be no integers between 0 and 1. For if there were then there would be a least such integer. Call this integer C. Then $0 < C < 1$. But if we multiply through this inequality by C we obtain $0 < C^2 < C$. Hence, C is not the least such integer.

II. Cite all the propositional rules used in each of the following. Reconstruct any lines that may have been omitted.

1. A v B, ~B; therefore, A.

2. A v B, ~A; therefore, B.

3.
> $[(A \supset B) \& A] \& [(B \supset C) \& \sim C]$
> A
> B
> C
> ~C
> C & ~C

Therefore, $\sim\{[(A \supset B) \& A] \& [(B \supset C) \& \sim C]\}$

4. $A \supset B$, ~~A; therefore, B.

5. A & B; therefore, ~~A & B.

6. A & ~~B; therefore, A & B.

7. ~~A & B; therefore, A & ~~B.

8. A, A $\supset$ B, B $\supset$ $\sim$A; therefore, A & $\sim$A; so C.

9. $\sim$A v B, $\sim\sim$A; therefore, B.

10. —— A $\supset$ C
   —— B $\supset$ C
   —— (A v B) $\supset$ $\sim$C
    —— A v B
       —A
        C
       —B
        C
       C
       $\sim$C
       C & $\sim$C
    $\sim$(A v B)

11. From A $\supset$ B and A $\supset$ $\sim$B, derive $\sim$A.

12. From $\sim$A $\supset$ $\sim$B, derive B $\supset$ A.

13. From $\sim$A v B, derive A $\supset$ B.

(In the following problems, missing premises may occasionally have to be supplied, and premises and conclusions may have to be paraphrased.)

14. Either the second trumpeter wasn't playing or the composer doubled the tonic. The second trumpeter was obviously playing; so the composer must have doubled the tonic.

15. If the light was red, the driver is guilty. It certainly was not the case that the light was not red; so the driver is certainly guilty.

16. A philosopher is a person who presents reasons and arguments in favor of his ideas. Nietzsche was a philosopher who never presented reasons and arguments; therefore he was a philologist.

17. A tree loses its leaves either when it's autumn or when the tree is dead. The tree behind the house had no leaves on it in June; so let's have it removed.

18. If Aristotle and Plato were both philosophers, it certainly is not the case that Aristotle was not a philosopher.

19. Logic supplies categories under which we can think correctly and is useful. And anything that is useful is worthwhile. But anything that categorizes one's thinking cannot be worthwhile, for categorized thinking cannot be applied in new ways; so we should all be politicians.

20. If God created light on the first day and the heavenly bodies on the fourth day, he created the sun on both the first and the fourth days. So it is obvious that he did not create light on the first day and the heavenly bodies on the fourth day.

21. Labor shall always demand better working conditions, and such a demand can never be unreasonable; so a demand for better working conditions is a reasonable demand.

22. Let us assume that Hume's position on causation is correct, and that his argument against miracles is sound. From Hume's position on causation, it follows that natural laws are never more than probably

		TABLE 2.1		
		INTRODUCTION	ELIMINATION	
$\&$	&I	p q $\therefore p \& q$	&E	$p \& q$ or $p \& q$ $\therefore p \quad \therefore q$
$\supset$	$\supset$ I	$\begin{array}{l} p \\ \vdots \\ q \\ \hline \therefore p \supset q \end{array}$	$\supset$ E	$p \supset q$ p $\therefore q$
$\vee$	vI	$\therefore \dfrac{p}{p \vee q}$ or $\therefore \dfrac{q}{p \vee q}$	vE	$p \vee q$ $\begin{array}{l} p \\ \vdots \\ r \end{array}$ $\begin{array}{l} q \\ \vdots \\ r \end{array}$ $\therefore r$
$\equiv$	$\equiv$ I	$(p \supset q) \& (q \supset p)$ $\therefore p \equiv q$	$\equiv$ E	$p \equiv q$ $\therefore (p \supset q) \& (q \supset p)$
$\sim$	$\sim$ I	$\begin{array}{l} p \\ \vdots \\ q \& \sim q \\ \hline \therefore \sim p \end{array}$	$\sim$ E	$p \& \sim p$ $\therefore q$
$\sim\sim$	$\sim\sim$ I	$\dfrac{p}{\therefore \sim\sim p}$	$\sim\sim$ E	$\dfrac{\sim\sim p}{\therefore p}$

true. But if natural laws are never more than probably true, it makes sense to speak of evidence that contradicts such laws, and thus it makes sense to claim that miracles have occurred. So if we assume that Hume's position on causation is correct, and that his argument against miracles is sound, it follows that his argument against miracles isn't sound. Consequently, we cannot assume that Hume's position on causation is correct and that his argument against miracles is sound.

23. Many good effects have followed from the development of the atomic bomb. But if good effects have followed from its development, humanity has been benefited, and it is not unfortunate that the United States developed the bomb. And if it is fortunate that the bomb was developed, we should all be grateful rather than sorry about its development. So let us not be ungrateful.

2.4   A List of Important Propositional Rules

The purpose of this section is to provide for easy reference to the rules. We begin by recapitulating, on page 39, the rules that we are treating as basic.

In preceding sections we have derived some further rules which serve as abbreviations in deductions, such as CD, MT, DS, and the laws of importation and exportation. In the table below we present the most useful rules that can be derived from those of Table 2.1:

TABLE 2.2

Modus Tollens (MT)	$p \supset q$	
	$\sim q$	
	$\therefore \sim p$	
Hypothetical Syllogism (HS)	$p \supset q$	
	$q \supset r$	
	$\therefore p \supset r$	
Disjunctive Syllogism (DS)	$p \vee q$	$p \vee q$
	$\sim p$	$\sim q$
	$\therefore q$	$\therefore p$
Constructive Dilemma (CD)	I	II
	$p \vee q$	$p \vee q$
	$p \supset r$	$p \supset r$
	$q \supset r$	$q \supset s$
	$\therefore r$	$\therefore r \vee s$
Destructive Dilemma (DD)	$\sim p \vee \sim q$	
	$r \supset p$	
	$s \supset q$	
	$\therefore \sim r \vee \sim s$	

Repeat

$$p$$
$$\therefore\ p \quad \text{within the scope of the assumption in which } p \text{ initially occurs.}$$

De Morgan's Laws (DM)

(a)	(b)	(c)	(d)
$\sim(p\ \&\ q)$	$\sim p \lor \sim q$	$\sim(p \lor q)$	$\sim p\ \&\ \sim q$
$\therefore\ \sim p \lor \sim q$	$\therefore\ \sim(p\ \&\ q)$	$\therefore\ \sim p\ \&\ \sim q$	$\therefore\ \sim(p \lor q)$

Commutative Laws (CM)

(a)	(b)	(c)	(d)
$p\ \&\ q$	$q\ \&\ p$	$p \lor q$	$q \lor p$
$\therefore\ q\ \&\ p$	$\therefore\ p\ \&\ q$	$\therefore\ q \lor p$	$\therefore\ p \lor q$

Distributive Laws (Dist)

(a)	(b)
$p\ \&\ (q \lor r)$	$(p\ \&\ q) \lor (p\ \&\ r)$
$\therefore\ (p\ \&\ q) \lor (p\ \&\ r)$	$\therefore\ p\ \&\ (q \lor r)$

(c)	(d)
$p \lor (q\ \&\ r)$	$(p \lor q)\ \&\ (p \lor r)$
$\therefore\ (p \lor q)\ \&\ (p \lor r)$	$\therefore\ p \lor (q\ \&\ r)$

Associative Laws (Assoc)

(a)	(b)	(c)	(d)
$p\ \&\ (q\ \&\ r)$	$(p\ \&\ q)\ \&\ r$	$p \lor (q \lor r)$	$(p \lor q) \lor r$
$\therefore\ (p\ \&\ q)\ \&\ r$	$\therefore\ p\ \&\ (q\ \&\ r)$	$\therefore\ (p \lor q) \lor r$	$\therefore\ p \lor (q \lor r)$

Law of Contraposition (Cp)

(a)	(b)
$p \supset q$	$\sim q \supset \sim p$
$\therefore\ \sim q \supset \sim p$	$\therefore\ p \supset q$

Law of Implication (Impl)

(a)	(b)
$p \supset q$	$\sim p \lor q$
$\therefore\ \sim p \lor q$	$\therefore\ p \supset q$

Law of Idempotence (Id)

(a)	(b)	(c)	(d)
p	$p\ \&\ p$	$p \lor p$	p
$\therefore\ p\ \&\ p$	$\therefore\ p$	$\therefore\ p$	$\therefore\ p \lor p$

Law of Exportation (Exp)

$$(p\ \&\ q) \supset r$$
$$\therefore\ p \supset (q \supset r)$$

Law of Importation (Imp)

$$p \supset (q \supset r)$$
$$\therefore\ (p\ \&\ q) \supset r$$

According to the rule of $\equiv$I, we could summarize the statement of such rules as DM, CM, Dist, Assoc, Cp, Impl, Exp, and Imp. Consider, for example, (a) of DM:

$$\textbf{1. } \sim(p \mathbin{\&} q)$$
$$\textbf{2. } \sim p \vee \sim q$$

Let us discharge line 1:

> **1.** $\sim(p \mathbin{\&} q)$
> **2.** $\sim p \vee \sim q$ 1, DM
>
> **3.** $\sim(p \mathbin{\&} q) \supset (\sim p \vee \sim q)$ 1–2, $\supset$I

Let us now continue by treating version (b) in the same way:

> **4.** $\sim p \vee \sim q$
> **5.** $\sim(p \mathbin{\&} q)$ 4, DM
>
> **6.** $(\sim p \vee \sim q) \supset \sim(p \mathbin{\&} q)$ 4–5, $\supset$I

We now use &I to conjoin lines 3 and 5:

$$\textbf{7. } [\sim(p \mathbin{\&} q) \supset (\sim p \vee \sim q)] \mathbin{\&}$$
$$[(\sim p \vee \sim q) \supset \sim(p \mathbin{\&} q)] \qquad 3, 6, \text{\&I}$$

This puts us in a position to use $\equiv$I:

$$\textbf{8. } \sim(p \mathbin{\&} q) \equiv (\sim p \vee \sim q) \qquad 7, \equiv\text{I}$$

We could similarly derive biconditional versions of CM, Dist, Assoc, Cp, and so on.

In addition to the derivation of these zero-premise biconditionals, we may also derive other zero-premise conclusions by discharging assumptions via rules $\vee$E, $\sim$I, and $\supset$I. Thus, we have the schema

> **1.** $p \mathbin{\&} \sim p$
> **2.** $p \mathbin{\&} \sim p$ 1, Repeat
>
> **3.** $\sim(p \mathbin{\&} \sim p)$ 1–2, $\sim$I

Line 3 is the *Law of Noncontradiction* (more often called the *Law of Contradiction*), and is traditionally regarded as a fundamental logical principle. Another example of a zero-premise conclusion is found in the Law of Excluded Middle for which we have already given the deduction schema.

As we shall see shortly, it is often desirable to refer to a zero-premise conclusion schema or instance of such a schema out of its context in a deduction schema or deduction. To do this we must distinguish it from lines that are not ZPC but use the same symbols. We make this distinction by prefixing $\vdash$ to the line which is a zero-premise conclusion. Thus, we may list the lines referred to so far as in Table 2.3.

TABLE 2.3

Repeat
$$\vdash \quad p \equiv p$$

DM
$$\vdash \quad \sim(p \mathbin{\&} q) \equiv (\sim p \mathbin{\mathbf{v}} \sim q)$$
$$\vdash \quad \sim(p \mathbin{\mathbf{v}} q) \equiv (\sim p \mathbin{\&} \sim q)$$

CM
$$\vdash \quad (p \mathbin{\&} q) \equiv (q \mathbin{\&} p)$$
$$\vdash \quad (p \mathbin{\mathbf{v}} q) \equiv (q \mathbin{\mathbf{v}} p)$$

Dist
$$\vdash \quad [p \mathbin{\&} (q \mathbin{\mathbf{v}} r)] \equiv [(p \mathbin{\&} q) \mathbin{\mathbf{v}} (p \mathbin{\&} r)]$$
$$\vdash \quad [p \mathbin{\mathbf{v}} (q \mathbin{\&} r)] \equiv [(p \mathbin{\mathbf{v}} q) \mathbin{\&} (p \mathbin{\mathbf{v}} r)]$$

Assoc
$$\vdash \quad [p \mathbin{\&} (q \mathbin{\&} r)] \equiv [(p \mathbin{\&} q) \mathbin{\&} r]$$
$$\vdash \quad [p \mathbin{\mathbf{v}} (q \mathbin{\mathbf{v}} r)] \equiv [(p \mathbin{\mathbf{v}} q) \mathbin{\mathbf{v}} r]$$

Cp
$$\vdash \quad (p \supset q) \equiv (\sim q \supset \sim p)$$

Impl
$$\vdash \quad (p \supset q) \equiv (\sim p \mathbin{\mathbf{v}} q)$$

Id
$$\vdash \quad p \equiv (p \mathbin{\&} p)$$
$$\vdash \quad p \equiv (p \mathbin{\mathbf{v}} p)$$

Exp
$$\vdash \quad [(p \mathbin{\&} q) \supset r] \equiv [p \supset (q \supset r)$$

Double Negation (DN)
$$\vdash \quad p \equiv \sim\sim p$$

Law of Excluded Middle
$$\vdash \quad p \mathbin{\mathbf{v}} \sim p$$

Law of Noncontradiction
$$\vdash \quad \sim(p \mathbin{\&} \sim p)$$

Any zero-premise conclusion schema may be thought of as an abbreviation for the deduction schema which results in it; hence, it may be introduced as a line into a deduction schema at any point, because the whole of its deduction schema could be introduced at any point. Similarly, any instance of a zero-premise conclusion schema may be introduced at any point in a deduction. We may illustrate this use of ZPC's in the following example.

> If the grid voltage is negative, there is a plate current. If the grid voltage is positive, there is a plate current. So there is always a plate current.

Assuming that the grid voltage is positive is equivalent to the grid voltage is not negative, we symbolize as

$$\text{—— 1. } N \supset P$$
$$\text{—— 2. } \sim N \supset P \quad /\therefore \; P$$

(The symbol $/\therefore$ sets off a conclusion alleged to follow from given premises.) Using Cp, Impl, DM, &E and other rules, we can deduce the conclusion without too much effort. But if we introduce N for p in $\vdash p \vee \sim p$, the desired conclusion follows immediately.

$$\text{3. } N \vee \sim N \qquad \text{ZPC}$$
$$\text{4. } P \qquad\qquad 1, 2, 3, \text{CD I}$$

Similar uses of ZPC's often facilitate proof.

EXERCISE 2.4

I. Derive each of the following rules, taken from Table 2.2, from those given in Table 2.1. (Study the derivations of DS, MT, CD, Exp, etc., given in the text, as a guide.)

1. Hypothetical Syllogism: $\quad p \supset q$
$\qquad\qquad\qquad\qquad\qquad\qquad q \supset r \quad /\therefore \quad p \supset r$

2. Idempotence: $\qquad\qquad\quad p \qquad\quad /\therefore \quad p \& p$
$\qquad\qquad\qquad$ and
$\qquad\qquad\qquad\qquad\qquad\qquad p \vee p \quad /\therefore \quad p$

3. Commutativity of $\vee$: $\qquad p \vee q \quad /\therefore \quad q \vee p$
$\qquad\qquad\qquad$ and
$\qquad\qquad\qquad\qquad\qquad\qquad q \vee p \quad /\therefore \quad p \vee q$

4. Contraposition: $\qquad\qquad p \supset q \quad /\therefore \; \sim q \supset \sim p$
$\qquad\qquad\qquad$ and
$\qquad\qquad\qquad\qquad\qquad\quad \sim q \supset \sim p \quad /\therefore \quad p \supset q$

5. Destructive Dilemma: $\qquad \sim p \vee \sim q$
$\qquad\qquad\qquad\qquad\qquad\qquad r \supset p$
$\qquad\qquad\qquad\qquad\qquad\qquad s \supset q \quad /\therefore \; \sim r \vee \sim s$

6. Implication: $\qquad\qquad\quad p \supset q \quad /\therefore \; \sim p \vee q$
$\qquad\qquad\qquad$ and
$\qquad\qquad\qquad\qquad\qquad\quad \sim p \vee q \qquad /\therefore \quad p \supset q$

II. Derive each of the following from the rules given in Table 2.1, those derived in the above exercises, and those derived in the text. (DS, Exp, Imp, MT, CD, Assoc, and CM of &.)

1. DeMorgan's Laws: $\sim(p \,\&\, q)$ $/\therefore$ $\sim p \vee \sim q$

        and

           $\sim p \vee \sim q$ $/\therefore$ $\sim(p \,\&\, q)$

        and

           $\sim(p \vee q)$ $/\therefore$ $\sim p \,\&\, \sim q$

        and

           $\sim p \,\&\, \sim q$ $/\therefore$ $\sim(p \vee q)$

2. Distributive Laws: $p \,\&\, (q \vee r) \;/\therefore\; (p \,\&\, q) \vee (p \,\&\, r)$

        and

           $(p \,\&\, q) \vee (p \,\&\, r) \;/\therefore\; p \,\&\, (q \vee r)$

        and

           $p \vee (q \,\&\, r) \;/\therefore\; (p \vee q) \,\&\, (p \vee r)$

        and

           $(p \vee q) \,\&\, (p \vee r) \;/\therefore\; p \vee (q \,\&\, r)$

III. Express each of the following rules as a conditional or biconditional zero-premise conclusion, or, where appropriate, as two such conclusions.

    1. $\supset$E

    2. $\vee$I

    3. $\sim$E

    4. $\sim\sim$I and $\sim\sim$E

    5. Modus Tollens

    6. Hypothetical Syllogism

    7. Disjunctive Syllogism

    8. Constructive Dilemma

    9. Destructive Dilemma

   10. DeMorgan's Laws

   11. Commutative Laws

   12. Distributive Laws

   13. Associative Laws

   14. Law of Contraposition

   15. Law of Implication

   16. Law of Idempotence

   17. Laws of Exportation and Importation

   18. Biconditional Introduction and Elimination

IV. Write out premises and conclusions in ordinary English to illustrate each of the rules given in Table 2.1 and Table 2.2.

2.5 Names, Statements, and Schemata

In the previous pages we have not only used many sentences and statements, we have talked *about* them. As a means of attaining clarity in speaking
about them, we have used a number of devices to which we are now going to
refer explicitly in order to achieve a more fundamental understanding of our
enterprise. However, an intuitive grasp of these devices has been sufficient
for understanding the exposition so far and will be sufficient through Chapter
Seven.

In Chapter One the following sentence occurs on page 7:

(1) Here for A and B one could substitute sentences like "It is before
eleven o'clock", "The earth is flat", $a < a$, and so on.

In the present chapter the following sentence occurs on page 19:

(2) Using N for "It is noon" and T for "The temperature is 84°",
we have

———1. N
———2. T
   3. N & T   1, 2, &1

A reflective examination of the use of italics, quotation marks, and display
in these passages raises important questions regarding usage. Let us introduce
some concepts permitting the analysis of such usage.

The first concept is that of a *name*. We normally use names in the following way:

(3) Tom is fat.
(4) Berlin is exciting.

We sometimes also say, for example,

(5) "Tom" is a short word.
(6) "Berlin" is the name of Berlin.

In (3), the word "Tom" is used as the name of a man. Sentence (5), on the
other hand, makes no use of the name of a man; it is concerned rather with
the name of a name, as is indicated by enclosing "Tom" in quotes. (4) and
(6) are similarly related. In (6) both the name of a city and the name of that
name are used.

It is customary to say that in (3) the word "Tom" is *used*, whereas in (5)
the word "Tom" is *mentioned*. Thus in (4) "Berlin" is used, whereas in (6)
it is first mentioned and then used. This use of quotation marks to designate
a name which is mentioned is standard. Notice that there are actually several
devices for mentioning a name. For example, the name may be separated from
the text and *displayed*. Thus, we say the word

Tom

is used in (3). Or, again, the name may be *italicized*. Thus we say *Berlin* is mentioned in (4). And we may use a phrase such as "the word . . . " or "the name . . . " to call attention to the fact that we are mentioning, not using, a word and hence feel no need to use any other device in addition.

Where it seems advisable, devices of this sort will be used to avoid confusion of use and mention. However, we do not take so much care in the case of symbols. It is standard mathematical usage to permit symbols to refer to themselves, for in most cases no real difficulties arise because of this. Hence, although symbols are often displayed, as when we say that

$$A, B, C, \ldots$$

are statements; symbols also appear in the context of a discussion as names. Thus in (2) N and T (as names) refer to themselves. That is, we could say

Using the letter N for . . .

or

Using "N" for . . .

We do not do this because it is contrary to mathematical practice and serves no real purpose.

Of course, names need not be limited to one word. Even the ordinary names of things are often quite long. In our discussion in previous chapters, furthermore, we have had occasion to refer to sentences as such. Thus in (1) above we mention the sentence "The earth is flat". This implies that sentences, like names, may be used or mentioned. Indeed, the sentence immediately preceding this one is used. There are many occasions, however, in a book on logic to mention sentences. For example,

(7) "The cat is black" is true.
(8) In (4) "Berlin" is used.
(9) (4) is false.

In (7) we mention the sentence "The cat is black" and assert a predicate of it. In (8) we mention the sentence "Berlin is exciting" by referring to one of its names, that is, (4). Hence (4), being a name, does not need quotes.

In the preceding pages (and in the following), we distinguish between actual sentences in ordinary language which are true or false as the case may be and logical statements, written with capital letters A, B, C, ... The logical statements are variables having particular true or false sentences as substituents. Thus we may say A is true or false, but unless we know what sentence has been substituted for it in a given case we cannot determine which it is. As indicated in Section 2, we also distinguish between logical statements and schemata. Schemata are written with lower case italic letters $p, q, r, \ldots$. The basis of this distinction is that, whereas A, B, C, . . . are variables having particular sentences as substituents, $p, q, r, \ldots$ are variables that take logical statements as substituents.

One additional point of nomenclature may now be introduced. The statements A, B, C, ... are simple in the sense that they contain no logical connectives. We shall call them *atomic statements* for this reason. On the other hand, statements built up from atomic statements and logical connectives are compound. We shall call such statements *compound* or *molecular*. An example of a molecular statement is (A v B) & C. Notice that we cannot always distinguish between atomic and molecular statements when we use schematic forms. Thus p may have as substituents either atomic or molecular statements, and $p \vee q$ can yield, as the result of substitution, not only A v B and X v Y, but also (C ⊃ D) v (E & F), etc.

The use of these variables introduces expressions made up of such variables and logical connectives. We have called these *schemata*. Examples of schemata are $p \& q$, $\sim p$, $(p \equiv q) \vee r$.

A schema, of course, is not a statement, but is rather a form of a statement. Consider, for example, the schema $p \& q$. What the rule of &E asserts is that when a line of a proof consists of a statement of the *form p & q*, we may write as a further line one of the component statements. We are thus able to express the logical rules with great generality. In terms of schemata we can now formulate an extremely useful definition of the conception of *statement*, to which we shall refer several times in this book.

Statement: (1) A, B, C, ... are statements.

(2) If p is a statement, then $\sim p$ is a statement.

(3) If p is a statement and q is a statement, then $(p \& q)$ is a statement.*

(4) If p is a statement and q is a statement, then $(p \supset q)$ is a statement.

(5) If p is a statement and q is a statement, then $(p \vee q)$ is a statement.

(6) If p is a statement and q is a statement, then $(p \equiv q)$ is a statement.

(7) Nothing else is a statement.

What we here define as a *statement* is also called a *well-formed formula*, often abbreviated as wff.

EXERCISE 2.5

I. Point out each instance of a name in the following, and decide whether it is (a) used, or (b) mentioned.

1. A is a statement.

2. A & B is a statement.

---

* Notice that as a matter of practice we omit the parentheses occurring in the definition of "statement" when no loss of clarity results.

3. A and B are statements.

4. Tom is tall and handsome.

5. "Tom is tall and handsome" is a sentence.

6. "Tom" is a shorter word than is "Thomas".

7. " 'Tom is tall and handsome' is a sentence" is itself a sentence.

8. That "Tom" is shorter than "Ed" is false.

9. " 'Tom' is shorter than 'Ed' " is false. " ' "Tom" is shorter than "Ed" ' is false" is a sentence.

10. Tom is shorter than Ed.

11. "Tom is shorter than Ed" is true.

12. If " 'Tom' is shorter than 'Ed' " is symbolized as A, then A is false.

13. (1) through (10) above are all false.

14. Statement (11) is false.

15. "Londres est belle" means "London is beautiful".

16. " 'Londres' est un beau mot" does not necessarily mean " 'London' is a beautiful word".

17. Any statement, *p*, must be either true or false.

18. A, B, C, . . . are statements, and if *p* is a statement, then ∼*p* is a statement.

19. The sentence " 'Tom' is a short word" may be used or mentioned; when it is used it refers to the name "Tom", but when it is mentioned it refers to itself.

20. $p \supset [q \equiv (r \,\&\, s)]$ is a form made up of variables and logical connectives.

II. Punctuate the following sentences where necessary.

1. Johann ist hier is a statement about a fellow named Johann.

2. If I know that John is here, I know something about John.

3. Gotham is one of the names for New York City, and New York is another.

4. Governor Rockefeller wishes to change the way New York State is governed.

5. Professor Jones wishes to change the way New York State is spelled.

6. Birmingham is an attractive city in spite of the fact that it is called the Pittsburgh of the South.

7. The name of the seventeenth-century philosopher Gottfried Wilhelm Leibniz is sometimes written in its latinized form, Leibnitz, although the German spelling Leibniz is generally preferred today.

8. That New York is larger than Yaoundé is generally accepted; so it is not the case that Yaoundé is larger than New York is true.

9. If Kano is south of Douala is false, then it cannot be true that Douala is south of Dschang unless Kano is south of Dschang.

10. $xy > z$ is a mathematical formula generally interpreted to mean the product of x and y is greater than z.

III. Each of the following statements can be thought of as exemplifying more than one logical schema, one of which forms is *the* schema (*i.e.*, the schema in which *each* distinct atomic statement is replaced by a distinct variable). Name as many schemata for each statement as you can, pointing out which one is *the* form. (*E.g.*, $p \vee q$ and $p \vee (q \mathbin{\&} r)$ are forms of (A & B) ∨ (C & D), but $(p \mathbin{\&} q) \vee (r \mathbin{\&} s)$ is *the* form.)

1. (A & B) ⊃ C

2. (A & B) ⊃ (C ∨ D)

3. (A & B) ⊃ (C ∨ A)

4. [A ⊃ (B ⊃ A)] ⊃ A

5. A ⊃ [(B & C) ⊃ A]

6. {A ⊃ [(B & C) ⊃ A]} ⊃ A

7. {A ⊃ [(B & C) ⊃ A]} ⊃ [A ∨ ∼(B & C)]

8. ∼A ⊃ [A ≡ (C & ∼C)]

9. A ∨ [A ⊃ (B & C)]

10. ∼[(A ∨ B) & (A ∨ ∼B) & (∼A ∨ B) & (∼A ∨ ∼B)]

11. ∼[∼(A ∨ ∼B) ∨ ∼(∼A ∨ B)] ≡ (A ≡ B)

12. (A ∨ B) ≡ {[A ≡ (A & B)] ≡ [A ≡ (A & B)]}

IV. Explain why each of the statements given in exercise III above is a statement. (*I.e.*, why or how does it fit the definition given on p. 48?)

2.6 Rule of Replacement

Considering the sentence "It is not the case both that it is not noon and that the temperature is not 84°", the following lines in deduction seem plausible:

(1)   —— 1. ∼(∼N & ∼T)
                —— 2. ∼∼N ∨ ∼∼T   1, DM
                    3. N ∨ T   2, ?

Nonetheless, this deduction is not the same as

(2) ————— **1.** $\sim\!\sim$N
                 2. N   1, DN

Here the second line is clearly an instance of the rule DN, but the third line in the first deduction is not. We might say that in the first deduction we used DN twice, once for $\sim\!\sim$N and once for $\sim\!\sim$T but this would be an ellipsis. What we did was to *replace* $\sim\!\sim$N by its equivalent N and $\sim\!\sim$T by its equivalent T.

The third line of the first deduction is justified by noting that $\vdash$ N $\equiv \sim\!\sim$N and $\vdash$ T $\equiv \sim\!\sim$T and by replacing $\sim\!\sim$N and $\sim\!\sim$T by their equivalents. Thus

(3) ————— **1.** $\sim$($\sim$N & $\sim$T)
                 2. $\sim\!\sim$N v $\sim\!\sim$T   1, DM
                 3. N v $\sim\!\sim$T   2, DN, Rep
                 4. N v T   3, DN, Rep

Here, Rep stands for the *Rule of Replacement*.

Another instance of the use of this rule (as a preliminary to stating it) may begin with a consideration of the sentence "It is not the case both that today is not Tuesday and that today is not Wednesday". We write

(4) ——— **1.** $\sim$($\sim$T & $\sim$W)
             2. $\sim\!\sim$(T v W)   1, DM, Rep
             3. T v W   2, DN, Rep (or 2, $\sim\!\sim$E)

The second line is reached by noting that $\vdash \sim$(p v q) $\equiv$ ($\sim p$ & $\sim q$) and replacing the instance of the right side in line 1 by its equivalent. This equivalence is formed from DM. Line 3 is reached by noting the biconditional $\vdash p \equiv \sim\!\sim p$ and by Rep.

The rule of replacement has this schematic form

Rep: Let L be a line of a deduction containing q at one place or more and let L* be like L except for containing p at one or more places where L contained q, and where p and q may be compound statements. Under these conditions

(1)   If $p \equiv q$, then
                            L   and   L*
                    $\therefore$ L* $\therefore$ L·
                        that is, L $\equiv$ L*

(2)   If $\vdash p \equiv q$, then $\vdash$ L $\equiv$ L*

The rule of replacement is a derived rule—for the proof of it see the next paragraphs—and it serves as an abbreviation for the specific deductions which would have to be found if it were unavailable. In general it is customary to omit reference to it in justifying steps in a deduction.

A derivation of the rule of replacement is not too difficult, although it must be reached by mathematical induction. It is given here for the reader familiar with this tool and in anticipation of many similar arguments in Part Two.*

The derived rules so far considered have been abbreviations for all specific deductions of a certain form. Fortunately, we have been able to present these specific deductions in a single deduction schema. Hence, the formulation of the relevant deduction schema provided the derivation of the rule. This kind of derivation is known as *metatheoretical*; it is not a specific deduction itself, but it is concerned with the establishment of specific deductions. Although the derivation of the rule of replacement is metatheoretical as well, there is no single deduction schema which can represent all the specific deductions involved. In fact, we need an infinite number of deduction schemata to do this.

The reason for the need of so many deduction schemata is that the rule of replacement justifies moving from *any* line in which a statement q might occur to another line in which it has been replaced at one or more instances by p. Thus we must consider every possible line in any deduction schema in order to derive the rule of Rep. Our method of considering these possible lines is to think of them in order of increasing complexity. Thus A ∨ B is more complex than A alone, because it embeds A in an alternative context. (A ∨ B) & C is still more complex; here the alternation in which A is embedded is itself embedded in a conjunctive context. Similarly, there are contexts of contexts of contexts, and so on. If we wish to prove that given $p \equiv q$ we can replace q by p in any line L, we must show that this is possible for an L of any complexity whatever. We want to be able to justify, for example, not only the inference

$$\begin{array}{lll} \text{1.} & \text{A} \equiv \sim\sim\text{A} & \text{ZPC} \\ \underline{}\ \text{2.} & \sim\sim\text{A} \vee \text{B} & \\ \text{3.} & \text{A} \vee \text{B,} & \end{array}$$

in which A is embedded in an alternative context, but also the inference

$$\begin{array}{lll} \text{1.} & \text{A} \equiv \sim\sim\text{A} & \text{ZPC} \\ \underline{}\ \text{2.} & \text{D} \equiv \sim[(\sim\sim\text{A} \vee \text{B}) \,\&\, \text{C}] & \\ \text{3.} & \text{D} \equiv \sim[(\text{A} \vee \text{B}) \,\&\, \text{C}], & \end{array}$$

where the context in which A is embedded is much more complex.

Our proof of Rep uses the principle of mathematical induction. We show that Rep holds for all lines of zero complexity—this is the basis of the induction. We then show that if Rep holds for a line of any given complexity it also

---

* The reader unfamiliar with the use of mathematical induction may omit these sections without loss of continuity by accepting Rep. Mathematical induction is, of course, a strictly deductive type of reasoning.

holds for a line of the next higher order of complexity—this is the induction step. Since the order of complexity of any line is measured by the number of connectives in it, we can express what we are trying to prove in this step by saying "If Rep holds for a line containing n connectives, it holds for a line containing $n + 1$ connectives". In any event, having established both the basis and the induction step, we conclude that Rep holds for all lines, regardless of their complexity or number of connectives.*

Let us discuss the basis and the induction step separately.

Basis: If we consider a line, L, in which q is embedded in no context whatever, there being no connectives in L, then L is just q. Since Rep stipulates that $p \equiv q$, and L* is p, we have immediately that $L \equiv L^*$ for all such maximally simple lines. This completes the proof of the basis.

Induction Step: We want to show now that if $(p \equiv q) \supset (L \equiv L^*)$ for L of any given complexity, then $(p \equiv q) \supset [f(L) \equiv f(L^*)]$, where $f(L)$ is either $\sim$L, or r & L, or r v L, or $r \supset L$, or $L \supset r$, or $r \equiv L$, and similarly for L*. (Since conjunction, alternation, and the biconditional commute, we do not have to consider L & r, L v r, or $L \equiv r$ separately.) In other words, we must show that when Rep holds for L of given complexity, it also holds for L of the next higher order of complexity. We proceed to consider separately each of the cases mentioned.

I. *Negative Context:* $\sim$L. We give a schema showing that the inference from $(p \equiv q) \supset (L \equiv L^*)$ to $(p \equiv q) \supset (\sim L \equiv \sim L^*)$ is justified.

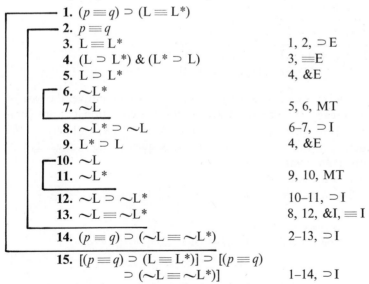

1. $(p \equiv q) \supset (L \equiv L^*)$		
2. $p \equiv q$		
3. $L \equiv L^*$	1, 2, $\supset$E	
4. $(L \supset L^*)$ & $(L^* \supset L)$	3, $\equiv$E	
5. $L \supset L^*$	4, &E	
6. $\sim L^*$		
7. $\sim L$	5, 6, MT	
8. $\sim L^* \supset \sim L$	6–7, $\supset$I	
9. $L^* \supset L$	4, &E	
10. $\sim L$		
11. $\sim L^*$	9, 10, MT	
12. $\sim L \supset \sim L^*$	10–11, $\supset$I	
13. $\sim L \equiv \sim L^*$	8, 12, &I, $\equiv$I	
14. $(p \equiv q) \supset (\sim L \equiv \sim L^*)$	2–13, $\supset$I	
15. $[(p \equiv q) \supset (L \equiv L^*)] \supset [(p \equiv q)$ $\supset (\sim L \equiv \sim L^*)]$	1–14, $\supset$I	

---

* When q is a compound statement, the connectives internal to it are not regarded as affecting the complexity of the line in which it occurs.

II. *Conjunctive Context.* We next give a schema showing that the inference from $(p \equiv q) \supset (L \equiv L^*)$ to $(p \equiv q) \supset [(r \& L) \equiv (r \& L^*)]$ is justified.*

1. $(p \equiv q) \supset (L \equiv L^*)$	
2. $p \equiv q$	
3. $L \equiv L^*$	1, 2, $\supset$E
4. $(L \supset L^*) \& (L^* \supset L)$	3, $\equiv$E
5. $r \& L$	
6. $L \supset L^*$	4, &E
7. L	5, &E
8. L^*	6, 7, $\supset$E
9. r	5, &E
10. $r \& L^*$	9, 8, &I
11. $(r \& L) \supset (r \& L^*)$	5–10, $\supset$I
12. $r \& L^*$	
13. $L^* \supset L$	4, &E
14. L^*	12, &E
15. L	13, 14, $\supset$E
16. r	12, &E
17. $r \& L$	16, 15, &I
18. $(r \& L^*) \supset (r \& L)$	12–17, $\supset$I
19. $(r \& L) \equiv (r \& L^*)$	11, 18, &I, $\equiv$I
20. $(p \equiv q) \supset [(r \& L) \equiv (r \& L^*)]$	2–19, $\supset$I
21. $[(p \equiv q) \supset (L \equiv L^*)] \supset \{(p \equiv q)$	
$\quad \supset [(r \& L) \equiv (r \& L^*)]\}$	1–20, $\supset$I

III. *Conditional Context.* Since conjunction is commutative, the case of L & r is already covered by II above. But the conditional is not commutative. Thus we have to consider both the situation in which L is the antecedent and that in which it is the consequent. These cases, as well as all others, are left as an exercise.

(a) L is the antecedent
To be proved: $[(p \equiv q) \supset (L \equiv L^*)] \supset \{(p \equiv q) \supset [(L \supset r)$
$\equiv (L^* \supset r)]\}$

(b) L is the consequent
To be proved: $[(p \equiv q) \supset (L \equiv L^*)] \supset \{(p \equiv q) \supset [(r \supset L)$
$\equiv (r \supset L^*)]\}$

---

* When r is a compound statement, the connectives internal to it are not regarded as affecting the order of complexity of the line in which it occurs unless r contains p, in which case we treat the compound by means of the arguments for the relevant connectives.

IV. *Alternative Context:*

To be proved: $[(p \equiv q) \supset (L \equiv L^*)] \supset \{(p \equiv q) \supset [(r \lor L)$
$$\equiv (r \lor L^*)]\}$$

V. *Biconditional Context:*

To be proved: $[(p \equiv q) \supset (L \equiv L^*)] \supset \{(p \equiv q) \supset [(r \equiv L)$
$$\equiv (r \equiv L^*)]\}$$

We have shown that the first form of Rep holds where there are no logical connectives outside p and q and that if it holds where there are n such logical connectives it holds for $n + 1$. It therefore holds in general.

The second form of Rep, if $\vdash p \equiv q$, then $\vdash L \equiv L^*$, follows directly. We have established the existence of deductions of the form

> **1.** $p \equiv q$
> **2.** $L \equiv L^*$

we may therefore add the following lines in every case:

> **3.** $p \equiv q \supset L \equiv L^*$ 1, 2, $\supset$I
> **4.** $p \equiv q$ ZPC Condition of Rep 2nd Version
> **5.** $L \equiv L^*$

In line 5, $L \equiv L^*$ is ZPC; hence $\vdash L \equiv L^*$.

EXERCISE 2.6

Carry out each of the proofs for the Rule of Replacement in the various elementary contexts for which proofs were not given in the text.

2.7   Rule of Substitution

Consider any rule discussed in this chapter; for example, &E:

$$p \& q$$
$$\therefore p$$

Now consider a specific deduction authorized by this schema; *e.g.*,

> **1.** N & T
> **2.** N   1, &E

How is the specific deduction related to the schema? Obviously there is a sense in which we have "substituted" N for p and T for q. This kind of substitution is justified by informal reasoning about the system and is not a rule of inference. In this respect it differs from the rule of replacement just considered. There is, however, a *Rule of Substitution* which is a rule of inference. We find it exemplified in

> **1.** A & B
> **2.** A   1, &E

when this deduction comes from the preceding one by substituting A for N, B for T.

In this we substitute one statement for another. Thus, we begin with a specific deduction and arrive at another specific deduction by substitution. Such substitution of one statement for another in a specific deduction is similar to the rule of replacement in being a rule of inference, but it differs in three important respects:

(1) The replacement of, say, $\sim\sim$A by A presupposes that A $\equiv$ $\sim\sim$A is a ZPC or an assumption. But when we substitute A for N, we are *not* presupposing that N $\equiv$ A is a ZPC or assumption.

(2) If we have, say, A v $\sim$A, and we know that $\vdash$ $\sim\sim$A $\equiv$ A, we can replace the left-hand A by $\sim\sim$A without touching the right-hand A in its negative context; we obtain $\sim\sim$A v $\sim$A. In other words, we do not have to replace A by $\sim\sim$A *throughout*. But if we wish to substitute in an instance of the rule of &E we must substitute the same letter for N throughout. Thus, we may form

> 1. A & T
> 2. A   1, &E

and we may form

> 1. X & Y
> 2. X   1, &E

but we are not permitted to form

> 1. N & T
> 2. X

(3) The statements substituted for must be atomic. Since substitution may be for atomic statements only, we may argue

> 1. A v $\sim$A
> 2. B v $\sim$B   1, Sub

but not

> 1. A v $\sim$A
> 2. A v C   1, (erroneous Sub)

Let us now speak briefly of some further ways in which substitution may occur.

(1) There is no reason why what we substitute for N and for T may not be compound statements. The following is perfectly permissible:

> 1. N & T
> 2. (A $\supset$ B) & (C $\supset$ D)   1, Sub in specific deduction
> 3. A $\supset$ B   2, &E

(2) On the other hand, there is no reason why what we substitute for N must differ from what we substitute for T. Thus

    1. N & T
    2. N & N   1, Sub in specific deduction
    3. N   2, &E

One thing we must avoid, however, is substituting anywhere within the scope of an assumption for the letters involved in the assumption itself. The following example illustrates the dangers arising from such illicit substitutions:

    1. A v B
    2. A v A   1, "Substitution"
    3. A   2, Id
    4. (A v B) ⊃ A   1–3, ⊃I

The obvious incorrectness of line 4 reveals the consequences of such an erroneous substitution. The root of the difficulty is that an assumption may hold for only some of the instances of the statements given or some other particular cases, but not in general.

We may summarize these points in a rule schema for substitution which can serve as justification for an inference in a deduction.

Sub: Where L_1 and L_2 represent any lines of a deduction and where L^*_1 and L^*_2 result from substitution for atomic statements throughout L_1 and L_2; and where the statements substituted are not necessarily different and may be compound; and the atomic statements substituted for do not occur in the assumptions within the scope of which the substitution takes place,

    if L_1
                           $\therefore\ L_2$

    then L^*_1
                           $\therefore\ L^*_2$

The rule of substitution can be derived. The derivation depends upon the fact that the form of a specific deduction remains intact through any correct substitution, as has been indicated in the examples given. In consequence, given a single specific deduction, we are entitled by Sub to write a deduction schema. That is, from

    1. E & F
    2. E   1, &E

we generalize to the schema

    $p\ \&\ q$
    $\therefore\ p$ 1, &E

Thus we may use any specific deduction as a deduction schema, as well as the converse.

The rule of substitution is, of course, not to be confused with the principle of substitution mentioned in Chapter One, the precise formulation of which is given in Chapter Five.

EXERCISE 2.7

I. **1.** Decide in each of the following cases whether the inference given is a valid substitution instance of &E.

   1. A & B, /∴ B

   2. A & A, /∴ A

   3. A & B, /∴ C

   4. (A & B) & (A & C), /∴ A & B

   5. A, B, /∴ A

   6. (A & B) & (A v C), /∴ A v C

   7. (A & B) & (A & C), /∴ B & C

   8. (A & B) & C, /∴ C

   9. (A & B) & C, /∴ A

  10. (A & B) v C, /∴ A & B

  11. A ⊃ (B & C), /∴ C

  12. A ⊃ (B & C), /∴ A ⊃ B

  13. [(A ⊃ B) v C] & D, /∴ (A ⊃ B) v C

  14. ∼A & ∼(B v C), /∴ ∼(B v C)

  15. (A & ∼B) ⊃ (∼C v ∼D), /∴ A ⊃ (∼C v ∼D)

2. For each of the following, decide whether it is (a) a valid substitution instance of one of DeMorgan's Laws as it stands, or whether it is (b) an instance of substitution plus replacement based on the Law of Double Negation ($p \equiv \sim\sim p$), or is (c) not a valid inference at all, or is (d) an instance of replacement based on the biconditional statements of DM.

   1. ∼[(A & B) v C], /∴ ∼(A & B) & ∼C

   2. ∼(A v B) & C, /∴ (∼A & ∼B) & C

   3. A & (B & C), /∴ ∼[∼A v ∼(B & C)]

   4. A & (B & C), /∴ ∼[∼A v (∼B v ∼C)]

   5. (A ⊃ B) v C, /∴ ∼(A ⊃ B) & C

   6. (A v B) v C, /∴ ∼(∼A & ∼B) v C

7. $\sim\{(A \vee B) \;\&\; [B \equiv (C \;\&\; D)]\}, \;/\therefore\; \sim(A \supset B) \vee \sim[B \equiv (C \;\&\; D)]$

8. $\sim[(A \vee B) \vee \sim(C \equiv D)], \;/\therefore\; \sim(A \vee B) \;\&\; (C \equiv D)$

9. $\sim\{(A \vee B) \equiv [\sim C \;\&\; \sim(D \vee B)]\}, \;/\therefore\; \sim\{(A \vee B) \equiv \sim[C \vee \sim(D \vee B)]\}$

10. $[\sim(A \;\&\; \sim B) \supset (C \;\&\; D)] \vee E, \;/\therefore\; [(\sim A \vee B) \supset (C \;\&\; D)] \vee E$

II. **1.** Consider the following axioms:

Ax. 1. $(x \vee x) \supset x$

Ax. 2. $x \supset (x \vee y)$

Ax. 3. $(x \vee y) \supset (y \vee x)$

Ax. 4. $(x \supset y) \supset [(z \vee x) \supset (z \vee y)]$

These axioms constitute the axiomatic basis given propositional logic by Hilbert and Ackermann.* Now consider the four following proofs of theorems from these axioms, and (1) point out all instances of substitution, (2) point out all instances of replacement, and (3) identify all the logical rules used in the proofs.

Th. 1. $\quad (x \supset y) \supset [(z \supset x) \supset (z \supset y)]$

1.	$(x \supset y) \supset [(z \vee x) \supset (z \vee y)]$	Ax. 4
2.	$(x \supset y) \supset [(\sim z \vee x) \supset (\sim z \vee y)]$	
3.	$(x \supset y) \supset [(z \supset x) \supset (z \supset y)]$	Q.E.D.

Th. 2. $\quad \sim x \vee x$

1.	$x \supset (x \vee y)$	Ax. 2
2.	$x \supset (x \vee x)$	
3.	$(x \vee x) \supset x$	Ax. 1
4.	$x \supset x$	
5.	$\sim x \vee x$	Q.E.D.

Th. 4. $\quad \sim\sim x \supset x$

1.	$(x \vee y) \supset (y \vee x)$	Ax. 3
2.	$(x \vee \sim x) \supset (\sim x \vee x)$	
3.	$(x \vee \sim x) \supset (\sim\sim\sim x \vee x)$	(By Th. 3)
4.	$x \vee \sim x$	Th. 2
5.	$\sim\sim\sim x \vee x$	
6.	$\sim\sim x \supset x$	Q.E.D.

Th. 5. $\quad (x \supset y) \supset (\sim y \supset \sim x)$

1.	$(x \vee y) \supset (y \vee x)$	Ax. 3
2.	$(\sim x \vee y) \supset (\sim\sim y \vee \sim x)$	
3.	$(\sim x \vee \sim\sim y) \supset (\sim\sim y \vee \sim x)$	
4.	$(\sim x \vee y) \supset (\sim x \vee \sim\sim y)$	
5.	$(\sim x \vee y) \supset (\sim\sim y \vee \sim x)$	
6.	$(x \supset y) \supset (\sim y \supset \sim x)$	Q.E.D.

---

* See *Principles of Mathematical Logic.* (New York: Chelsea Publishing Company, 1950), p. 27.

2. In a similar way, prove the following theorems from the given formulas, and identify instances of replacement and substitution.

Th. 3. Given $x \vee \sim x$, prove $x \supset \sim\sim x$

Th. 6. Given $x \supset \sim\sim x$, prove $(\sim x \vee \sim y) \supset \sim(x \& y)$

Th. 7. Given $x \supset \sim\sim x$, prove $\sim(x \vee y) \supset (\sim x \& \sim y)$

Th. 8. Given $x \supset \sim\sim x$, prove $(\sim x \& \sim y) \supset \sim(x \vee y)$

Th. 9. Given $x \supset x$, prove $(x \& y) \supset (y \& x)$

2.8 A Brief Note on Translation

When we are analyzing arguments from mathematics, or any other technical system, there is usually no doubt about which of the logical connectives— $\supset$, &, $\vee$, $\equiv$, $\sim$ —should be used or how the reasoning should be symbolized. On the other hand, when we reason in English the problem of deciding upon a symbolic rendering is sometimes complicated by a certain vagueness of usage and by the variety of synonyms available in English.

Although our concern is not primarily that of analyzing English usage, we need to observe that problems do arise and to be prepared to deal with some of the simpler of them. Perhaps the first task in dealing with reasoning as it occurs in English sentences is that of picking out the conclusion of the argument—that which is claimed to be proved. It is not uncommon in ordinary discourse to put this first (or last or in the center of the argument). On the other hand, wherever it occurs, a conclusion is often designated by certain words.

TABLE 2.4

WORDS THAT OFTEN CALL ATTENTION TO A CONCLUSION

therefore	for this reason	it follows that
in consequence	it must be	it is evident that
consequently	then	evidently
so	thus	apparently
	hence	obviously, etc.

It is not uncommon in ordinary discourse to omit some of the premises. For example, if someone says, "If you win that bet, I'm a monkey's uncle", he probably takes for granted an additional premise, "I'm not a monkey's uncle", so that the proper symbolic translation would be

1. $W \supset M$

2. $\sim M$

3. $\sim W$

Here, indeed, there is one premise missing and so obvious does the speaker think this premise to be that he even omits stating the conclusion as well. Actually, it follows from the premises by MT.

When premises are explicitly stated in ordinary discourse, they may be grouped together or split up by the conclusion. Sometimes they may be identified by the occurrence of certain words.

TABLE 2.5

WORDS THAT OFTEN DESIGNATE PREMISES

because	inasmuch as	granted that
for	the facts are	on the hypotheses
since	it is known that	etc.

Whether a premise is designated by certain words or not, it is our task to detect it and state it in explicit symbolic form. Often enough in ordinary discourse this can be done only by considering the context of the discussion, including the intentions of the discussants. Actually, it is not the primary purpose of our symbols to express English meanings completely or exactly. One additional comment about ordinary discourse will suffice for our purposes. There is occasionally a misunderstanding of how various phrases related to "if . . . then . . . " should be symbolized. We shall list these together with a preferred translation. It would be good practice to satisfy one's intuition concerning the correctness of the translation. This may be done by writing out versions in English.

TABLE 2.6

If A then B	$A \supset B$
A if B	$B \supset A$
A only if B	$A \supset B$
A provided that B	$B \supset A$
not A unless B	$A \supset B$
A if and only if B	$A \equiv B$
A is the same as B	$A \equiv B$
A is necessary for B	$B \supset A$
A is sufficient for B	$A \supset B$
A is necessary and sufficient for B	$A \equiv B$

EXERCISE 2.8

I. Pick out the premises and conclusions in the following.

  1. Because A and B, C.

  2. Because A, B, since C.

   3. A, so B, since C.

   4. Evidently A, since B and C.

   5. A because B and C.

   6. It is known that A; consequently, B.

   7. A, inasmuch as B.

   8. A, then B, inasmuch as C.

   9. A and B; for this reason, C.

   10. A, granted that B.

   11. On the hypothesis A, it must be B and C.

   12. Obviously A, for B and C.

   13. The facts are A; hence, B and C.

   14. It follows that A, for it is known that B and C.

   15. Therefore, granted A, it follows that B if C.

   16. It is known that A; thus, on the hypothesis B, it is evident that C.

   17. Apparently A, inasmuch as B if C.

   18. A and B; so C, because D and E.

   19. A, and B if C; thus D.

   20. It is known that A; so granted that B, it must be that C or D.

   21. A, inasmuch as B is the case if C and D.

   22. A or B, if C; thus D if both E and F.

   23. A, because the facts are B, C, D, and E.

   24. On the grounds that A or B, and C, we may assert D.

   25. It must be A, for it follows from B if C, and from D.

II. Symbolize the arguments in I above.

III. Verify Table 2.6 by using actual English clauses instead of A and B. Provide
   explanations wherever you think it necessary.

IV. Symbolize the following statements.

   1. Either A or B.

   2. Either A or not B, and C.

   3. If A, then B and C.

   4. If A, then B, if C.

   5. If A and C, then B.

   6. If either A and B or C, and not C, then A.

   7. Not A if and only if B.

8. If A implies B, or A implies C, then C if A.

9. Either A implies B, or A implies not B.

10. Either A or B, but not both.

11. If A, then either B or not B.

12. If A implies not B, and A implies B, then not A.

13. It is not true that if A implies B, and not A, then not B.

14. If A implies B, but B does not imply A, then B but not A.

15. If it is false that A implies not A, then it cannot be true that B and not A.

16. If A is equivalent to B, then it is not false that either A and B or not A and not B.

17. If A and not B or B and not A, then A is not equivalent to B.

18. Not A and neither B nor C implies that either not B and not C, or D.

19. If A implies B, then B if and only if C or D.

20. If A is not equivalent to B, but B is equivalent to C, then either A does not imply B, or B implies that neither A nor C.

21. If A implies that B if C, then not B implies that neither A nor C.

22. A if and only if B, but neither C nor B, implies not B.

23. If A and B imply C, and if C implies neither A nor not B, then B is not equivalent to C if A is true.

24. If A and B if C and D, and not B if D, then not both C and D.

25. That A is not sufficient for B, nor is C sufficient for B, implies that A and C together are not sufficient for B.

2.9 Some Applications of the Rules

Now that the most useful propositional rules have been presented, we can employ them in the analysis of those arguments to which they are appropriate. An example is the following:

> If you do not transfer this wire to a new post, that resistance will be overloaded. If you do transfer this wire or redesign the circuit you will lose too much time. But you cannot overload the circuit, so your time is lost!

First, we symbolize this argument, using appropriate symbols. We write the alleged conclusion to the right of the final premise, separating it from this premise by the symbol $/\therefore$. Thus

$$\text{1. } \sim T \supset O$$
$$\text{2. } (T \vee R) \supset L$$
$$\text{3. } \sim O \quad /\therefore \ L$$

We proceed to derive the alleged conclusion, if we can. (Note: in the exercises for this section, all conclusions given are in fact deducible.) Thus

4.	$\sim\sim$T	1, 3, MT
5.	T	4, $\sim\sim$E (or DN)
6.	T v R	5, vI
7.	L	2, 6, $\supset$E

In practice we might combine lines 4 and 5 as a single row. In general, we shall consolidate steps as we go along, sometimes without any comment upon the consolidation.

The deduction we shall present in connection with each of the examples of this section is a test of the correctness of the conclusion given. It should be borne in mind, however, that all that we can test for is the conformity of the examples to the logical rules we have been discussing. We cannot test any extra-logical reasoning that may be involved in the examples. For instance, the reasoning involved in arriving at the conclusion $\sim$T $\supset$ O, used as the first premise in the example immediately above, is beyond our province. By studying logic, we gain no special prowess in reasoning about electrical circuits, subatomic particles, factors that influence the stock market, or the merits of capital punishment. The most that we can hope to gain is an insight into the types of argument common to reasoning in all areas.

Let us turn now to a second example.

> If the pilot was conscious and knew the rate of descent of his airplane, then if the altimeter was accurate, mechanical failure was responsible for the crash. Inspection of the wreckage shows that there was no mechanical failure and that the altimeter was accurate. Therefore, if the pilot was conscious, he did not know the rate of descent of his airplane. (C,K,A,M)

Here appropriate symbols are suggested at the end of the problem, as they will usually be suggested in the exercise. We proceed to symbolize and deduce as follows:

1.	(C & K) $\supset$ (A $\supset$ M)	
2.	$\sim$M & A $/\therefore$ C $\supset$ $\sim$K	
3.	C	
4.	K	
5.	C & K	3, 4, &I
6.	A $\supset$ M	1, 5, $\supset$E
7.	A	2, &E
8.	M	6, 7, $\supset$E
9.	$\sim$M	2, &E
10.	M & $\sim$M	8, 9, &I
11.	$\sim$K	4–10, $\sim$I
12.	C $\supset$ $\sim$K	3–11, $\supset$I

But there is no standard procedure for most problems of this sort. A different way of solving the present one is shown by

    ────**1.** (C & K) ⊃ (A ⊃ M)
    ────**2.** ∼M & A   /∴ C ⊃ ∼K
        3. A & ∼M   2, CM
        4. ∼(∼A v M)   3, DM (also DN)
        5. ∼(A ⊃ M)   4, Impl (also DN)
        6. ∼(C & K)   1, 5, MT
        7. ∼C v ∼K   6, DM
        8. C ⊃ ∼K   7, Impl (also DN)

This version is shorter, but makes use of logical relations that would not be obvious to everyone. Mere brevity is not in itself a virtue, of course.

Let us look at one more argument.

> The Company will waive the premiums on this policy only if the insured becomes disabled. But if the Company has not waived the premiums, and said premiums are not paid when due, this policy will lapse, and the Company will either refund its cash value to the insured, or issue term insurance for a limited period. Therefore, if the insured is not disabled, then if the premiums are not paid when due, this policy will lapse. (W,D,P,L,R,I)

Using the suggested symbols, we write

    ────**1.** W ⊃ D
    ────**2.** (∼W & ∼P) ⊃ [L & (R v I)]   /∴ ∼D ⊃ (∼P ⊃ L)
        3. ∼D
        4. ∼W   1, 3, MT
        5. ∼P
        6. ∼W & ∼P   4, 5, &I
        7. L & (R v I)   2, 6, ⊃E
        8. L   7, &E
    9. ∼P ⊃ L   5-8, ⊃I
    10. ∼D ⊃ (∼P ⊃ L)   3-9, ⊃I

This deduction illustrates an important practical procedure; if the conclusion is a conditional, assume its antecedent and see whether its consequent can be derived. In the present case, that consequent is a conditional itself; so we assume *its* antecedent within the scope of our first assumption.

Of course, it is not *necessary* to assume the antecedent of the conclusion. The second version of the solution of the second problem above exemplifies an alternative procedure for deriving conditional conclusions.

EXERCISE 2.9

I. A. Symbolize the following arguments, using the suggested notation.

B. Derive the conclusion of each from its premises, and justify each step by citing the propositional rules which are used.

1. Pitchblende contains uranium, so either pitchblende contains uranium or iron ore does. (P,I)

2. Hydrogen is the lightest of the elements, so it is true that hydrogen either is or is not the lightest element. (L)

3. It is certainly not the case that John's statement was not true. Therefore, his statement was true. (T)

4. Because the fire department was called, it is obviously not the case that it was not called. (C)

5. If I improve my study habits, I shall pass with honors. I shall improve those habits, so I shall pass with honors. (I,P)

6. If the current is flowing, then the light is on. So if the light is not on, then the current is not flowing. (C,L)

7. If the Earth were a flat disk atop the back of a tortoise, as some have asserted, then Magellan and others would never have been able to circumnavigate the globe. But Magellan and others have been able to circumnavigate the globe. Therefore, it cannot be true that the Earth is a flat disk on the back of a tortoise. (F,C)

8. Insofar as (if) the laws of mathematics refer to reality, they are not certain. Hence, insofar as they are certain, they do not refer to reality. (R,C)

9. This statement must be either true or false, and it is not true. Therefore, it is false. (T,F)

10. If the enemy is fully prepared, we had better increase our strength. To increase our strength we must conserve our natural resources. Therefore, if the enemy is fully prepared, we must conserve our natural resources. (P,I,R)

11. If n is either positive or negative, n^2 is positive. So if n is negative, n^2 is positive. (P,N,P^2)

12. If n is positive, then n^2 is positive. If n is negative, then n^2 is positive. n is either positive or negative. Consequently, n^2 is positive. (P,N,P^2)

13. If n is even, then n^2 is even, and if n is odd, then n^2 is odd. n is either odd or even. Thus, n^2 is either odd or even. (E,E^2,O,O^2)

14. Either this number is not less than 87 or it is not more than 87. If it is 79, then it is less than 87, and if it is 91 it is more than 87. Consequently, it is either not 91 or else it is not 79. (L,M,S,N)

15. It is impossible that *n* is both greater than *m* and less than *m*. Thus, either *n* is not greater than *m*, or it is not less than *m*. (G,L)

16. It is impossible that *n* is both greater and less than *m*. So if *n* is greater than *m*, then it is not less than *m*. (G,L)

17. My statement is true if and only if it is not false. Furthermore, it is not the case that my statement is true. So it must be false. (T,F)

18. Either this line is not curved, or it is not straight, and from this it follows that it cannot be both curved and straight. (C,S)

19. If line *a* is perpendicular to line *b*, and line *c* is perpendicular to line *b*, then line *a* is parallel to line *c*. Thus, we can infer that if *a* is not parallel to *c*, then either *a* is not perpendicular to *b*, or *c* is not perpendicular to *b*. (A,C,P)

20. If line *a* is tangent to circle *c*, then it meets the circumference of *c* at one point *p* only and is perpendicular to the radius drawn to *p*. Line *a* is perpendicular to that radius, but it intersects the circumference at more than one point. Therefore, line *a* is not tangent to circle *c*. (T,M,P)

21. Line *a* is either longer than *b*, or shorter than *b*. If it is longer than *b*, it is not the same length as *b*, and if it is shorter than *b*, it is not the same length. Therefore, line *a* is not the same length as line *b*. (L,S,E)

22. If log *z* is equal to the sum of log *x* and log *y*, then *z* is the product of *x* and *y*. If log *z* equals the sum of log *x* and log *y*, and log *z* equals two times log *x*, then *z* equals x^2. If *z* is the product of *x* and *y*, and is equal to x^2, then *x* equals *y*. So we may conclude that if log *z* equals log *x* plus log *y*, then if log *z* is equal to two times log *x*, then *x* equals *y*. (A,P,T,S,E)

23. Angle A is a right angle if it measures exactly ninety degrees, but if it is less than ninety degrees it is acute, and if it is greater, it is obtuse. If it is not exactly ninety degrees, then it is either less or greater. Hence, if angle A is not a right angle, it is either acute or obtuse. (R,E,L,G,A,O)

24. If *x* is a positive number, then 2*x* is a positive number. *x* is either positive or negative. If *x* is a negative number, then 2*x* is not a positive number. Hence, *x* is a positive number if and only if it is not a negative number. (P,2P,N)

25. *x* is a positive number if and only if x^3 is a positive number. Hence, *x* is not a positive number if and only if x^3 is not a positive number. (X,C)

26. If a given space is Euclidian, then no two straight lines in that space can meet more than once. But in Riemannian space straight lines do meet more than once. Therefore, it is evident that a given space may not be both Euclidian and Riemannian. (E,M,R,)

27. If two gases are at the same temperature, then their molecules have the same average kinetic energy. Equal volumes of two gases contain the same number of molecules. The pressures of two gases are equal if the numbers of molecules and their kinetic energies are equal. Thus, if two gases have the same temperature and volume, they must have the same pressure. (T,E,V,N,P)

28. Either n is not less, or else it is not more, than m; n equals m if and only if n is neither more nor less than m. Therefore, if n is less than m, it is neither more than nor equal to m. (L,M,E)

29. Line CM is perpendicular to line AB at point M if and only if angle AMC is a right angle. Therefore, line CM is perpendicular to line AB at point M and is parallel to line DE if and only if angle AMC is a right angle and line CM is parallel to line DE. (P,R,L)

30. x is a negative number if and only if x^3 is a negative number. x is a positive number if and only if it is not a negative number. x^3 is a positive number if and only if it is not a negative number. So x is positive if and only if x^3 is positive. (N,N^3,P,P^3)

31. If forces A and B are equal and are the sole forces acting on point p, the resultant force R will either be nil, or will have the direction of the bisector of the angle between A and B. But R does not have this direction. If R is nil, then A and B are equal and directly opposed. Hence, if A and B are equal but not directly opposed, then they are not the sole forces acting on p. (E,S,N,D,O)

32. In one interpretation, A > B is equivalent to A is to the right of B. If A > B and B > C, then A is to the right of C. Furthermore, A > B, but A is not to the right of C. Consequently, it is not true that B > C if A is to the right of B.

33. If ABC is a triangle, then $AC = BC$ if and only if angle $CAB =$ angle CBA. If ABC is a triangle, and is isosceles, then $AC = BC$ if AB is the shortest side. Hence, if ABC is an isosceles triangle and AB the shortest side, then $AC = BC$ and angle $CAB =$ angle CBA. (T,L,A,I,S)

34. Side AB of triangle ABC equals side DE of triangle DEF, and AC equals DF. If angle BAC is not greater than angle EDF, then it is either equal to or less than angle EDF. If AB equals DE and AC equals DF, then it is true that if angle BAC equals angle EDF then BC equals EF and that if angle BAC is less than angle EDF then BC is less than EF. BC is greater than EF if and only if it is neither less than nor equal to EF. Therefore, angle BAC is greater than angle EDF if BC is greater than EF.

35. $ad = bc$ if and only if $a/b = c/d$. If it is not the case that $a/b > c/d$, then either $a/b < c/d$ or $a/b = c/d$. If $a/b = c/d$ then it is not the case that either $a/b > c/d$ or $a/b < c/d$. Therefore, $ad = bc$ if and only if it is not the case that $a/b > c/d$ or $a/b < c/d$. (P,E,G,L)

36. If triangle *ABC* is isosceles, then side *AC* equals side *BC* if *AB* is the shortest side. If *ABC* is isosceles and if *M* is the midpoint of *AB*, angle *ACM* equals angle *BCM*. Triangle *ACM* is congruent with triangle *BCM* if and only if angle *ACM* equals angle *BCM*, *AC* equals *BC*, and *CM* equals *CM*. *M* is the midpoint of *AB*, and of course *CM* equals *CM*. If triangle *ACM* is congruent with triangle *BCM*, then angle *CAB* equals angle *CBA*. So if triangle *ABC* is isosceles and *AB* is the shortest side, then angle *CAB* equals angle *CBA*.(I,Q,S,M,A,C,L,E)

37. If *ABCD* is a quadrilateral, then if it has four right angles and four equal sides, it is a rectangle and a square. If the four sides are not equal, then it is not a square, and if the four angles are not equal it is neither a square nor a rectangle. Hence, either *ABCD* is not a quadrilateral, or else if it is a rectangle and has four equal sides then it is a square. (Q,A,E,R,S)

38. *ABCD* is a parallelogram if and only if diagonal *AC* bisects diagonal *BD* at *M* and *BD* bisects *AC* at *M*. If *AB* is parallel to *DC*, then angle *ACD* equals angle *CAB* and angle *ABD* equals angle *BDC*. Triangle *AMB* and triangle *DMC* are congruent if *AB* equals *DC*, angle *ACD* equals angle *CAB*, and angle *ABD* equals angle *BDC*. *AC* bisects *BD* at *M* if *BM* equals *MD*, and *BD* bisects *AC* at *M* if *AM* equals *MC*. If triangles *AMB* and *DMC* are congruent, then *BM* equals *MD* and *AM* equals *MC*. Therefore, if *AB* equals *DC* and is parallel to *DC*, then *ABCD* is a parallelogram.

39. If the universe is infinite and is not expanding, and if its matter is distributed uniformly, then the number of stars at any given distance from the earth increases as the square of that distance. Now the light from any particular source (star) decreases as the square of the distance; and if the number of stars at any given distance increases as the square of the distance, while the light from each source decreases by the same factor, then the light reaching the earth from all of the sources at any given distance is equal to that reaching the earth from any other given stellar distance whatsoever. If the universe is infinite, then if the light from any distance is equal to that from any other, then the night sky is not dark, but is ablaze with light. But the night sky is dark. Thus, we must infer that if the universe is infinite, and if matter is distributed uniformly, then the universe is expanding. (I,E,M,S,L,O,D,A)

40. If $\sqrt{2}$ is a rational number, then $\sqrt{2} = p/q$. p/q is the relationship between two integers expressed in its lowest terms. If p/q is such a relationship, then it cannot be the case that both p is even and q is even. If $\sqrt{2} = p/q$, then $2 = p^2/q^2$, and $p^2 = 2q^2$. If $p^2 = 2q^2$ then p^2 is even, and if p^2 is even, then p is even. If p is even then $p = 2r$, and if $p = 2r$ and $p^2 = 2q^2$, then $4r^2 = 2q^2$ and $q^2 = 2r^2$. If $q^2 = 2r^2$ then q is even. So $\sqrt{2}$ is not a rational number.

41. If *ABC* is a triangle, then *AB* = *AC* if and only if angle *CBA* = angle *BCA*. If it is not the case that *AB* = *AC* if *BC* is the odd side, then *ABC* is not an isosceles triangle. Hence, if either *AB* ≠ *AC* or angle *CBA* ≠ angle *BCA*, then either *ABC* is not an isosceles triangle, or else *BC* is not the odd side. (T,L,A,O,I)

42. I'll either have to give her my raincoat or my umbrella. If I give her my raincoat, my body will get wet; if I give her my umbrella, my head will get wet. So I'm bound to get wet; and if I get wet, I'll catch cold. Here come the sniffles!

43. A body in motion must either be moving in a place where it is or in a place where it is not. Now it cannot be moving in a place where it is; if it were, it would not be there. Neither can it be moving where it is not, for it is not there; so no body can be in motion.

(Zeno of Elea)

44. If the books in the library of Alexandria contain the same doctrines that are to be found in the Koran, they are unnecessary. If they contain doctrines that are opposed to those to be found in the Koran, they are pernicious. Now both what is unnecessary and what is pernicious should be destroyed; therefore, the books contained in the library of Alexandria should be destroyed. (Caliph Omar)

45. If you tell me that you have never been bad, you are a liar and, therefore, bad. And if you tell me you have been bad, you should be punished for being bad. Since you say one or the other, you really deserve to be punished.

46. Since musical purists maintain that a composition should be performed only on the instrument for which it was composed, they must also maintain that Bach's four suites for lute should not be played nowadays. But anyone who maintains that cannot be a music lover, for all music lovers maintain that all great music should be performed. Therefore, musical purists are not great music lovers.

47. Both snakes and lizards are reptiles, and both reptiles and birds are oviparous; so it follows that lizards and snakes are oviparous.

48. Either the conclusion of an argument is contained in the premises or it isn't. If it is contained in the premises, it tells us nothing and is useless. If it is not contained in the premises, the argument is invalid, and everyone knows that nothing useful can be learned from an invalid argument, so all conclusions are useless.

II. The following arguments are informal. Premises may have been omitted. Points may have been repeated. Intermediate conclusions may have been drawn. Analyze the arguments as well as the rules permit.

1. Either the Yankees or the White Sox won the Pennant. The Yankees could not have won, for the series was not played in New York. So that means that the series was played in Chicago.

2. If the ground is wet, it has rained, and if it has rained, the hay has got wet. The ground is wet all right; so our hay needs drying.

3. Either the standard of living or else the quantity of military production must fall, for military production can be increased only if the supply of consumer goods is decreased, which means a decrease in the standard of living. And the standard of living cannot increase unless military production decreases, for it is impossible to increase both the quantity of consumer goods produced and either maintain or increase the quantity of military production.

4. It was observed that when certain substances, say A and B, were rubbed together and then separated again, each exerted a force upon the other and upon other bodies which were brought near them. It was also noticed that if another body, say C, were brought near A and then brought near B, the effects on C were opposite in character. Now if the forces exerted by A and B were the same in character, the effects of each would also be the same in character. But since the effects of A and B are opposite in character, the forces exerted by each must also be opposite in character. If body C now is shown to exert on other objects a force that is similar to one of the forces exerted by either A or B, it can be shown that the effects of A and B upon C are as follows: if A and C each affect a body D in the same way, A and C will repel each other; and if A and C each affect a body D in different ways, A and C will attract each other. So it follows that, as regards forces of this sort, like forces repel each other and unlike forces attract each other.

5. A revolutionary movement has many of the features of a religious movement, and its success is dependent upon the movement's becoming fashionable; for revolutionary movements are essentially a response to mass frustration, and such responses characterize religious movements. Too, if a movement is a success, it presents a pattern of behavior that is acceptable to a society, but such patterns characterize fashion movements, *i.e.*, they are fashionable.

6. Much of the sensitivity customarily attributed to gustation is actually due to the odor of the stimulus, for it can be shown that when olfactory reception is eliminated, recognition of many common substances by taste is impossible.

7. If we are to avoid depressions, industry must constantly be in the process of expansion, for if industry cannot expand, savings will not return to circulation since savings are either kept out of circulation or invested. But either savings must return to circulation or incomes must decline, for every cent of anyone's income, be it wages, salaries, rents, profits, or interest, ultimately derives from money which someone else has spent. And everyone knows that whenever incomes decline, the economy is in a state of depression.

8. The League of Nations could not have been a success regardless of whether or not the United States had been a member, for the assembly and the council fell under the domination of France and Great Britain; and the United States could not have prevented this, for both France and Great Britain were very insistent about the payment of reparations and would not have relinquished these claims (for they both had a strong fear of a powerful Germany). This being the case, the policies of the League were dictated by the policies of France and Great Britain, and thus were not sympathetic to promoting a commonwealth of nations, for France insisted upon pursuing a policy of encircling Germany and Britain one of balancing the continental forces. And obviously, if the League could not pursue policies sympathetic to promoting a commonwealth of nations, it could not have been a success, for its object was just to pursue such policies.

9. Let us assume that the population of the world doubles every twenty-five years. If so, the world's population will have increased two hundred and fifty-six times in two centuries. Now we know that our ability to produce food cannot increase proportionally. Consequently, there will be a time when there are more people than we could possibly feed. That is, the fact that we cannot double the world's output of food every twenty-five years implies that if the world's population doubles every twenty-five years, then there will be a time when there are more people than we could possibly feed. What really follows is that either the world's population must not increase by a factor "x" over a period of years "y" or our ability to increase the production over the same period of years cannot be less than by the factor "x". So if there are limits to our ability to increase the production of food, there are limits to the factor by which population can increase.

10. Either government subsidies to education will increase or universities will be unable to expand and thus many future adults will be deprived of higher education. So unless government subsidies to education increase, universities will be unable to expand; and if universities are unable to expand, many future adults will be deprived of higher education. For this reason, if we do not choose to deprive many future adults of higher education, government subsidies to education must increase.

11. Neither Socrates nor Aristotle disbelieved in the existence of the external world, and if Socrates did not disbelieve in the existence of the external world, then Plato's dialogues misrepresent the thinking of Socrates. Now either Plato's dialogues do not misrepresent the thinking of Socrates or Aristotle was right in criticizing Plato. Evidently, then, Aristotle believed in the existence of the external world and was right in criticizing Plato.

12. I ask, should I believe what you say or should I not? To say that I shouldn't is the same as saying that what you say is false, for if your doctrines are false, I should disbelieve them, and if I should disbelieve them, they are as good as false. But if you say I should believe them, then you must be able to produce convincing reasons for the truth of what you say—since one should believe only what is true and to know that something is true is to have convincing reasons for your views—or be silent about it.

13. If the president's party elects a legislative majority, the president's platform will be enacted into law. But if the president's party does not elect a legislative majority, his platform will not be enacted into law. It follows then that either the voters do not want a platform enacted into law or they will elect the president's party to a legislative majority, and that they either want a platform enacted into law or they will not elect the president's party to a legislative majority. Obviously, then, if the voters elect a president and not his party, the voters do not want either of the offered platforms enacted into law.

14. Let us assume that we raise the gasoline tax one cent per gallon. It follows that the net income from taxes will increase by three million dollars. But if we increase the price of auto registrations, the net income will increase only two and a half millions. Furthermore, if we increase the gasoline tax, the burden will not fall entirely on state residents, since travelers must also buy gasoline, and if we increase the price of registrations, the burden will fall entirely on state residents. Now, certainly the latter is not desirable, and, furthermore, two and a half millions is not sufficient to cover current appropriations. Since we must either increase the gasoline tax or the price of automobile registrations, it is obvious that we must increase the gasoline tax and not the price of automobile registrations.

15. We have a conception of God as being the most perfect being. There-fore, we conceive of Him as existing, since if we did not conceive of Him as existing, we would not have a conception of Him as being the most perfect being, for a being that exists is more perfect than one that doesn't. So we either conceive of God as existing, or we do not con-ceive of Him as being the most perfect being.

2.10 Recapitulation: The Materials of Proof

In this chapter we have said that a line in a deduction is sound when justified by one of the rules of inference. More generally than this, however, we have implicitly formulated a set of conditions for an acceptable line in a deduction. It is time to make this characterization explicit, for, as far as it goes, it tells us something of the nature of proof.

Thus we can say that a propositional *deduction* consists of lines each of which is a statement and each of which is either

(A) a premise; or

(B) any arbitrary assumption provided that it is discharged at a succeeding line; or

(C) a line inferred from a previous line not in the scope of assumptions already discharged by an underived or derived rule; or

(D) a zero-premise conclusion.

All zero-premise conclusions ultimately arise from $\supset$ I, **v** E, $\sim$ I, the rules which discharge assumptions; if these rules did not occur in our system, we should be unable to generate such conclusions. Now many systematizations of PL (propositional logic) do, in fact, lack such rules. Such systems have to "import" their zero-premise conclusions from the outside, so to speak. They do this in the form of axioms. One such set of axioms is the following:*

(1) (A **v** A) $\supset$ A

(2) A $\supset$ (A **v** B)

(3) (A **v** B) $\supset$ (B **v** A)

(4) [A **v** (B **v** C)] $\supset$ [B **v** (A **v** C)]

(5) (B $\supset$ C) $\supset$ [(A **v** B) $\supset$ (A **v** C)]

This system must be supplemented by some further statements defining A $\supset$ B as $\sim$A **v** B and A & B as $\sim$($\sim$A **v** $\sim$B). As a result of the introduction of axioms, the rules can be reduced in number to only $\supset$ E and Substitution. In general, there seems to be a choice between a plurality of rules but no axioms or a plurality of axioms but a small number of rules. It is true that formulations of PL involving no more than a single axiom and a single rule have been given,† but such formulations are so unwieldy as to serve technical purposes only.

When the motive for formulating PL is that of analyzing deductions in axiom systems, it is somewhat unsatisfactory to present PL as itself an axiom system. The question of the nature of deductive reasoning seems to be postponed rather than answered when this is done. On the other hand, it cannot be denied that there are advantages in an axiomatic formulation of PL. The rules discharging assumptions, which in some form or another must be adopted if all axioms are to be omitted, are such powerful rules that they must be used with care. For example, we noted restrictions on the rule Sub when used within the scope of an assumption which is discharged by **v**E, $\sim$I, or $\supset$I. (We shall see that similar restrictions are necessary whenever individual variables occur in an assumption to be discharged—see Chapter Five.) The

---

* Russell and Whitehead, *Principia Mathematica* (Cambridge, England: Cambridge University Press, 1910–13). The fourth axiom here was later shown to be unnecessary.

† Nicod, J. G. P., "A Reduction in the Number of the Primitive Propositions of Logic" in *Proceedings of the Cambridge Philosophical Society*, Vol. 19 (1916), pp. 32–40.

reason for such restrictions lies in the fact that an assumption is usually not a zero-premise conclusion.

What we have done in this chapter has been to state the rules for the propositional reasoning that underlies mathematical and other axiomatic systems. We could see from our discussions in Chapter One that such rules existed. In the present chapter we have tried to state these rules in such a way as to make clear some of the interrelations between them, so as to suggest that most of them can be derived from a relatively small number. The separation of the rules in Table 2.1 from those in Table 2.2 expressed this point. In addition, we have tried to gain a certain familiarity with and facility in the use of these rules, showing through the solution of problems how they are used in various areas of human thought.

Also, if we wish, we may think of this chapter as an introductory analysis of what is meant by deduction and proof. Deductive reasoning is clearly evident in the context of mathematical and other systematic reasoning. Although there is nothing new about such systems and the kind of reasoning associated with them—they are at least as old as Euclid—there has been a growing emphasis upon them in recent and contemporary thinking, both in mathematics and in science. This emphasis is reflected by a concern with axiomatic method. If we take this method seriously, certain questions about it inevitably arise, perhaps the most central and fundamental of these being "What is deduction?"

In Chapter One, we began to answer this question. But the answer given in Chapter Two is in many ways fuller, although it is restricted to deductions using propositional rules. In any event, we have been at pains in the present chapter to state something of the nature of a deduction. We have agreed that a sequence of lines which meets the standards formulated as A through D above constitutes a deduction. Of course a great deal more precision in statement is possible, but not necessarily advisable, at the outset. What is more important than the maximum precision at this stage in our enquiry is just the realization that we can say something about deduction—that we can characterize it.

Once we characterize deduction, whether with maximum precision or not, the question arises as to whether deduction so characterized is adequate to our needs. So long as we are vague about deduction, relying on our intuition to tell us when things go right or wrong, we can suppose that the deductive method itself is quite satisfactory in doing whatever it is supposed to do. It is only when we pin down the deductive method, seeing in a more formal way when mistakes are made, that we come to realize the possibility that the method we have specified need not necessarily be wholly satisfactory. Is the method of deduction specified in A–D a *consistent* method, for example?

As we shall be able to show when we reach Part Two, deduction of the sort specified by A–D is consistent. This means that wherever we use the rules of a logic based on Table 2.1 we can never get p & $\sim p$ as a ZPC. The fact that we can show this raises the further question as to the consistency of deductions in which nonpropositional rules are used. These questions have yet to be faced, and will not be faced until considerably later in the book.

Another question arising about deductive methods concerns their *completeness*. If we consider our rules of logic (as so far stated), we may ask whether these rules are all that we need to get the results that we want. By way of analogy, we might ask of a systematic formulation of Euclidian plane geometry whether the axioms stated were sufficient to get all the truths about a Euclidian plane. Here, what we wish to know is whether the logical rules used in A–D above are sufficient to get all of the truths of a system, or whether there are truths of a system which could never occur as lines of a deduction as specified by A–D.

As we shall see, deductions specified by A–D cannot give us all truths of a system. There are truths, involving the "internal structure" of statements, for example (see Chapter Five), which no deductions of the sort we have used could attain. By way of analogy, Euclidian geometry cannot serve as the basis for all geometrical truths, for some are peculiar to non-Euclidian geometry. In a narrower sense, however, the rules we have formulated are complete. That is, we can get all propositional truths, namely those having to do with statements, by deductions of the sort we have specified. This means that when we use this logic in connection with mathematical or scientific systems, all the propositional truths that there are in connection with these systems can be attained as final lines of deductions as specified in A–D.

The problem of how we demonstrate the consistency and completeness of logic and questions about independence of rules belong to the study called *metatheory*, and will be reserved for Part Two.

EXERCISE 2.10

I. Consider the following proofs and state in accordance with the four reasons of Section 10 just why each line is acceptable as a line in the proof.

1. (A & B) $\supset$ (C & D), (B $\supset$ $\sim$D), therefore, $\sim$A v $\sim$B.

1. (A & B) $\supset$ (C & D)
2. B $\supset$ $\sim$D
3. A & B
4. C & D
5. D
6. $\sim$B
7. B
8. B & $\sim$B

9. $\sim$(A & B)
10. $\sim$A v $\sim$B

2. $[p \mathbin{\&} (q \lor r)] \equiv [(p \mathbin{\&} q) \lor (p \mathbin{\&} r)]$

1. $p \mathbin{\&} (q \lor r)$
2. $q \lor r$
3. p
4. q
5. p
6. $p \mathbin{\&} q$
7. $q \supset (p \mathbin{\&} q)$
8. r
9. p
10. $p \mathbin{\&} r$
11. $r \supset (p \mathbin{\&} r)$
12. $(p \mathbin{\&} q) \lor (p \mathbin{\&} r)$
13. $[p \mathbin{\&} (q \lor r)] \supset [(p \mathbin{\&} q) \lor (p \mathbin{\&} r)]$
14. $(p \mathbin{\&} q) \lor (p \mathbin{\&} r)$
15. $p \mathbin{\&} q$
16. p
17. q
18. $q \lor r$
19. $p \mathbin{\&} (q \lor r)$
20. $p \mathbin{\&} r$
21. p
22. r
23. $q \lor r$
24. $p \mathbin{\&} (q \lor r)$
25. $p \mathbin{\&} (q \lor r)$
26. $[(p \mathbin{\&} q) \lor (p \mathbin{\&} r)] \supset [p \mathbin{\&} (q \lor r)]$
27. $\{[(p \mathbin{\&} q) \lor (p \mathbin{\&} r)] \supset [p \mathbin{\&} (q \lor r)]\} \mathbin{\&}$
     $\{[p \mathbin{\&} (q \lor r)] \supset [(p \mathbin{\&} q) \lor (p \mathbin{\&} r)]\}$
28. $[p \mathbin{\&} (q \lor r)] \equiv [(p \mathbin{\&} q) \lor (p \mathbin{\&} r)]$

II. In a similar manner prove $p \equiv (p \mathbin{\&} p)$ and justify each line as a line in the proof.

SUGGESTED READINGS

1. I. M. Copi, *Symbolic Logic* (New York: The Macmillan Co., 1954), Ch. III.

2. Haskell B. Curry, *A Theory of Formal Deducibility* (South Bend, Ind.: Notre Dame Math. Lect., No. 6, 2nd Ed., 1957).

3. F. B. Fitch, *Symbolic Logic* (New York: The Ronald Press Co., 1952), Ch. I, II.

4. Gerhard Gentzen, "Untersuchungen über das logische Schliessen", *Mathematische Zeitschrift*, vol. 39 (1934–5), pp. 176–210, 405–431.

5. S. C. Kleene, *Introduction to Metamathematics* (New York: Van Nostrand Co., 1952), Ch. V, VI.

6. P. H. Nidditch, *Introductory Formal Logic of Mathematics* (London: University Tutorial Press Ltd., 1957), Ch. I–III.

Chapter 3

Matrices, Normal Forms, and Duality

3.1 Truth-Functional Tests of Deductions

It is trivial to remark that when we have a deduction the conclusion is deducible from the given premises. We must not, however, confuse this innocuous remark with its converse. For, if we have failed to find a deduction of a conclusion from certain premises, this does *not* prove that the deduction *cannot* be found. All that it may mean is that we have not tried hard enough or been lucky enough. Perhaps with more effort we should succeed in finding the deduction. On the other hand, if a certain conclusion is in fact not deducible from given premises, we may go on indefinitely trying to deduce it with no assurance that our failure has any significance at all. Thus, while deducibility can be asserted on the basis of the rules, something else is needed as a basis for asserting nondeducibility.

When the deduction of a conclusion from given premises can be found, we shall speak of the *inference* by which this conclusion is reached as a *sound inference*. (The phrase "valid argument" is sometimes used in this connection, but we shall want to use the word "valid" for a different purpose later.) In a sound inference, if the premises are all true, the conclusion must be true; to use language we shall adopt in a later chapter (Chapter Nine), the propositional rules *transmit* truth from premises to conclusion in any sound inference. If there is a deduction—*i.e.*, a sound inference—then it is impossible for all its premises to be true when its conclusion is false. Thus, whenever anyone claims to have inferred a conclusion from given premises by the rules, we can show conclusively that he is wrong if the premises can be true while the conclusion is false. This is the nucleus of the technique we now develop as a basis for demonstrating nondeducibility.

We begin with a very simple case. Suppose we consider the inference "It is Wednesday or Thursday; therefore, it is Wednesday". How could we exhibit the unsoundness of this inference? Let us first symbolize it, writing it out horizontally rather than vertically for reasons that will soon be obvious. The diagonal line indicates that there is a claim for sound inference.

$$\text{W} \vee \text{T} \quad /\!\therefore \text{ W}$$

We now assume that the conclusion is false. Under the right-hand W we accordingly write **f**. But if the W forming the conclusion is false, the W in the premise must likewise be false (in the interests of consistency), and we record this fact by writing **f** under this W.

$$\text{W} \vee \text{T} \quad /\!\therefore \text{ W}$$
$$\text{f} \qquad\qquad \text{f}$$

Next we examine the premise to see whether there is any way of making it true. Obviously there is; if T were true, then W ∨ T would be true. We write

$$\text{W} \vee \text{T} \quad /\!\therefore \text{ W}$$
$$\text{f t t} \qquad \text{U} \quad \text{f}$$

The **t** under the ∨ means that the whole alternation W ∨ T is true; in general, a **t** or an **f** under ∼, &, ⊃, ∨, or ≡ ascribes truth or falsity to the statement formed by using the symbol. The **U** under the three dots indicates that, since the premise can be true while the conclusion is false, the inference is *unsound*.

Why did we assign **t** rather than **f** to T? If we had assigned **f** to it, the alternation W ∨ T would have been *false*; and we should not have shown the premise can be true while the conclusion is false. The procedure we have carried out presupposes that we have in mind at least some of the conditions that render an alternation true or false. It is in fact easy to specify all of these conditions in summary form: *an alternation is true unless both members are false*. Using the **t**'s and **f**'s of the present example, we can express this by writing a *truth table*.

A	∨	B
t	t	t
f	t	t
t	t	f
f	f	f

This means that when A is true and B is true, A ∨ B is true (the first row of **t**'s), that when A is false and B is true, A ∨ B is true (the second row), and so on.

The same result can be put compactly in terms of the following *matrix*:

v	t	f
t	t	t
f	t	f

Here the column to the left expresses possible assignments of **t** and **f** to A and the row at the top expresses possible assignments to B. The remaining letters express the resultant *truth-value* of A **v** B; *i.e.*, they indicate whether A **v** B is true or false. We always take the left-hand column as indicating the truth-value of the left-hand member of an alternation, conjunction, conditional, or biconditional, and the top row as indicating the truth-value of its right-hand member.

This matrix constitutes a definition of **v**, and is a convenient alternative to the table it summarizes.

Let us turn to a second sample of inference and test it for soundness: "It is noon. Therefore it is noon and the sun is shining". In symbols this is

$$N \quad /\therefore \; N \,\&\, S$$

Can we make the conclusion false at the same time that the premise is true? We can, by assuming truth and falsity as follows:

$$N \quad /\therefore \; N \,\&\, S$$
$$t \qquad U \quad t\;f\;f$$

We have to assume N is true; otherwise we defeat our purpose of showing that the premise can be true while the conclusion is false. The truth table for **&** presupposed by this analysis is

A	&	B
t	t	t
f	f	t
t	f	f
f	f	f

The matrix is

&	t	f
t	t	f
f	f	f

In other words, *a conjunction is false unless both conjuncts are true.*

The next argument we shall analyze is one involving two premises. A person, whose friend Jones has declined to see him on Wednesday, might reflect

> Either Jones has to be out of town on Wednesday or he has a prior engagement on that day. Now that I think of it, he does have a prior engagement. So he doesn't have to be out of town on Wednesday.

This can be symbolized as follows:

$$O \vee P, \quad P \quad /\therefore \quad \sim O,$$

and if we assume truth and falsity as follows:

$$O \vee P, \quad P \quad /\therefore \quad \sim O$$
$$t\ t\ t \qquad t \quad \mathbf{U} \quad f\ t$$

the inference is shown to be unsound because *both* premises can be true while the conclusion is false. Notice how our assumption of the truth of O presupposes that *A is true if and only if* ∼*A is false.* In tabular and matrix forms,

∼	A		∼	t	f
f	t		—	f	t
t	f				

We still need defining matrices for ⊃ and ≡. The easiest way of obtaining these will be to use Impl in its biconditional form $\vdash (p \supset q) \equiv (\sim p \vee q)$ rather than to analyze any further specific deductions. By virtue of results already obtained, ∼A v B can be analyzed in the following way:

∼	A	v	B
f	t	t	t
t	f	t	t
f	t	f	f
t	f	t	f

In this truth table we obtain the left-hand column before the column under the v, because the statement as a whole is an alternation, whose truth-value we cannot compute until we know the truth-values of its constituents, ∼A and B. The final computation is as follows: a **t** appears in the first, second, and fourth rows under the **v** because in each of these cases one or both of ∼A and B is true. In the third row, however, both ∼A and B are false, so the alternation as a whole is false.

Now by Impl, $\vdash \sim p \vee q \equiv p \supset q$, so that when A and B have the truth-values given them in the truth table just constructed, A ⊃ B has the values computed for ∼A v B and written under the **v**. In other words, the truth table for ⊃ is the following:

A	⊃	B
t	t	t
f	t	t
t	f	f
f	t	f

The matrix is

⊃	t	f
t	t	f
f	t	t

This result can be expressed in ordinary English by saying that *a conditional is always true except when its antecedent is true and its consequent is false.*

The definition just stated often seems paradoxical. Consider the conditional "If water is malleable, tomorrow is Tuesday". Since the antecedent is false, the one condition under which a conditional can be false is not fulfilled, and so the conditional must be true. In mathematical reasoning, nonetheless, we do regard such a conditional as true, the point being that in mathematical reasoning M $\supset$ T is regarded as truth-functional.

A compound statement is *truth-functional* when its truth or falsity is determined by the truth or falsity of its constituent statements. Thus A v $\sim$B is truth-functional because if we know, for example, that A is false and B is true we can determine its truth or falsity by using the matrices for v and $\sim$. In mathematical reasoning compound statements are always built up in this way from elementary statements. However, most sentences used in ordinary discourse are not. The truth or falsity of "Brown said that Sligo is in Scotland" is independent of the falsity of "Sligo is in Scotland", to mention just one case. It is doubtful that in ordinary discourse the truth or falsity of "If water is malleable, tomorrow is Tuesday" is determined by the truth or falsity of its constituents. Its truth or falsity in ordinary discourse might be thought to depend upon the lack of connection between its antecedent and its consequent.

We have illustrated the operation of some of the logical rules in terms of conditional premises drawn from ordinary discourse; *e.g.*, "If it is before eleven, the library is open". It is essential to point out now that such conditionals can be used as appropriate examples only by treating ordinary discourse as if it were a logical or mathematical system. For, strictly speaking, the logic we are developing in this book is the logic of mathematics. It is, after all, a logic of deduction, and it is only in a manner of speaking that deductions can be said to occur at all in ordinary language.

In mathematics, we use a truth-functional conditional. And in view of this need, it is the present matrix for $\supset$ that we must accept; for the composition of this matrix agrees with Impl and the matrices for v and $\sim$, and we have no hesitation in accepting either of these.

Having the matrix for $\supset$, we can now test inferences with conditional premises. Let us observe the *caveat* of the next to the last paragraph by discreetly refusing to interpret the symbols we use to express such premises. Consider, for instance,

A $\supset$ B,	C $\supset$ D,	C $\supset$ B	$/\therefore$	A $\supset$ D
t t t	f t f	f t t	U	t f f

This inference is unsound because, as in previous cases, all its premises can be made true while its conclusion is false. Of course, it would be equally possible for one or more premises to be false while the conclusion is false.

Consider the following assignment of truth-values:

$$
\begin{array}{ccccc}
A \supset B, & C \supset D, & C \supset B & /\therefore & A \supset D, \\
\text{t f f} & \text{t f f} & \text{t f f} & & \text{t f f}
\end{array}
$$

But such an assignment is inconclusive. The question whether all the premises can be true is not answered by the statement that some or all *can* be false. The best way to answer it is to try to make all the premises true. As we proceed with the work of assuming truth and falsity in the premises, we may find cases in which such assumption is crucial. Thus, since we begin with

$$
\begin{array}{ccccc}
A \supset B, & C \supset D, & C \supset B & /\therefore & A \supset D, \\
\text{t} & \text{f} & & & \text{t f f}
\end{array}
$$

the assumptions of truth and falsity in each of the first two premises is crucial; B must be true and C false in order for these premises to be true. But the third premise is not a crucial case, for, as matters stand, there are three different ways in which it could be true. The best way to work problems of this sort is to begin with the crucial assignments.

It is easy to obtain the defining matrix for $\equiv$. We can begin with

$$\vdash (A \equiv B) \equiv [(A \supset B) \& (B \supset A)].$$

We then construct the following truth table for the right-hand side, which is the required truth table for $\equiv$.

$$
\begin{array}{ccccccc}
[(A & \supset & B) & \& & (B & \supset & A)] \\
\text{t} & \text{t} & \text{t} & \text{t} & \text{t} & \text{t} & \text{t} \\
\text{f} & \text{t} & \text{t} & \text{f} & \text{t} & \text{f} & \text{f} \\
\text{t} & \text{f} & \text{f} & \text{f} & \text{f} & \text{t} & \text{t} \\
\text{f} & \text{t} & \text{f} & \text{t} & \text{f} & \text{t} & \text{f}
\end{array}
$$

The column under & can be summarized by the matrix

$\equiv$	t	f
t	t	f
f	f	t

In other words, *a biconditional is true if and only if its members agree in truth-value.*

Let us consider an inference with a biconditional conclusion:

$$
\begin{array}{cccc}
A \supset B, & B \supset C & /\therefore & A \equiv C
\end{array}
$$

We might proceed to assume truth and falsity as follows:

$$
\begin{array}{cccc}
A \supset B, & B \supset C & /\therefore & A \equiv C \\
\text{t} & \text{f} & & \text{t f f}
\end{array}
$$

It is clear that at least one of these premises must be false: if B is true, the first premise will be true but the second will be false, while if B is false, the second premise will be true but the first false. Is this inference, then, a sound one? The answer appears if we reflect that there is also another way of making the conclusion false,

$$
\begin{array}{ccc}
A & \equiv & C, \\
\mathbf{f} & \mathbf{f} & \mathbf{t}
\end{array}
$$

from which we can proceed as follows:

$$
\begin{array}{cccccc}
A \supset B & & B \supset C & /\therefore & A \equiv C \\
\mathbf{f} & & \mathbf{t} & \mathbf{U} & \mathbf{f} \ \mathbf{f} \ \mathbf{t}
\end{array}
$$

With this assumption of truth and falsity both premises are true regardless of whether B is true or false.

In general, there may be a number of ways of rendering the conclusion of an inference false, and the inference is unsound if the premises can be made all true for any of these ways. Four rows of truth-values, for instance, may be needed to test a conclusion of the form $(p \equiv q) \equiv r$ and seven may be needed when the conclusion is $\sim(p \vee q \vee r)$.

What of the cases in which we are sure that no assumptions of truth or falsity could exhibit an inference as unsound? Such a case is the following:

$$
\begin{array}{cccccc}
A \supset B, & & B \supset C & /\therefore & A \supset C \\
\mathbf{t} & & \mathbf{f} & & \mathbf{t} \ \mathbf{f} \ \mathbf{f}
\end{array}
$$

From the analysis of the preceding inference, which was like this except for having $A \equiv C$ as its conclusion, we can see that not both premises could be true when the conclusion is false. The conclusion, then, necessarily follows from the premises. In other words, the inference is sound, and the conclusion is deducible from the premises. Thus, in our search for a test for unsound inferences, we find not merely a way of identifying unsound ones but a way of identifying sound ones as well. Any inference that we do not succeed in showing to be unsound by present methods is definitely sound; and we shall write S under the three dots to indicate this:

$$
\begin{array}{cccccc}
A \supset B, & & B \supset C & /\therefore & A \supset C \\
\mathbf{t} & & \mathbf{f} & \mathbf{S} & \mathbf{t} \ \mathbf{f} \ \mathbf{f}
\end{array}
$$

A method that allows us to decide whether a given inference is sound or unsound is called a decision procedure, and will be discussed further in Part Two.

A natural question at this point is whether the decision procedure we have developed does not render obsolete the entire apparatus of Chapter Two. Since we now have a purely mechanical test for the soundness of an inference, why continue to use the rules at all? Several points must be made in reply to this question. The first is that although truth-value assignments may tell us *that* a certain conclusion can be reached from certain premises, they do not tell us *how* to reach that conclusion. Only the rules tell us *how* statements can be deduced from one another. A related point is that if logic is the theory of mathematical reasoning, then the fundamental way in which we formulate logic cannot be in terms of matrices and truth-value assignments. For although matrices and truth-value assignments can be used to check the results of mathematical reasoning, they most emphatically do not embody that reasoning. Theorems are derived from axioms by means of logical rules, not by means of tables of **t**'s and **f**'s. Finally, even if a satisfactory theory of propositional deduction could be formulated in terms of a decision procedure, such a theory could not be formulated for certain more complex kinds of reasoning for which it is known that there cannot be a decision procedure. And the propositional rules turn out to be a highly useful adjunct of the formulation of some of these kinds of reasoning, as we shall see in Chapter Six. This is a central reason for adopting these rules at the outset.

TABLE 3.1

RÉSUMÉ OF THE BASIC TRUTH TABLES

A	B	A & B	A ⊃ B	A v B	A ≡ B	A	~A
t	t	t	t	t	t	t	f
f	t	f	t	t	f	f	t
t	f	f	f	t	f		
f	f	f	t	f	t		

EXERCISE 3.1

I. **1.** Show by assignment of truth-values that the deductions presented in the exercises for Chapter Two were sound; especially those of Exercise 2.9.

   2. (a) By the same method, decide which of the following inferences are sound and which are unsound.

       (b) Then, as a review, deduce the conclusion from the premises of each sound inference.

           1. I can get to Yugoslavia on time only if I fly. If I want to close the uranium deal, I must get to Yugoslavia on time. But, in fact, I do not need to close the uranium deal. Therefore, I need not fly.

           2. If Anderson comes to the party, then, if Brown is not there, Clark will make a fool of himself. If Brown is there, then Davis will get drunk. If Davis gets drunk, Anderson will not come. Therefore, Anderson will not come unless Brown is there.

3. If I can find the key to my car, I am going to start the engine if and only if the nearby service station is open. Either the nearby service station is open or I shall have to change the tire myself. I will do no such thing. Therefore, if the nearby service station is open, I am going to start the engine.

4. Either there was a picnic here or somebody is using this spot for a private dump. If someone is using this spot for a private dump, I am going to notify the game warden. But if I notify the game warden, he may ask me about that illegal doe I got last year. I would not want him to ask me about that. If those are paper cups, it must have been a picnic. So it was a picnic.

5. Either Smith is stupid or he is playing it safe. Either he is rich or he is bluffing. If he is rich, he is not playing it safe. If he is bluffing, he is not stupid. Therefore, if he is not rich, he is stupid.

6. $A \supset A$ /∴ $(A \lor B) \supset A$

7. $A \supset A$ /∴ $A \lor (B \supset A)$

8. $\sim A \supset A$ /∴ A

9. $\sim A \supset A$ /∴ $A \supset \sim A$

10. $\sim A \supset A$ /∴ $\sim A \supset B$

11. $A \supset \sim A$ /∴ $A \supset B$

12. $A \supset \sim A$ ∴ $B \supset \sim A$

13. $\sim(A \supset \sim A)$ /∴ $\sim(A \lor B)$

14. $\sim(A \supset A)$ /∴ A

15. $\sim(A \supset A)$ /∴ $\sim A$

16. $\sim(A \supset B)$ /∴ A

17. $\sim(A \supset B)$ /∴ $\sim(A \& \sim B) \supset A$

18. $\sim A \supset (B \supset A)$ /∴ $\sim A \supset \sim B$

19. $A \& B$ /∴ $A \lor B$

20. $A \lor B$ /∴ $A \& B$

21. $A \lor B$ /∴ $\sim(\sim A \& \sim B)$

22. $A \lor B$ /∴ $(A \& B) \lor (A \& \sim B) \lor (\sim A \& B)$

23. $A \lor B$ /∴ $(A \lor B) \& (A \lor \sim B) \& (\sim A \lor B)$

24. A & B   /∴ (A ∨ B) & (A ∨ ~B) & (~A ∨ B)

25. ~(~A ⊃ ~B)   /∴ A ⊃ B

26. A ⊃ (B ⊃ C)   /∴ (A ⊃ B) ⊃ C

27. (A ⊃ B) ⊃ C   /∴ A ⊃ (B ⊃ C)

28. (A ⊃ B) ⊃ C   /∴ ~(B ⊃ C) ⊃ A

29. (A ⊃ B) ∨ C   /∴ (C ⊃ A) ⊃ B

30. (A ⊃ B) ∨ C   /∴ A ⊃ (B ∨ C)

31. A ⊃ (B ∨ C)   /∴ (A ⊃ B) ∨ (A ⊃ C)

32. A ⊃ (B & C)   /∴ (A ⊃ B) & (A ⊃ C)

33. A ⊃ B, A ⊃ ~B   /∴ ~B

34. A ⊃ B, A ⊃ ~B   /∴ ~A

35. (A ⊃ ~A) ∨ B, ~[(A ⊃ ~A) & B]   /∴ ~B

36. (A ∨ B) ⊃ (B ⊃ C)   /∴ (A ⊃ B) ⊃ C

37. (A ⊃ B) ⊃ B   /∴ B

38. (A ⊃ B) ⊃ A   /∴ A

39. A   /∴ (A ⊃ B) ⊃ A

40. A   /∴ A ⊃ (B ⊃ A)

41. A   /∴ A ⊃ (A ⊃ B)

42. A ⊃ B, A ⊃ ~B   /∴ ~A ∨ C

43. A ⊃ B, ~A ⊃ B   /∴ A

44. A ⊃ B, ~A ⊃ B   /∴ B ∨ A

45. A ⊃ [A ⊃ (B ∨ ~B)]   /∴ ~A

46. ~A ⊃ [A ⊃ (B ∨ ~B)]   /∴ ~A

47. A ⊃ [A ⊃ (B & ~B)]   /∴ ~A

48. A ⊃ [A ⊃ (B & ~B)], A ⊃ B   /∴ C

49. (A & ~B) ⊃ C, C ⊃ D, ~(D ∨ C)   /∴ A ⊃ B

50. ~A, ~(~B ∨ C), B ⊃ (D & C)   /∴ B ⊃ A

51. ~A ⊃ (B ⊃ A), B ⊃ (A ∨ C)   /∴ ~B & A

52. A v B, ∼(∼A ⊃ ∼C), C ⊃ D   /∴ ∼(∼D v ∼B)

53. (A v B) ⊃ (∼C ⊃ D), (∼B v C) ⊃ ∼E /∴ E ⊃ (A ⊃ D)

54. (A & B) v (A ⊃ B), A ⊃ (B v C) /∴ (A & C) v (A ⊃ C)

55. (A ⊃ B) & (C v A), (C ⊃ A) & (C ⊃ ∼A) /∴ ∼(A & ∼B)

3.2 Statements and Truth-Values

In Section 2.5 we observed that A, B, C, . . . were used as variables having the sentences of ordinary language as substituents. In this chapter we have used them in the same way. We have used them, however, in another way as well, and this new use requires a word of explanation. We begin by observing that any particular sentence possesses **t** or **f**, as the case may be. Thus "The grass is green" is true and "The $\sqrt{2}$ is rational" is false. If, then, the first of these sentences be taken as a *substituent* for A, we might regard **t** as a *value* of A. Similarly, if the second of these sentences be taken as a substituent for A, we might regard **f** as a value of A. In general, since A, B, C, . . . are variables having as substituents sentences in ordinary language some of which possess **t** and some **f**, **t** and **f** may be regarded as values of these variables.

The use of **t** and **f** as values for the variables A, B, C, . . . permits a summary of the result of replacing them by particular true and false statements. Indeed, a truth table is just such a summary including the truth-functionally determined truth-values of the molecular statement for the different possible values. When we write the truth table for a molecular statement, we write all possible different combinations of the values **t** and **f** for that statement. Thus the truth table

A	&	B
t	t	t
f	f	t
t	f	f
f	f	f

presents in its four lines all the different cases of the values **t** and **f** as well as the value of the molecular statement for each case. Clearly, A may have the value **t** or **f**. For the case where A is **t**, B may have the value **t** or **f**. Similarly, where A has the value **f**, B may have the value **t** or **f**. Thus there are four possible cases for each of which the value of the molecular statement is determined as indicated.

Any molecular statement of PL can be built up from atomic statements and the logical connectives ⊃, v, &, ≡, and ∼. Since a matrix exists for each of these logical connectives, it is possible to determine the truth-value of any molecular statement on the assumption of the various possible combinations of truth-values of its constituents. Thus, for example, the molecular statement

$$(A \lor B) \supset C$$

is constructed from the atomic statements A, B, and C, and the logical connectives $\lor$ and $\supset$. The truth table determining its truth-value for all possible
values of its constituents is

(A	$\lor$	B)	$\supset$	C
t	t	t	t	t
f	t	t	t	t
t	t	f	t	t
f	f	f	t	t
t	t	t	f	f
f	t	t	f	f
t	t	f	f	f
f	f	f	t	f

In general, as this example suggests, we can construct a truth table for any such
statement. There will be 2^k lines in the truth table, where k is the number of
different atomic statements in the molecular statement. In determining the
value of the molecular statement for the values of its atomic statements, we
use the functional relation given in the matrices of the relevant logical connectives.

Each line of a truth table of a molecular statement built up from A, B,
C, ... presents one possible combination of truth-values of its atomic constituents and the resulting truth-value for these values of the successive compounds constructed from the constituents. All the lines of a truth table
together represent a truth-function, that is, a unique correspondence between
the truth-values of the atomic statements and the truth-value of the molecular
statement. Thus we might write the above truth table in functional notation as

$$f(A, B, C) = p$$

where we see in familiar mathematical notation that the truth-value of p is
functionally determined by the truth values of A, B, and C.

Consideration of truth-functions in this way reminds us that each of the
matrices for the logical connectives represents a truth-function of two variables, and we may ask how many such functions (and so connectives) there
are. The answer is sixteen, for there are sixteen ways in which one may determine the possession of t or f for the four possible combinations of t and f for
the two variables A and B. These sixteen possibilities are stated in Table
3.2. The reader may wish to see if he can state an ordinary language meaning
of the types of connectives not discussed or used in this book and hence not
identified in the spaces across the top. The connectives $|$ and $\downarrow$ are discussed
in Section 3.3.

TABLE 3.2

A	B		A v B	A ⊃ B				A ≡ B	A & B	A | B						A ↓ B	
t	t	t	t	t	t	t	t	t	t	f	f	f	f	f	f	f	f
f	t	t	t	t	t	f	f	f	f	t	t	t	t	f	f	f	f
t	f	t	t	f	f	t	t	f	f	t	t	f	f	t	t	f	f
f	f	t	f	t	f	t	f	t	f	t	f	t	f	t	f	t	f

The conception of truth tables which express the relation between the truth-values of constituent atomic statements and the truth-value of the molecular statement of which they are a part is the basis for the design of computers for the solution of problems in logic. The possibility of such computers has been imagined for a long time. Some work in the direction of logic machines was done as early as the eighteenth century by Charles Stanhope, and further work was carried out by W. S. Jevons in the nineteenth century on a machine based on Boolean algebra.* Today, of course, computers are available for the solution of all sorts of problems. The Burroughs Truth Function Evaluator developed by the Burroughs Corporation is an electrical computer designed to solve problems in genetics, electrical engineering, and insurance rapidly and easily. Such machines as this depend upon the fact that the truth tables can be represented by switches, circuits, vacuum tubes, or mechanical devices.†

We have so far used the variables $p, q, r, \ldots$ to have as substituents any of the atomic statements A, B, C, ... as well as any molecular statements built up from these with the connectives ⊃, v, &, ≡, and ∼. Since any molecular statement, as we have seen, evaluates to **t** or **f**, we can, if we like, write the truth table for a schema. Clearly if p and q have as substituents A and B there is no significant difference between the statement

$$A \text{ v } B$$

and the schema

$$p \text{ v } q$$

It is also evident that in this case the truth table for the statement can serve

---

* Boolean algebra is a variant form of PL, expressing the principles of logic in algebraic form. See Chapter Eight, Section 8.3.

† See William Miehle, *Burroughs Truth Function Evaluator* (Detroit: Burroughs Corporation, 1955). See also Robert V. Oakford and James F. Gere, *Introduction to BALGOL* (Belmont, California: Wadsworth Publishing Company, Inc., 1961).

for the schema. Even when *p* and *q* have as substituents molecular statements, however, these molecular statements will be either **t** or **f**. Hence in such a case the table for

$$
\begin{array}{ccc}
p & \textbf{v} & q \\
\textbf{t} & \textbf{t} & \textbf{t} \\
\textbf{f} & \textbf{t} & \textbf{t} \\
\textbf{t} & \textbf{t} & \textbf{f} \\
\textbf{f} & \textbf{f} & \textbf{f}
\end{array}
$$

(which is also that for A **v** B) still provides the evaluation of the disjunction of molecular statements in all possible cases. It is sometimes useful to analyze schemata by means of truth tables, and we shall occasionally do so. When we do so, we must remember that *p*, *q*, *r*, ... are not necessarily atomic.

EXERCISE 3.2

I. **1.** How many lines are needed for the truth table for each of the following?

    1. A **v** ~A

    2. (A **v** ~A) & (A & ~A)

    3. (A ⊃ B) **v** (A & ~B)

    4. [(A **v** B) ⊃ (C **v** D)] ⊃ A

    5. [(A & B) **v** ~A] ⊃ [~B & (A **v** C)]

    6. (A & B) ⊃ [(A & B) **v** C]

    7. [(A **v** C) & (B ⊃ S)] ⊃ [(T & U) **v** ~A]

    8. A /∴ A **v** [B & (A ⊃ C)]

    9. A ≡ B, C ⊃ (D **v** A), ~B ⊃ ~D /∴ C ⊃ A

    10. A ⊃ [B ≡ (C **v** D)], (D ⊃ E) & {(C **v** D) ⊃ [B ≡ (C **v** D)]}
       /∴ E ⊃ [A ⊃ (B **v** D)]

  2. Write the truth tables for the above inferences.

II. **1.** Assume that, instead of the two values **t** and **f**, there are three possible values for each variable (*e.g.*, **t**, **p** (possible), and **f**). How many lines would be needed for the truth table for each of the formulas in part one above?

  2. Can you write a general formula which expresses the number of lines needed for the three-valued table for any formula of *k* variables?

III. **1.** Assign a symbol to each of the ten connectives which are not identified explicitly in Table 3.2. For each of the connectives which is the negation of another, use the symbol of that other cut by a diagonal line, so that your final list contains eight distinct symbols and the negation of each.

2. Find the best ordinary language meaning for each of these ten connectives.

3. Is there any particular relationship between the ordinary language meaning of each connective and that of its negation?

IV.   A notation which perhaps makes more explicit the nature of the logical connectives as functions is that devised by J. Łukasiewicz and used widely by the Polish logicians. In this system ∼*p* is written *Np*, *p* & *q* is written *Kpq*, *p* ∨ *q* is written *Apq*, and *p* ⊃ *q* is written *Cpq*. Note that this notation is unambiguous without punctuation.

1. Why may it be said that this notation makes more evident the functional nature of the logical connectives?

2. Translate the following into the notation of this text.

   1. *CpKqr*

   2. *CKpqr*

   3. *NCpAqr*

   4. *CpCqp*

   5. *KCpqr*

   6. *CCpqANpq*

   7. *CCNqNpCpq*

   8. *CNCpqKpNq*

   9. *CCpqCNKqrNKrp*

   10. *CCpCqrCCpqCpr*

   Schemata 4, 7, and 10 are the postulates of Łukasiewicz's own system.

3. Write the truth tables for the schemata of 2 above.

4. Translate the formulas of part one above into the Polish notation.

3.3   Tautology, Contradiction, and Interdefinability

A statement that is always true—*i.e.*, evaluates as true no matter how truth-values are assigned to its constituents—is called a *tautology*. An example is provided by the following conditional, known as Peirce's Law:

$$[(A \supset B) \supset A] \supset A$$

	A	⊃	B	⊃	A]	⊃	A
	t	t	t	t	t	t	t
	f	t	t	f	f	t	f
	t	f	f	t	t	t	t
	f	t	f	f	f	t	f

The appearance of a solid column of t's under the main ⊃ shows that this statement is indeed a tautology. It will sometimes be of use to refer to tautologies apart from their truth tables. We shall designate a statement as tautological by the symbol $\vdash$. Thus we write an instance of Peirce's Law $\vdash [(A \supset B) \supset A] \supset A$. We shall also indicate the tautological character of the instances of a schema by prefixing $\vdash$ to the schema. Since in Chapter Two we prefixed $\vdash$ to each ZPC, the present usage suggests that ZPC's are tautologies, which is indeed the case, as may be verified in any instance and as we shall prove in Chapter Nine.

Any inference is sound when the conditional that has the conjunction of the premises as antecedent and the conclusion as consequent is a tautology. Consider, for example, a case of DS:

[(A	v	B)	&	~A]	⊃	B
t	t	t	f	f t	t	t
f	t	t	t	t f	t	t
t	t	f	f	f t	t	f
f	f	f	f	t f	t	f

If an inference is unsound, on the other hand, the conditional written as above is not a tautology. This is exemplified by one of the unsound arguments of Section 3.1:

[(O	v	P)	&	P]	⊃	~O
t	t	t	t	t	f	f t
f	t	t	t	t	t	t f
t	t	f	f	f	t	f t
f	f	f	f	f	t	t f

This statement is not a tautology, because it is false for at least one assignment of truth-values to its elements.

Observe that the first row of the truth table we have just written out involves precisely the same assignment of truth-values to constituents that we used in Section 3.1 to condemn the same deduction as unsound. The method of Section 3.1 is a way of writing out just the crucial lines of the truth table of an inference.

A statement that is always false—*i.e.*, evaluates as false no matter how truth-values are assigned to its elements—is called a *contradiction*. An example is

A	&	~A
t	f	f t
f	f	t f

A statement that is neither a tautology nor a contradiction is called *contingent*. For example, $[(O \lor P) \& P] \supset {\sim}O$ as above, or more simply

(A	⊃	~A)
t	f	f t
f	t	t f

In Chapter Two we asserted that all contradictions could be reduced to the form $p \mathbin{\&} \sim p$. It is easy to see now why this should be so. Any two contradictions, say r and s, have precisely the same truth-value, namely **f**, for every assignment of truth-values to their constituents; and the biconditional $r \equiv s$ is true if and only if r and s both have the same truth-value. Thus

$$\vdash r \;\equiv\; s$$
$$ \mathbf{f} \quad \mathbf{t} \quad \mathbf{f}$$

Therefore, any contradiction is equivalent to (and hence replaceable by) $p \mathbin{\&} \sim p$. Similarly, all tautologies are equivalent. But of course not all contingent statements are equivalent, because they receive **f** under various conditions.

Let us symbolize any statement that is a tautology by T, and any statement that is a contradiction by C. The following schemata, which concern tautologies and contradictions, may now be verified.

(a) $\vdash p \supset \mathrm{T}$ —"Any statement implies a tautology"— "Given any tautology, every statement implies it". The following deduction schema suggests a reason for this.

> 1. p
> 2. $p \vee \sim p$ ZPC
> 3. $p \supset (p \vee \sim p)$ 1–2, $\supset$I

Of course, $p \vee \sim p$ is a tautological form.

(b) $\vdash \mathrm{C} \supset p$ —"A contradiction implies any statement".
For

> 1. C
> 2. p 1, $\sim$E
> 3. $\mathrm{C} \supset p$ 1–2, $\supset$I

(c) $\vdash (p \mathbin{\&} \mathrm{T}) \equiv p$
(d) $\vdash (p \mathbin{\&} \mathrm{C}) \equiv \mathrm{C}$
(e) $\vdash (p \vee \mathrm{T}) \equiv \mathrm{T}$
(f) $\vdash (p \vee \mathrm{C}) \equiv p$
(g) $\vdash (p \equiv \mathrm{T}) \equiv p$
(h) $\vdash (p \equiv \mathrm{C}) \equiv \sim p$

To these we may add discharged forms of the laws of Idempotence:

(i) $\vdash (p \mathbin{\&} p) \equiv p$
(j) $\vdash (p \vee p) \equiv p$

In Section 3.1 we introduced the matrix for $\supset$ on the basis of the schema $\vdash (p \supset q) \equiv (\sim p \vee q)$. This suggests that we could formulate PL without writing any conditionals. In fact, we could do without conjunctions, too, since the schema $\vdash (p \mathbin{\&} q) \equiv \sim(\sim p \mathbin{\textbf{v}} \sim q)$ can readily be proved. The biconditional is also eliminable, since

$$\vdash (p \equiv q) \equiv [(p \supset q) \mathbin{\&} (q \supset p)]$$

which reduces to

$$\vdash (p \equiv q) \equiv [(\sim p \mathbin{\textbf{v}} q) \mathbin{\&} (\sim q \mathbin{\textbf{v}} p)]$$

and thus to

$$\vdash (p \equiv q) \equiv \sim[\sim(\sim p \mathbin{\textbf{v}} q) \mathbin{\textbf{v}} \sim(\sim q \mathbin{\textbf{v}} p)]$$

Thus specific conditionals, conjunctions, and biconditionals can all be defined in terms of alternation and denial.

Conjunction and denial could equally well serve as the undefined basis for PL, as is shown by the following schemata:

$$\vdash (p \supset q) \equiv \sim(p \mathbin{\&} \sim q)$$
$$\vdash (p \mathbin{\textbf{v}} q) \equiv \sim(\sim p \mathbin{\&} \sim q)$$
$$\vdash (p \equiv q) \equiv [\sim(p \mathbin{\&} \sim q) \mathbin{\&} \sim(q \mathbin{\&} \sim p)]$$

Conditional and negative operations could also be used as the undefined basis for defining statements involving other operations since

$$\vdash (p \mathbin{\&} q) \equiv \sim(p \supset \sim q)$$
$$\vdash (p \mathbin{\textbf{v}} q) \equiv (\sim p \supset q); \quad \text{also} \quad \vdash (p \mathbin{\textbf{v}} q) \equiv [(p \supset q) \supset q]$$
$$\vdash (p \equiv q) \equiv \sim[(p \supset q) \supset \sim(q \supset p)]$$

In terms of the biconditional and negation, however, it is impossible to define statements involving all three of the other operations.

If we begin with biconditionals and conjunctions, we have

$$\vdash (p \supset q) \equiv [p \equiv (p \mathbin{\&} q)]$$

Then, using $\vdash (p \mathbin{\textbf{v}} q) \equiv [(p \supset q) \supset q]$ (cited just above) we can introduce alternation

$$\vdash (p \mathbin{\textbf{v}} q) \equiv [[p \equiv (p \mathbin{\&} q)] \equiv \{[p \equiv (p \mathbin{\&} q)] \mathbin{\&} q\}]$$

The reader may wish to use a truth table to check this equivalence. But this is as far as we can go in making $\equiv$ and $\mathbin{\&}$ the undefined basis of PL, for there is no way of defining negative statements in terms of biconditionals, conjunctions, conditionals, and alternations without moving beyond PL. To do so requires introducing the notion of "For all p". Thus "For all p, $p \equiv p$" is clearly true, but "For all p, $p \mathbin{\&} p$" is false. In fact, "For all p, $p \mathbin{\&} p$" may be taken as the *definition* of contradiction.

$$\vdash \text{C} \equiv (\text{For all } p, p \mathbin{\&} p)$$

Once we have C, we can easily introduce negation as

$$\vdash \sim p \equiv (p \supset \text{C})$$

This extension of PL, involving what is called the quantification of statement schemata, is called *protothetic*, and has been developed primarily by the Polish logicians Tarski and Lesniewski.*

If we begin with the operations discussed and used in this book, then, there is no way of choosing one so as to define the other four in terms of it, and there are only three ways of choosing two and defining the other three without going beyond the terms of PL. But there are operations that we have not yet discussed or used and which permit the formulation of PL on the basis of one undefined operation. One is *joint denial*; that is, "Neither p nor q"; symbolized $p \downarrow q$†. The essential equivalences for definition are

$$\vdash \sim p \equiv (p \downarrow p)$$
$$\vdash p \vee q \equiv \sim(p \downarrow q)$$
$$\equiv (p \downarrow q) \downarrow (p \downarrow q)$$
$$\vdash p \,\&\, q \equiv \sim p \downarrow \sim q$$
$$\equiv (p \downarrow p) \downarrow (q \downarrow q)$$

$p \supset q$ and $p \equiv q$ can now be defined. Another type of statement in terms of which all other types can be defined is the *alternative denial* $p \mid q$, meaning "Either not p or not q".‡ The connectives $\downarrow$ and $\mid$ were anticipated in Table 3.2.

EXERCISE 3.3

I. By using truth tables, determine which of the following formulas are (1) tautologies, (2) contradictions, (3) contingencies, (4) equivalent with one another, (5) compatible with one another, and (6) contradictories of one another (Note: p and q are *equivalent* when either both are true or both are false. They are *compatible* when both could be true. And they are *contradictories* when they are incompatible and $\sim p$ and $\sim q$ are also incompatible.)

   1. $A \supset (A \vee B)$

   2. $A \supset (A \equiv B)$

   3. $A \,\&\, (A \vee B)$

   4. $\sim(A \vee \sim A)$

   5. $A \supset (B \,\&\, C)$

   6. $\sim A \vee (\sim A \,\&\, \sim B)$

---

* See Łukasiewicz and Tarski, "Untersuchungen über den Aussagenkalkül", *Comptes Rendus des Séances de la Société des Sciences et des Lettres de Varsovie*, Classe III, Vol. 23 (1930), pp. 30–50; especially pp. 44–50. (English translation in Tarski, *Logic, Semantics, and Metamathematics*, Oxford, Clarendon Press, 1956, pp. 54–59.)

† This was first discovered by Peirce. See *The Collected Papers of Charles Sanders Peirce*, Vol. IV, pp. 13–14.

‡ See H. M. Sheffer, "A Set of Independent Postulates for Boolean Algebras", *Trans. Amer. Math. Soc.*, vol. 14 (1913), pp. 481–488.

    7. $\sim$A $\supset$ (A & $\sim$B)

    8. (A & B) $\equiv$ ($\sim$A v $\sim$B)

    9. (A & B) & $\sim$(A v B)

    10. (A v B) $\supset$ (A & B)

    11. [(A $\supset$ B) & (B $\supset$ C)] $\supset$ (A $\supset$ C)

    12. [(A & B) v (A & $\sim$C)] $\supset$ (B $\equiv$ C)

    13. $\sim$A v [(A & B) v ($\sim$A & $\sim$B)]

    14. [A $\supset$ (A v C)] $\supset$ $\sim$($\sim$A v A)

    15. (A $\supset$ B) $\equiv$ [($\sim$A v B) & ($\sim$B & A)]

    16. [(A $\supset$ B) & (A $\supset$ C)] $\supset$ (B $\supset$ C)

    17. [$\sim$A v (B & C)] & (B & $\sim$C)

    18. [(A v B) & C] $\equiv$ [(A & C) v (B & C)]

    19. [(A & C) $\supset$ (B & D)] $\equiv$ [A $\supset$ (C & D)]

    20. [(A & B) v (A $\supset$ B)] $\equiv$ {[(A & C) v (A $\supset$ C)] & [A $\supset$ (B & C)]}

II. 1. Verify the tautologous schemata (a) through (j) given on page 95 by
      (a) truth-table technique
      (b) providing for each a deduction schema which shows it to be a ZPC

   2. (a) Define each of the other standard connectives, and joint denial, in terms of alternative denial.

      (b) Define each of the fifteen possible connectives in terms of (1) joint denial (2) alternative denial.

   3. Restate each of the formulas of part I above in terms of (where appropriate):

      (a) conjunction and denial
      (b) alternation and denial
      (c) implication and denial
      (d) joint denial
      (e) alternative denial

3.4   Normal Forms

By means of the rules of Impl and $\equiv$E, it is easy to reduce any propositional statement to an equivalent involving just conjunction, alternation, and negation, if it is not already in this form. Thus the tautological schema

$$\vdash p \supset p$$

becomes

$$\vdash \sim p \text{ v } p.$$

From

$$p \equiv \sim p$$

we proceed as follows:

    ——**1.** $p \equiv \sim p$
        2. $(p \supset \sim p) \mathbin{\&} (\sim p \supset p)$ 1, $\equiv$E
        3. $(\sim p \mathbin{v} \sim p) \mathbin{\&} (\sim\sim p \mathbin{v} p)$ 2, Impl (twice), Rep
        4. $\sim p \mathbin{\&} p$ 3, Id (twice), DN, Rep

Since each of the rules used here can be expressed as a biconditional, the inference is reversible, so $\vdash (p \equiv \sim p) \equiv (\sim p \mathbin{\&} p)$.

When a statement has been reduced to an equivalent in terms of conjunction, disjunction (*i.e.*, alternation), and negation, then, if it satisfies certain additional conditions, it is said to be in *Disjunctive Normal Form* (DNF) or *Conjunctive Normal Form* (CNF), as the case may be.

DNF: A statement is in Disjunctive Normal Form provided it is of the form $p \mathbin{v} q \mathbin{v} r \mathbin{v} \ldots$, where all contradictory disjuncts are dropped and each remaining disjunct is either
(1) an atomic statement
(2) the negation of an atomic statement
(3) a conjunction of atomic statements and/or negations of atomic statements.

If we allow a disjunction to have just one disjunct, we count all of the following as being in DNF:

           A
           $\sim$A
           A & B   DNF's with just one disjunct.
           A & $\sim$B & C

           A $\mathbin{v}$ B
           (A & B) $\mathbin{v}$ $\sim$C
           (A & B) $\mathbin{v}$ (A & $\sim$C)
           A $\mathbin{v}$ (B & C & D) $\mathbin{v}$ (B & $\sim$C)

But the following are not in DNF, for reasons which the reader should make sure he understands:

           $\sim$(A & B)
           (A $\supset$ B) $\mathbin{v}$ (C & D)
           [A & (B $\mathbin{v}$ C)] $\mathbin{v}$ (A & C)
           $\sim$[A $\mathbin{v}$ (B & C) $\mathbin{v}$ D]
           A $\mathbin{v}$ B $\mathbin{v}$ (C & $\sim$C)

CNF, on the other hand, is defined as follows:

CNF: A statement is in Conjunctive Normal Form, provided it is of the form
p & *q* & *r* & . . . , where all tautologous conjuncts are deleted and each
remaining conjunct is either
(1) an atomic statement
(2) the negation of an atomic statement
(3) a disjunction of atomic statements and/or negations of atomic
statements.

The reader should make lists like those above—one consisting of statements in
CNF, and the other of statements that do not qualify. Notice that some statements may be in both DNF and CNF. Thus A clearly has both forms, as
does ∼A. A & ∼B & C, furthermore, can be interpreted either as the sole
disjunct of a statement in DNF or as a CNF having three conjuncts.

There are two methods for putting a statement in normal form; namely,
by using its truth table and by using a list of standard equivalences. We
illustrate the latter first. Suppose our problem is to put (A v B) & (∼A v ∼B)
in DNF (note that it is already in CNF). We can feel our way to the answer
as follows:

     1. (A v B) & (∼A v ∼B)
     2. [(A v B) & ∼A] v [(A v B) & ∼B]   1, Dist, Rep
     3. [(A & ∼A) v (B & ∼A)] v
             [(A & ∼B) v (B & ∼B)]   2, Dist, Rep
     4. (B & ∼A) v (A & ∼B)   By equivalence (f) of Sec-
                                     tion 3.3: $(p \lor C) \equiv p$; and
                                       Rep

Let us now put A ≡ (A v B) in CNF:

     1. A ≡ (A v B)
     2. [A ⊃ (A v B)] & [(A v B) ⊃ A]   1, ≡E
     3. [∼A v (A v B)] & [∼(A v B) v A]   2, Impl, Rep
     4. [(A v ∼A) v B] & [∼(A v B) v A]   3, Assoc, CM, Rep
     5. T & [∼(A v B) v A]   4, ⊢ $(p \lor T) \equiv T$, Rep
     6. [∼(A v B) v A]   5, ⊢ $(p \& T) \equiv p$, Rep
     7. [(∼A & ∼B) v A]   6, DM, Rep
     8. [(A v ∼A) & (A v ∼B)]   7, Dist
     9. A v ∼B   8, ⊢ $(p \& T) \equiv p$, Rep

Line 9 is a statement in CNF having just one conjunct. Notice that this
deduction is fairly streamlined; we skip a number of steps, following the
suggestions made in Chapter Two, Section Nine.

These two examples should serve to suggest what equivalences make up the "standard" list referred to above. There are the biconditional versions of the following:

CM	Impl
Dist	Exp, Imp
Assoc	$\equiv$I, $\equiv$E
DM	Id
DN	

together with equivalences (c)–(f) of Section Three of this chapter. Indeed, any tautological equivalence of PL may be used. The only steps we must *not* take in deriving normal forms are those involving rules that cannot be stated as equivalences. Consider the following attempt to put (A & B) v C in CNF:

> **1.** (A & B) v C
> **2.** [(A & B) v C] v ~C   1, vI
> **3.** (A & B) v (C v ~C)   2, Assoc
> **4.** C v ~C   3, (p v T) $\equiv$ T

But this cannot be the right answer, because, while a statement is equivalent with any of its DNF's and CNF's, the tautology C v ~C is obviously not equivalent with the contingent statement (A & B) v C. The trouble is that the rule of vI is irreversible and so cannot be used in the derivation of normal forms. Since the derivation must be possible in both directions—from the statement to its normal form and back again—only reversible rules, that is, equivalences, can be used.

     The use of the plural expressions "DNF's" and "CNF's" suggests that any given statement has several normal forms of each kind. In fact, it has an indefinitely large number of them. The following, for example, are all DNF's of A $\supset$ B:

> ~A v B
>
> (A & B) v (~A & B) v (~A & ~B)
>
> (~A & C) v (B & C) v (~A & ~C) v (B & ~C), etc.

     Let us turn now to the second of the two ways of constructing normal forms—the method of using truth tables. Suppose we want a DNF for (A & B) $\equiv$ B. We begin by writing out its truth table:

(A	&	B)	$\equiv$	B
t	t	t	t	t
f	f	t	f	t
t	f	f	t	f
f	f	f	t	f

One way of understanding this table is to see that it means that (A & B) $\equiv$ B is true if and only if either A is true and B is true, or A is true and B is false, or A is false and B is false, or any combination of these possibilities holds true. In other words,

$$\vdash [(A \& B) \equiv B] \equiv [(A \& B) \lor (A \& \sim B) \lor (\sim A \& \sim B)]$$

But what we have done is to write the right-hand side out in DNF.

The statement that we have just written in DNF deserves special attention. Notice that each atomic statement appearing on the left-hand side appears just once in each disjunct on the right. When this sort of regularity occurs, we have what is called an *Expanded Disjunctive Normal Form* (EDNF). We always get an EDNF when we read a truth table in this way.

EDNF: A statement is in Expanded Disjunctive Normal Form provided it is in DNF and each atomic statement in the original formula occurs just once in each disjunct.

We can use the method of equivalences to derive an EDNF. To do this we make use of $\vdash p \& T \equiv p$. Given $A \supset B$, we proceed as follows:

——1. $A \supset B$
    2. $\sim A \lor B$ 1, Impl
    3. $[\sim A \& (B \lor \sim B)] \lor [B \& (A \lor \sim A)]$ 2, $\vdash (p \& T) \equiv p$
    4. $(\sim A \& B) \lor (\sim A \& \sim B) \lor (A \& B) \lor (\sim A \& B)$ 3, Dist, CM
    5. $(\sim A \& B) \lor (\sim A \& \sim B) \lor (A \& B)$ 4, Id

This procedure can be applied in general. Thus the tautological disjunction of each statement and its negation occurring in the original formula can be successively conjoined to the disjuncts of DNF to form the EDNF.

Expanded Conjunctive Normal Form (ECNF) is CNF in which each atomic statement appears once and only once in every conjunct. $(A \lor B) \&$ $(\sim A \lor \sim B)$ would be an example. ECNF, too, can be read from a truth table. Thus, in the table for $(A \& B) \equiv B$ above, the second line means that the statement is false when A is false and B is true. In other words, $\sim(\sim A \& B)$, or, by DM and DN, $A \lor \sim B$. But this is in ECNF. Another illustration is provided by $A \& \sim B$, which is not, as it stands, in ECNF because B does not appear in the first conjunct, nor A in the second.

(A	&	~B)
t	f	f t
f	f	f t
t	t	t f
f	f	t f

This table can be interpreted to mean that none of three different conditions is fulfilled: to wit,

$$\sim(A \& B) \& \sim(\sim A \& B) \& \sim(\sim A \& \sim B)$$

If we use DM and DN we obtain the derived statement in ECNF:

$$(\sim A \text{ v} \sim B) \text{ \& } (A \text{ v} \sim B) \text{ \& } (A \text{ v } B)$$

ECNF: A statement is in Expanded Conjunctive Normal Form provided it is in CNF and each atomic statement in the original formula occurs just once in each conjunct.

We can use the method of equivalences to derive an ECNF. To do this we make use of $\vdash p \text{ v } C \equiv p$. Given $A \text{ \& } \sim B$ we proceed as follows:

——1. A & ~B
  2. [A v (B & ~B)] & [~B v (A & ~A)]   1, $\vdash (p \text{ v } C) \equiv p$
  3. (A v B) & (A v ~B) & (A v ~B) & (~A v ~B)   2, Dist, CM
  4. (A v B) & (A v ~B) & (~A v ~B)   3, Id
  5. (~A v ~B) & (A v ~B) & (A v B)   4, CM

This is the same result as that just obtained by the truth-table method. The procedure can be generalized by successively disjoining with each conjunct of a CNF the conjunction of each statement occurring in the CNF and its denial.

Notice that while, say, A & B can be viewed as being in both CNF and DNF, it cannot be viewed as being both in ECNF and EDNF. It is not in ECNF because the first conjunct lacks an occurrence of B while the second lacks an occurrence of A. The only statements that can be viewed as being in both ECNF and EDNF are those like A and ~B.

We saw that the ECNF of A & ~B was (~A v ~B) & (A v ~B) & (A v B). Now the ECNF of the statement B ⊃ A is ~B v A, or A v ~B. Notice that this is one of the conjuncts in the ECNF of A & ~B. Since a conjunction implies any of its conjuncts, this shows that A & ~B implies B ⊃ A; in other words, (A & ~B) ⊃ (B ⊃ A). In general, when the ECNF of q is included in the ECNF of p, then $p \supset q$ is true. On the other hand, when the EDNF of p is included in that of q, $p \supset q$ is true.

When the n atomic statements are to be accounted for, 2^n different disjuncts or conjuncts are possible. Thus the three statements A, B, and C combine as follows:

A	B	C
A	B	~C
A	~B	C
A	~B	~C
~A	B	C
~A	B	~C
~A	~B	C
~A	~B	~C

How are we to interpret an expanded normal form in which all 2^n different conjuncts or disjuncts appear? Consider the following EDNF:

$$(A \mathbin{\&} B \mathbin{\&} C) \vee (A \mathbin{\&} B \mathbin{\&} {\sim}C) \vee (A \mathbin{\&} {\sim}B \mathbin{\&} C) \vee (A \mathbin{\&} {\sim}B \mathbin{\&} {\sim}C)$$
$$\vee ({\sim}A \mathbin{\&} B \mathbin{\&} C) \vee ({\sim}A \mathbin{\&} B \mathbin{\&} {\sim}C) \vee ({\sim}A \mathbin{\&} {\sim}B \mathbin{\&} C)$$
$$\vee ({\sim}A \mathbin{\&} {\sim}B \mathbin{\&} {\sim}C)$$

Since each disjunct represents a condition under which the statement as a whole is true, this statement must be true under *all possible* conditions; *i.e.*, it is a tautology. Similarly, an ECNF having 2^n different conjuncts would be a contradiction, since it would be false under all possible conditions.

Expanded normal forms can be used not only to identify tautologies and contradictions, and cases in which one statement implies another, but also to discover other logical relations among statements. They are quite useful in working practical problems. The following tables summarize the most important results of this kind:

TABLE 3.3

INTERPRETATION OF EDNF'S

p has 2^n disjuncts:	$\vdash p \equiv \mathrm{T}$
p has no disjuncts (*i.e.*, they all disappear in the process of reduction):	$\vdash p \equiv \mathrm{C}$
p and q both have the same disjuncts:	$\vdash p \equiv q$
Every disjunct in p is also in q:	$\vdash p \supset q$
p and q have no common disjunct:	$\vdash {\sim}(p \mathbin{\&} q)$
p and q have at least one common disjunct:	p and q could be true at the same time (*i.e.*, they are compatible)
p and q together contain all possible disjuncts:	$\vdash p \vee q$
p and q have no common disjunct but together contain all possible disjuncts:	$\vdash p \equiv {\sim}q$
p contains all those disjuncts that occur both in q and in r:	$\vdash p \equiv (q \mathbin{\&} r)$
p contains all those disjuncts that occur either in q or in r or in both:	$\vdash p \equiv (q \vee r)$

TABLE 3.4

INTERPRETATION OF ECNF'S

p has 2^n conjuncts:	$\vdash p \equiv C$
p has no conjuncts:	$\vdash p \equiv T$
p and q have the same conjuncts:	$\vdash p \equiv q$
Every conjunct in q is also in p:	$\vdash p \supset q$
p and q have no common conjunct:	$\vdash p \mathbin{\mathbf{v}} q$
At least one possible conjunct is neither in p nor in q:	p and q are compatible
p and q together contain every possible conjunct:	$\vdash \sim(p \mathbin{\&} q)$
p and q have no common conjunct but together contain all possible conjuncts:	$\vdash p \equiv \sim q$
p contains those conjuncts that occur both in q and in r:	$\vdash p \equiv (q \mathbin{\mathbf{v}} r)$
p contains those conjuncts that occur either in q or in r or in both:	$\vdash p \equiv (q \mathbin{\&} r)$

There is a kind of parallel between these two tables—a fact we can understand better in terms of the study of duality in the next section.

EXERCISE 3.4

I. **1.** Which of the following may be regarded as being in ECNF, in EDNF, in CNF, in DNF, or in more than one, or in none of these? Which would be in normal form if tautologous conjuncts or contradictory disjuncts were dropped?

     1. A

     2. A $\mathbf{v}$ B

     3. A & B

     4. A $\mathbf{v}$ A

     5. (A $\mathbf{v}$ A) & B

     6. (A $\mathbf{v}$ B) $\mathbf{v}$ $\sim$A

     7. (A & B) $\mathbf{v}$ $\sim$A

8. (A v B) & ~A

9. (~A v A) & ~A

10. (A ≡ B) v ~A

11. (A v B) & (A v ~B)

12. (A v B) & (~A v ~B)

13. (A & B) v (~A & ~B) v (C & ~C)

14. (~A & ~B) v (A & ~B)

15. (A & B & C) v (~A & ~B & ~C)

16. (~A v B) & (~B v A) & (~C v A)

17. (A v ~B) & (~A v ~B) & (A v ~A)

18. (A & B) v (A & ~C)

19. [(A v B) & ~A] v ~B

20. [(A v B) & (~A v ~B)] v (B & ~B)

21. (A v B) & (B v C) & (~D v ~E)

22. [A v (B & ~B)] & [B v (A & ~A)]

23. [A & (B v ~B)] v [B & (A v ~A)] v [~B & (A v ~A)]

24. [A & (B v ~B)] & {[B & (A v ~A)] v [~B & (A v ~A)]}

25. (A v B v C) & (A v ~B v ~C) & [~A v ~B v (C & ~C)]

II. **1.** From the truth tables constructed in the previous exercises, write the respective disjunctive and conjunctive normal forms.

2. By means other than truth tables, construct normal forms of the following formulas:

1. A & (A v B)

2. ~A ⊃ (A & B)

3. (A & B) ⊃ C

4. (A v B) ⊃ C

5. [(~A v B) ⊃ A] ≡ ~A

6. (A ⊃ B) & (B ⊃ A)

7. ~A ≡ B

8. ~(~A v ~B)

9. (A ≡ B) ≡ (B ≡ A)

10. [(A & B) ⊃ C] ⊃ [A ⊃ (B ⊃ C)]

3. Expand any of the above that are not already in expanded normal form.

III. **1.** For each of the statements in part I of this exercise not in expanded normal form, write an equivalent ECNF or EDNF, using truth tables.

   2. Reduce each of the statements of part I to its simplest equivalent statement.

   3. By examining their expanded normal forms, find pairs of the above statements which are equivalent with each other, compatible with each other, and contradictions of each other. Can you check these results against those of part II, Question 3, of this exercise?

3.5 Duality*

A powerful rule of PL which has not yet been introduced is the principle of *Duality*. Like normal forms, this rule has many uses in practice and is also of considerable theoretical importance. In particular, it enables us to establish biconditionals with a minimum of labor and is of especial value in dealing with biconditionals in predicate logic (see Chapter Six). Like Rep, the principle of Duality is a derived rule and is proved by use of mathematical induction.

We have observed in Section 3.3 that the connectives essential to expressing statements in PL can be reduced to three: $\sim$, &, and v. Thus, by replacing statements by equivalents, $p \supset q$ becomes $\sim p \lor q$ and $p \equiv q$ becomes $(\sim p \lor q)$ & $(\sim q \lor p)$. In the further discussion of this section we assume that all compound statements are built up out of the three connectives $\sim$, &, and v.

In particular let $p_1, p_2, \ldots, p_n$ be statements (either atomic or molecular) and X be a molecular statement built up out of some or all of $p_1, p_2, \ldots, p_n$, repeating a statement as often as desired. Under these conditions we define the *dual* of X, symbolized as X^+, as the statement obtained by

(1) changing p_i to $\sim p_i$, and where this results in $\sim\sim p_i$, using DN and Rep to get p_i.

(2) changing & to v and v to &.

For example:

Statement	Dual
p	$\sim p$
$p \lor q$	$\sim p$ & $\sim q$
$p \lor \sim p$	$\sim p$ & p
$\sim p$ & $(\sim q \lor q)$	$p \lor (q$ & $\sim q)$

Note that the formulas on the left are also the duals of those on the right.

The definition of a dual is relative to $p_1, p_2, \ldots, p_n$, which may be molecular; their duals may be formed as long as their inner structure is carried along unchanged.

---

* The balance of this chapter may be omitted without loss of continuity until the end of Chapter Six.

We may now state the derived rule of duality. We state it in three parts in order to facilitate its proof.

Dual: Let X, Y, and Z be statements constructed of $p_1, p_2, \ldots, p_n$ and using only the connectives $\sim$, **v**, &. Let X^+ be a statement constructed from X by changing each p_i to $\sim p_i$ (and where this results in $\sim\sim p_i$ replacing it by p_i) and changing & to **v** and vice versa throughout. Under these conditions

    (a) $\vdash \sim X \equiv X^+$
    (b) If $\vdash Y \equiv Z$ and we change & for **v** and vice versa throughout Y and Z giving Y' and Z', then $\vdash Y' \equiv Z'$.
    (c) If $\vdash Y \supset Z$ and we change & for **v** and vice versa throughout Y and Z giving Y' and Z', then $\vdash Z' \supset Y'$.

Proof of (a): We proceed by induction to show that for any molecular statement X, $\vdash \sim X \equiv X^+$. We do this by showing, *first*, that where X is constructed of one of the statements $p_1, p_2, \ldots, p_n$ the conclusion follows—*the basis of the induction. Second*, we enumerate the X's depending on how many occurrences of $p_1, p_2, \ldots, p_n$ and the connective $\sim$ are in them. Thus each of

$$\sim p \text{ v } q,$$

$$\sim\sim p,$$

and

$$\sim p \text{ \& } q$$

has three occurrences of relevant symbols while each of

$$\sim[(p \text{ v } q) \text{ \& } \sim r]$$

and

$$\sim[(p \text{ \& } q) \text{ \& } \sim r]$$

has five such occurrences. We now assume as hypothesis of the induction that the result $\sim X \equiv X^+$ holds for any X having n or fewer such occurrences and show that the conclusion follows for $n + 1$ occurrences.

    Basis: X is one of the statements $p_1, p_2, \ldots, p_n$, say p_1. Then $\sim X$ is $\sim p_1$. But X^+ is $\sim p_1$. Hence

$$\vdash \sim X \equiv X^+$$

    Induction Step: We assume that the result holds when X is constructed of $p_1, p_2, \ldots, p_n$ and the connectives **v**, &, and $\sim$ in such a way that there are n or fewer occurrences of these statements and $\sim$. If, now, there are $n + 1$ occurrences of relevant symbols, X will have one of the forms $\sim Y$, Y v Z, Y & Z. We consider each in turn.

    Case 1. X is $\sim Y$.

        Subcase a. Y is a single statement, say p. Then X^+ is p and $\sim X$ is $\sim\sim p$. By DN $\sim\sim p$ is p. Hence

$$\vdash \sim X \equiv X^+$$

Subcase b. Y is a compound of $p_1, p_2, \ldots, p_n$. Then X^+ is $\sim Y^+$. By the hypothesis of the induction

$$\vdash \sim Y \equiv Y^+$$

So

$$\vdash \sim Y^+ \equiv \sim\sim Y$$

But $\sim X$ is $\sim\sim Y$. Hence

$$\vdash \sim X \equiv X^+$$

Case 2. X is $Y \& Z$. Then X^+ is $Y^+ \vee Z^+$. By the hypothesis of the induction, $\vdash \sim Y \equiv Y^+$ and $\vdash \sim Z \equiv Z^+$. By DM

$$\vdash \sim(Y \& Z) \equiv \sim Y \vee \sim Z$$

Thus by Rep

$$\vdash \sim(Y \& Z) \equiv Y^+ \vee Z^+$$

Hence

$$\vdash \sim X \equiv X^+$$

Case 3. X is $Y \vee Z$. Then X^+ is $Y^+ \& Z^+$. By the hypothesis of the induction, $\vdash \sim Y \equiv Y^+$ and $\vdash \sim Z \equiv Z^+$. By DM

$$\vdash \sim(Y \vee Z) \equiv \sim Y \& \sim Z$$

Thus by Rep

$$\vdash \sim(Y \vee Z) \equiv Y^+ \& Z^+$$

Hence

$$\vdash \sim X \equiv X^+$$

The rule DM is a special case of this theorem.

Proof of (b): Assume $\vdash Y \equiv Z$. First, we substitute $\sim p_1$, $\sim p_2$, $\sim p_3, \ldots$ respectively in $Y \equiv Z$. By Sub we have

$$\vdash Y_1 \equiv Z_1$$

where Y_1 and Z_1 are the results of this substitution. Second, we replace each $\sim\sim p_i$, by p_i, using Rep and get

$$\vdash Y_{12} \equiv Z_{12}$$

where Y_{12} and Z_{12} are the results of this replacement. By the deduction schema given in Chapter Two, Section Six, in the proof of Rep under

I. Negative Context

$$\vdash (p \equiv q) \equiv (\sim p \equiv \sim q),$$

we have

$$\vdash \sim Y_{12} \equiv \sim Z_{12}$$

However, since

$$\vdash \sim Y_{12} \equiv Y_{12}^+$$

and

$$\vdash \sim Z_{12} \equiv Z_{12}^+$$

We have by Rep

$$\vdash Y_{12}^+ \equiv Z_{12}^+$$

But since Y_{12}^+ and Z_{12}^+ change & for v and vice versa as well as restoring the negations and nonnegations originally in X' and Y',

$$Y_{12}^+ \quad \text{is} \quad Y'$$
$$Z_{12}^+ \quad \text{is} \quad Z'$$

Hence

$$\vdash Y' \equiv Z'$$

Example: The various operations in the proof performed may be better understood in an illustration. We begin with

$$\vdash (\sim A \text{ v } B) \equiv (B \text{ v } \sim A)$$

First, we substitute negations

$$\vdash \sim\sim A \text{ v } \sim B \equiv \sim B \text{ v } \sim\sim A$$

Second, we replace double negations

$$\vdash A \text{ v } \sim B \equiv \sim B \text{ v } A$$

Then, we negate the left and right sides

$$\vdash \sim(A \text{ v } \sim B) \equiv \sim(\sim B \text{ v } A)$$

And taking the dual of each side in turn,

$$\vdash \sim(A \text{ v } \sim B) \equiv (\sim A \text{ \& } B)$$
$$\vdash \sim(\sim B \text{ v } A) \equiv (B \text{ \& } \sim A)$$

Whence

$$\vdash (\sim A \text{ \& } B) \equiv (B \text{ \& } \sim A)$$

Proof of (c): X is $\vdash Y \supset Z$. We follow the pattern of the proof of (b), except that instead of referring to the deduction schema in Chapter Two in the proof of Rep, we note that

$$\vdash p \supset q \equiv \sim q \supset \sim p$$

Hence, our final result is

$$\vdash Z' \supset Y'$$

The earliest recognition of duality seems to date from 1877 in the work of Schröder.* The value of the rule Dual, even with the availability of truth-table

---

* See Ernst Schröder, *Der Operationskreis des Logikkalküls* (Leipzig, 1877).

methods, is very great. Something of this can be seen if we note that the following schemata are justified by Dual.

I.	**1.**	$[(p \ \& \ q) \ \& \ r] \equiv [p \ \& \ (q \ \& \ r)]$	ZPC
	2.	$[(p \lor q) \lor r] \equiv [p \lor (q \lor r)]$	1, Dual
II.	**1.**	$(p \ \& \ q) \equiv (q \ \& \ p)$	ZPC
	2.	$(p \lor q) \equiv (q \lor p)$	1, Dual
III.	**1.**	$[p \ \& \ (q \lor r)] \equiv [(p \ \& \ q) \lor (p \ \& \ r)]$	ZPC
	2.	$[p \lor (q \ \& \ r)] \equiv [(p \lor q) \ \& \ (p \lor r)]$	1, Dual
IV.	**1.**	$(p \ \& \ p) \equiv p$	ZPC
	2.	$(p \lor p) \equiv p$	1, Dual
V.	**1.**	$[p \ \& \ (p \lor q)] \equiv p$	ZPC
	2.	$[p \lor (p \ \& \ q)] \equiv p$	1, Dual
VI.	**1.**	$[p \ \& \ (q \lor \sim q)] \equiv p$	ZPC
	2.	$[p \lor (q \ \& \ \sim q)] \equiv p$	1, Dual
VII.	**1.**	$[p \ \& \ (q \ \& \ \sim q)] \equiv (q \ \& \ \sim q)$	ZPC
	2.	$[p \lor (q \lor \sim q)] \equiv (q \lor \sim q)$	1, Dual

EXERCISE 3.5

I. Write the duals of the following formulas:

     1. $A \lor (B \ \& \ C)$

     2. $A \ \& \ \sim A$

     3. $A \supset B$

     4. $A \equiv B$

     5. $\sim\{D \ \& \ \sim[C \lor \sim(A \ \& \ B)]\}$

     6. $[(A \supset B) \ \& \ A] \supset \sim B$

     7. $(A \ \& \ B) \supset (A \lor B)$

     8. $A \supset (B \supset \sim B)$

     9. $A \supset [(A \supset B) \supset \sim B]$

     10. $(A \supset A) \supset (B \supset \sim B)$

II. We have seen that the connectives & and ∨ are duals of each other. Now consider the other fourteen binary connectives and decide (1) which are duals of each other, (2) which are duals of themselves, (3) what is the dual of the unary connective $\sim$?

III. Decide whether each of the following is true or false, and explain your answer.

1. $p \equiv p^{++}$

2. The dual of the EDNF of a statement is the ECNF of the same statement.

3. The dual of a tautology is a contradiction.

4. The dual of an ECNF with no conjuncts is an EDNF with infinitely many disjuncts.

5. $(p^+ \& q^+)^+ \equiv p \vee q$

SUGGESTED READINGS

1. I. M. Copi, *Symbolic Logic* (New York: The Macmillan Co., 1954), Ch. II.

2. E. L. Post, "Introduction to a General Theory of Elementary Propositions", *American Journal Math.*, Vol. 43 (1921), pp. 163–185.

3. W. V. Quine, *Methods of Logic*, rev. ed. (New York: Holt, Rinehart and Winston, Inc., 1959), Part I.

4. W. V. Quine, *Mathematical Logic*, rev. ed. (Cambridge, Mass.: Harvard University Press, 1951), Ch. I.

5. J. B. Rosser, *Logic for Mathematicians* (New York: McGraw-Hill Book Co., 1953), Ch. II.

Chapter 4

Some Other Propositional Logics

4.1 Multi-valued Logics

Not all systems of axioms have the same underlying logic. Most mathematical systems, for instance, require complex additions to the rules of the propositional logic we have been discussing, as we shall see in succeeding chapters.

Yet if some systems require a more complicated logic than the propositional, some mathematical reasoning seems to require a simpler version of propositional logic than the one presented, and still other reasoning a different if not simpler version. It will pay us to consider some of these simpler and different propositional systems. Since we cannot consider all of them, it is important to understand the motivation for developing them. One way of viewing logic is as the theory of formalizing axiom systems. If we view logic in this way, it becomes the structure implicit in any given axiom system. We might, however, argue that logic is not relative to axiom systems, but is to be found only in intuitive mathematical reasoning. This is the view of a school of logicians deriving from Brouwer who are known as Intuitionists. In consequence, they reject all mathematical arguments which, when formalized, make unrestricted use of the law of excluded middle, as we shall see in Section 4.2. Since this includes a considerable part of classical mathematics, their views on the law of excluded middle have significant consequences. In fact, they have found it necessary to try to rebuild mathematics without it. To some extent they have succeeded.

What makes anyone suppose that there could be a logic in which $\vdash p \lor \sim p$ does not hold? Intuitively, we seem to take this law for granted, so much so that we regard $p \mathbin{\&} \sim p$, to which all inconsistency reduces, as equivalent with

$\sim(p \vee \sim p)$; *i.e.*, we suppose it *inconsistent* to deny $\vdash p \vee \sim p$. On the other hand, of course, some statements that we make do not exclude the middle. If you ask yourself whether you are in this room or not, your answer may be definitely "yes". But suppose that you ask yourself this question at the very moment that you are leaving by the door. Perhaps in this case you could hardly say yes or no. In the interests of your intuition concerning the law of excluded middle, you might wish to say that in fact you were either in the room or outside, even if you weren't sure which. You might define "being in this room" as being on the roomward side of the plane of the doorframe, and not intersecting this plane. In this case, if a person's foot or nose intersected the plane of the doorframe, he would definitely be out of the room. Notice that this definition cannot be used as *evidence* for the law of excluded middle, for the law is presupposed in the very application of the definition. Suppose, in any event, that you had no feeling about the excluded middle at all. Then you might well say that it is undecidable, "50–50", whether you are in this room. Let us consider a logic which operates on this basis. Such a logic will at least make the issue plausible to us.

Let us begin with *three-valued logic*. This gets its name from the fact that it involves the use of three truth-values in truth-value analysis. In ordinary PL, the two truth-values are **t** and **f**. If we introduce a third value, we deny what the law of excluded middle asserts; *i.e.*, that any statement must be either true or false. Instead of **t** and **f** let us use the symbols 1 and 0, with $\frac{1}{2}$ as the intermediate value. Assigning these three values to a statement, say P, is easily done, even if their meanings are not clear. We might say with some plausibility that 1, $\frac{1}{2}$, and 0 can be interpreted to mean true, doubtful, and false respectively. But for the moment we need not press the question as to whether this is fully warranted.

Can we extend the analogy between P with three values and A with two values? Are there tables corresponding to the ordinary operations, for example? The answer is certainly "yes", at least, formally. Consider $\sim$A in a two-valued system having the matrix

A	$\sim$A
1	0
0	1

What would correspond to this in a three-valued system? Let us use N in place of $\sim$ to distinguish the systems. What, then, is NP? Suppose we say

P	NP
1	0
$\frac{1}{2}$	$\frac{1}{2}$
0	1

On the basis of our interpretations this seems fairly plausible. When P is true, NP is false and vice versa; when P is doubtful, NP is also doubtful. Plausible or not, however, we must pause to consider some alternatives which might just as well have been put down, for example:

P	$N'P$
1	0
$\frac{1}{2}$	1
0	1

This is equally plausible, and it calls our attention to the fact that a unary operation in a three-valued logic can have more than one truth table. In fact, there are many unary operations. In a two-valued logic we usually think of negation as being the only unary operation, although we might also think of the following table as defining a second one:

A	*A
1	1
0	0

The operation in this case would be called an identity operation, of course. In a three-valued logic, however, there are still more unary operations, some of which we can indicate:

P	NP	MP	DP	RP
1	0	1	0	0
$\frac{1}{2}$	$\frac{1}{2}$	1	1	1
0	1	0	0	1

The rest of the unary operations are obtainable by introducing all the various arrangements of 1, 0, and $\frac{1}{2}$ in similar tables. This is an arbitrary procedure, yet the results can be plausibly interpreted. Thus if we regard N as *not*, we can think of M as meaning *possible*. We read MP as "P is possible". Similarly, DP might be read as "P is doubtful", for, if we deny that P is true and affirm P only when P is $\frac{1}{2}$, this is not far from the ordinary meaning of "P is doubtful". RP, finally, means simply that P is not true.

Altogether there are twenty-seven unary operations in three-valued logic, and in general there are n^n unary operations in n-valued logic. This means that there are actually four unary operations in two-valued logic.

One of the characteristics of a two-valued logic is that unary operations can be *iterated*, or applied successively. In the case of $\sim$ we can have $\sim\sim A$

or ∼∼∼A, etc. Clearly, the same situation exists in a three-valued logic. N N*P*, for example, turns out to have the following table:

P	NP	NNP
1	0	1
$\frac{1}{2}$	$\frac{1}{2}$	$\frac{1}{2}$
0	1	0

We could proceed as in a two-valued logic to say that NN*P* is equivalent to *P*; *i.e.*, that N obeys a law of double negation. If we had defined N in the alternative way above, however, this would not have been true. What about the other unary operations? Can we apply these to one another? There is no reason why we cannot—and very often in doing so we make a surprising amount of sense, judging by our interpretations. Thus, if we examine NM*P*, we obtain

P	MP	NMP
1	1	0
$\frac{1}{2}$	1	0
0	0	1

Here, the final line tells us that NM*P* holds true only when *P* is false—hence it means something like "*P* is impossible". MN*P*, on the other hand, gives us

P	NP	MNP
1	0	0
$\frac{1}{2}$	$\frac{1}{2}$	1
0	1	1

which probably means something like "*P* is possibly false". NMN*P* gives us

P	NP	MNP	NMNP
1	0	0	1
$\frac{1}{2}$	$\frac{1}{2}$	1	0
0	1	1	0

which comes close to "*P* is necessarily true". At this point one can easily guess that ND*P* means "*P* is not doubtful".

Apparently, then, one thing that can be done with a three-valued logic is to symbolize subtler nuances of ordinary language than can be handled by ordinary PL. It seems that such phrases as "*P* is necessary", "it is not impossible that *P*", etc., can be given symbolic expression with this logic.

We can also extend our three-valued logic beyond the unary operations to binary ones. In a two-valued logic, for example, we combine A and B with the operation

&	t	f
t	t	f
f	f	f

The analogue in a three-valued logic we shall call $P \wedge Q$ and we set up a matrix as follows:

$\wedge$	1	$\frac{1}{2}$	0
1	1	$\frac{1}{2}$	0
$\frac{1}{2}$	$\frac{1}{2}$	$\frac{1}{2}$	0
0	0	0	0

This matrix agrees with that for a two-valued logic where the sentences have only the values 1 and 0 (*i.e.*, **t** and **f**), and it is about what our intuition suggests for other values. Note that, according to the two- and three-valued matrices alike, a conjunction always assumes the smaller of the values of its conjuncts.

Now let $P \circ Q$ be the three-valued version of $p \vee q$. What happens if we define $P \circ Q$ as $N(NP \wedge NQ)$, on the analogy of the two-valued definition of A $\vee$ B as $\sim(\sim A \& \sim B)$? The resulting three-valued truth table is the following:

N	(N	P	$\wedge$	N	Q)
1	0	1	0	0	1
1	$\frac{1}{2}$	$\frac{1}{2}$	0	0	1
1	1	0	0	0	1
1	0	1	0	$\frac{1}{2}$	$\frac{1}{2}$
$\frac{1}{2}$	$\frac{1}{2}$	$\frac{1}{2}$	$\frac{1}{2}$	$\frac{1}{2}$	$\frac{1}{2}$
$\frac{1}{2}$	1	0	$\frac{1}{2}$	$\frac{1}{2}$	$\frac{1}{2}$
1	0	1	0	1	0
$\frac{1}{2}$	$\frac{1}{2}$	$\frac{1}{2}$	$\frac{1}{2}$	1	0
0	1	0	1	1	0

The column under the initial N is summarized in the following matrix:

$\circ$	1	$\frac{1}{2}$	0
1	1	1	1
$\frac{1}{2}$	1	$\frac{1}{2}$	$\frac{1}{2}$
0	1	$\frac{1}{2}$	0

This is exactly what we might have expected. Notice that, as in two-valued alternation or disjunction, a disjunction always assumes the larger of the values of its disjuncts.

Suppose, now, we proceed with the development of three-valued operations on the analogy of two-valued ones, and define the three-valued conditional $P \rightarrow Q$ as $N(P \wedge NQ)$. We shall attain the following matrix, which the reader can verify:

$\rightarrow$	1	$\frac{1}{2}$	0
1	1	$\frac{1}{2}$	0
$\frac{1}{2}$	1	$\frac{1}{2}$	$\frac{1}{2}$
0	1	1	1

Consider now the $\frac{1}{2}$ in the very center. This is the alleged value of $P \rightarrow Q$ when the value of P is $\frac{1}{2}$ and that of Q is likewise $\frac{1}{2}$. Now, this means that $P \rightarrow P$ would have the value $\frac{1}{2}$ when P has this value. But it is very difficult to find any interpretation of three-valued logic on which this result is acceptable. It surely is not acceptable on the interpretation we have adopted; even though "It will rain" may be doubtful, "If it will rain, then it will rain" is not in the least doubtful.

What should we conclude from this anomaly? Only that the analogy with two-valued logic breaks down in the case of the definition of $P \rightarrow Q$. Let us then pursue a different analogy. As we saw in Chapter Three, it is possible to define A v B as (A ⊃ B) ⊃ B. Let us, then, *begin* with the desired matrix for the three-valued conditional; namely,

$\rightarrow$	1	$\frac{1}{2}$	0
1	1	$\frac{1}{2}$	0
$\frac{1}{2}$	1	1	$\frac{1}{2}$
0	1	1	1

and proceed by defining $P \circ Q$ as $(P \rightarrow Q) \rightarrow Q$, and $P \wedge Q$ as $N(NP \circ NQ)$. The reader who tries this will see that the resulting matrices are exactly the ones suggested by the discussion so far.

If we define the three-valued biconditional $P \leftrightarrow Q$ as $(P \rightarrow Q) \wedge (Q \rightarrow P)$, we shall have achieved all the matrices we will normally need. These may be summarized in schematic form as follows:

TABLE 4.1

P	Q	$P \rightarrow Q$	$P \circ Q$	$P \wedge Q$	$P \leftrightarrow Q$
1	1	1	1	1	1
$\frac{1}{2}$	1	1	1	$\frac{1}{2}$	$\frac{1}{2}$
0	1	1	1	0	0
1	$\frac{1}{2}$	$\frac{1}{2}$	1	$\frac{1}{2}$	$\frac{1}{2}$
$\frac{1}{2}$	$\frac{1}{2}$	1	$\frac{1}{2}$	$\frac{1}{2}$	1
0	$\frac{1}{2}$	1	$\frac{1}{2}$	0	$\frac{1}{2}$
1	0	0	1	0	0
$\frac{1}{2}$	0	$\frac{1}{2}$	$\frac{1}{2}$	0	$\frac{1}{2}$
0	0	1	0	0	1

In a two-valued logic we know that $p \supset (p \vee p)$ is a tautology. Is $P \to (P \circ P)$ the analogue of a tautology in a three-valued logic? Let us check.

$$P \to (P \circ P)$$

$$1 \; 1 \; 1 \; 1 \; 1$$

$$\tfrac{1}{2} \; 1 \; \tfrac{1}{2} \; \tfrac{1}{2} \; \tfrac{1}{2}$$

$$0 \; 1 \; 0 \; 0 \; 0$$

Clearly $P \to (P \circ P)$ is a three-valued tautology. In a two-valued logic $\vdash (A \& B) \equiv (B \& A)$. Is $(P \wedge Q) \leftrightarrow (Q \wedge P)$ equally a theorem?

P	Q	$(P \wedge Q)$	$\leftrightarrow$	$(Q \wedge P)$
1	1	1	1	1
$\tfrac{1}{2}$	1	$\tfrac{1}{2}$	1	$\tfrac{1}{2}$
0	1	0	1	0
1	$\tfrac{1}{2}$	$\tfrac{1}{2}$	1	$\tfrac{1}{2}$
$\tfrac{1}{2}$	$\tfrac{1}{2}$	$\tfrac{1}{2}$	1	$\tfrac{1}{2}$
0	$\tfrac{1}{2}$	0	1	0
1	0	0	1	0
$\tfrac{1}{2}$	0	0	1	0
0	0	0	1	0

Clearly this formula holds in a three-valued logic. But what about $P \circ NP$?

P	$P \circ NP$	
1	1	0
$\tfrac{1}{2}$	$\tfrac{1}{2}$	$\tfrac{1}{2}$
0	1	1

We see that the analogue of $A \vee \sim A$ is not a tautology in a three-valued logic, as we might expect from the existence of three values. So we do not have a law of excluded middle in this logic if we agree that $P \circ NP$ represents this law.

The question of the usefulness of three-valued logic still remains. In the discussion above we have assumed that ordinary English argumentation could constitute an interpretation of it. There is some basis for this, since the additional subtlety implicit in a three-valued logic makes possible a more exact symbolic representation of ordinary language. Thus we observe what can be done with English sentences such as the following:

> If it is necessarily false that the postman came on Tuesday, or I don't get any mail, then it is impossible to reply to his letter tomorrow. But it is doubtful that I could reply tomorrow, so the postman probably didn't come on Tuesday.

Symbolically, this gives us:

$$\{[(\text{NM}C \circ \text{N}G) \to (\text{NM}R)] \wedge (DR)\} \to \text{MN}C$$

This can be tested by truth tables. The variety of such possible formulations will suggest the richness of the logic.

This sort of interpretation of a three-valued logic by a three-valued proposition has been suggested by D. A. Bochvar and by Hans Reichenbach. Reichenbach has applied his interpretation to a physical situation in a book, *Philosophic Foundations of Quantum Mechanics.** Logics of this sort have been applied to the analysis of electrical circuits.† Šéstakov‡ has done a similar analysis published in Russian. An application to physics has been made by Destouches.§ So far none of these interpretations has met with general approval, but they do suggest that there is interest and possible significance in logics of this sort.

Indeed, work at the theoretical level is being carried forward not only for three-valued logics, but for logics with any number of values. A recent book on the general theory of such logics, *Many-Valued Logics* by Rosser and Turquette,¶ provides a good example of this work.

EXERCISE 4.1

I. 1. (a) Generate those unary operations of three-valued logic that were not presented in the text.

    (b) Can you find an English phrase that states the meaning of each?

    (c) How many different binary operations are there in all, in any three-valued logic?

    (d) How many in a four-valued logic? In an n-valued logic?

2. By defining each of the unary operations generated in exercise 1 (a) above, in terms of those unary and binary operations presented in the text, show that the formal presentation and naming of each is not necessary in three-valued logic.

3. Can any one of the unary operations N, M, D, or R be defined in terms of the others? In terms of the others plus the binary operations?

4. Determine which of the derived rules of PL (Chapter Two) have valid analogues in three-valued logic.

---

* Hans Reichenbach, *Philosophic Foundations of Quantum Mechanics* (Berkeley: University of California Press, 1944).

† See, for example, C. A. Metze, *Many-valued Logics and the Design of Switching Circuits*, doctoral dissertation, University of Illinois, Urbana, Ill., 1955.

‡ V. I. Šéstakov, in *Izvéstiá Akadémii Nauk SSSR*, Sériá matématičéskaá, Vol. 10 (1946), pp. 529–554.

§ Jean-Louis Destouches, *Principes Fondamentaux de Physique Théorique* (Paris, 1942).

¶ J. B. Rosser and A. R. Turquette, *Many-Valued Logics* (Amsterdam: North Holland Publishing Co., 1952).

II. Decide whether each of the following is a three-valued tautology, contingency, or contradiction.

    1. $P \rightarrow NP$

    2. $P \circ NP$

    3. $DP \rightarrow MP$

    4. $MP \rightarrow DP$

    5. $MNP \circ P$

    6. $NP \rightarrow RP$

    7. $NP \rightarrow NRP$

    8. $NRP \rightarrow NMP$

    9. $MNP \leftrightarrow NRP$

    10. $MP \rightarrow NDP$

    11. $DP \rightarrow RP$

    12. $(NP \wedge P) \rightarrow Q$

    13. $NP \leftrightarrow (P \rightarrow NP)$

    14. $RP \leftrightarrow (DP \circ NP)$

    15. $(DP \circ NP) \leftrightarrow NRP$

    16. $N(DP \wedge NP) \leftrightarrow (NDP \circ P)$

    17. $(MP \circ RP) \rightarrow N(P \circ RP)$

    18. $(MP \wedge RP) \leftrightarrow DP$

    19. $(MP \wedge DP) \leftrightarrow (MP \wedge RP)$

    20. $(DP \circ NP) \rightarrow (MNP \wedge P)$

    21. $NRP \leftrightarrow (P \rightarrow NP)$

    22. $(NP \rightarrow P) \circ NMP$

    23. $NMP \leftrightarrow (NP \rightarrow P)$

    24. $(P \circ NP) \rightarrow (P \wedge NP)$

    25. $(P \wedge NP) \rightarrow (P \circ NP)$

    26. $N[(P \circ NP) \rightarrow (P \wedge NP)] \circ DP$

    27. $N[(P \circ NP) \rightarrow (P \wedge NP)] \leftrightarrow DP$

    28. $(P \circ NP) \wedge (P \wedge NP)$

    29. $(P \rightarrow NP) \circ (NP \rightarrow P)$

30. $(P \rightarrow Q) \leftrightarrow (NQ \rightarrow NP)$

31. $[P \wedge (Q \circ P)] \leftrightarrow NP$

32. $[P \wedge (Q \circ P)] \leftrightarrow [(P \wedge Q) \circ (P \wedge P)]$

33. $[NP \wedge (Q \rightarrow P)] \rightarrow NQ$

34. $(NP \circ NQ) \rightarrow N(P \wedge Q)$

35. $(NP \wedge NQ) \wedge (P \circ Q)$

36. $(NP \wedge NQ) \rightarrow D(P \circ Q)$

37. $MN[(NP \wedge NQ) \wedge (P \circ Q)]$

38. $NR[(NP \wedge NQ) \wedge (P \circ Q)]$

39. $DN\{(RNP \circ NRP) \leftrightarrow [MP \circ (MNQ \leftrightarrow NRQ)]\}$

40. $M[(P \circ Q) \wedge (Q \rightarrow P) \wedge (NR \rightarrow NP)] \rightarrow R$

III. Which of the following formulas, tautologous in two-valued logic, have tautologous analogues in three-valued logic?

  1. $A \supset A$

  2. $(A \vee A) \supset A$

  3. $A \supset \sim\sim A$

  4. $A \supset (A \ \& \ A)$

  5. $\sim\sim A \supset A$

  6. $(A \ \& \ B) \supset A$

  7. $(A \ \& \ \sim A) \supset B$

  8. $(A \ \& \ B) \supset B$

  9. $A \supset (A \vee B)$

10. $B \supset (A \vee B)$

11. $(A \ \& \ B) \equiv (B \ \& \ A)$

12. $(A \supset B) \equiv (\sim B \supset \sim A)$

13. $\sim(A \vee B) \equiv (\sim A \ \& \ \sim B)$

14. $(A \vee B) \equiv (B \vee A)$

15. $[(A \supset B) \ \& \ A] \supset B$

16. $[A \supset (B \ \& \ \sim B)] \supset \sim A$

17. $[(A \supset B) \ \& \ \sim B] \supset \sim A$

18. $[(A \supset B) \ \& \ (B \supset C)] \supset (A \supset C)$

19. [(A v B) & ∼A] ⊃ B

20. ∼(A & B) ⊃ (∼A v ∼B)

21. [A ⊃ (B ⊃ C)] ≡ [B ⊃ (A ⊃ C)]

22. (A ⊃ B) ⊃ [(B ⊃ C) ⊃ (A ⊃ C)]

23. (A ⊃ C) ⊃ [(A ⊃ B) ⊃ (A ⊃ C)]

24. [A & (B v C)] ≡ [(A & B) v (A & C)]

25. [A v (B & C)] ≡ [(A v B) & (A v C)]

26. [A & (B & C)] ≡ [(A & B) & C]

27. [A v (B v C)] ≡ [(A v B) v C]

28. [(A & B) ⊃ C] ≡ [A ⊃ (B ⊃ C)]

29. [(A ⊃ B) & (B ⊃ A)] ≡ (A ≡ B)

30. {(A v B) & [(A ⊃ C) & (B ⊃ C)]} ⊃ C

31. [(A ⊃ B) ⊃ A] ⊃ A

IV. Symbolize the following statements and then assess them as in part II above:

1. If it is possible that statement A is doubtful, then it is doubtful that A is possible.

2. If it is doubtful that the candidate's claims are possible, then it is possible that they are doubtful.

3. If it is not possible that men live on the planet Venus, then it is not doubtful that they do.

4. Only if it is doubtful that a plane angle can be trisected is it not impossible that it can be.

5. Space flight is possible if and only if it is not impossible.

6. If it is possible that the iceman cometh, then it is doubtful that it is impossible that he cometh.

7. It is doubtful that the theory is adequate only if it is not necessary that it is adequate.

8. It is either possible that angels exist, or else it is impossible.

9. It is doubtful that his statement is either possible or doubtful.

10. The truth of an assertion is not doubtful if and only if it is either impossible or necessarily true.

11. It is not necessarily the case that if a fact is doubtful it must be either possible or impossible.

12. To say that something is possibly doubtful is to say no more than that it is doubtful.

13. If it is possibly doubtful that the painting is a forgery, then it is possible that the painting is not a forgery.

14. A third world war is possible if it is not the case that it is impossible whenever it is doubtful.

15. The watch can be repaired if and only if it is not irreparable.

16. Either it is possible to take the bus if the train is missed, or else it is possible only if the train is missed.

17. That either his honesty is doubtful or I shall eat my hat implies that if he proves to be honest, then I shall not eat my hat.

18. If it is possible that the water will not boil when the heat is raised, then it is also possible that it will boil when the heat is raised.

19. To say that if it is possible for him to save the union, the President will do it, is equivalent to saying that if he does not do it, we shall at least know that his failure was necessary.

20. It is possible for man to conquer the stars only if he solves his planetary difficulties; thus if it is doubtful that he will succeed in solving his planetary difficulties, it is doubtful that he will conquer the stars.

4.2 Intuitionistic Logic

It is perfectly possible to develop a three-valued (or *n*-valued) logic by starting with axioms and drawing conclusions from them, instead of relying on matrices. When one first begins to work with strange logics, however, it is good to follow a line that forces the results—as, for example, truth tables demand the clearly defined handling of operations and meanings. Since we are now familiar with one unusual logic, we can approach a second such logic from a somewhat different angle.

This time let us suppose that we believe that there are certain situations to which the law of excluded middle does not apply, even though there may be others to which it is applicable. Arguments over whether a person is or is not in a room he is leaving are quite possibly settled by more precise definitions of the limits of the room and what is to be meant by being in the room. But there are cases in mathematics that hardly allow for this sort of solution.

To see how such cases can arise, let us consider what are known as *perfect numbers*. A perfect number is defined as an integer that is equal to the sum of all of its own divisors except itself. Thus, 6 is a perfect number because $6 = 1 + 2 + 3$. Similarly, $28 = 1 + 2 + 4 + 7 + 14$. Besides 6 and 28, only four perfect numbers are known at present, although there seems to be no reason why further ones should not be discovered in the future. All six of the perfect numbers so far brought to light are even numbers, but once again no one has proved that there cannot be odd perfect numbers.

Now consider the statement "There is an odd number that is perfect". Suppose this statement were true. Then it would mean that if we run through the odd numbers, we shall at last come to one that is perfect. Now consider the denial of the statement. Does this mean, if we run through the odd numbers, we shall *never* come to one that is perfect? The intuitionist points out that it could not possibly mean that. He explains that to speak of "running through" —*i.e.*, examining and rejecting—each member of an *infinite* set of numbers makes no sense. But there is obviously an infinite set of odd numbers. So when we say that it is false that there is an odd number that is perfect, we cannot mean merely that no odd perfect number will be discovered. What we must mean, according to the intuitionist, is that there is a *contradiction* in the notion of an odd perfect number.

To summarize, let S stand for "There is an odd number that is perfect". Then what S means to the intuitionist is that if we run through the odd numbers, we shall at last come to one that is perfect. And what ∼S means to him is that the notion of an odd perfect number is inconsistent. But obviously S and ∼S do not exhaust the alternatives. They do so only if the problem of determining whether there is or is not an odd perfect number is solvable. But if the problem cannot be solved, then neither will anyone ever discover an odd perfect number nor will anyone ever discover a contradiction in the idea of one. The intuitionist asserts that not all mathematical problems can be solved; he attacks the belief that they all can be solved as a groundless dogma. In particular, he claims that many problems involving infinite sets can never be solved. And since they cannot, we shall have to settle for many pairs of statements of the forms *p* and ∼*p* which do not exhaust the alternatives and hence violate the traditional law of excluded middle.

Notice that the thesis of intuitionistic logic arises only in connection with *infinite* sets, such as that of *all odd numbers*. The intuitionist does not question any application of this law to a finite set. For example, he regards the statement "There is at least one odd perfect number between 1 and 10^{100}" as definitely either true or false, because, at least in principle, one could "run through" all the odd numbers between 1 and 10^{100}.

What we need, then, is a logic without the law of excluded middle, but one to which we can add this law in those cases where it applies. It was the need for this kind of care in the use of logic which led Brouwer to write a paper entitled "The Untrustworthiness of the Principles of Logic".* He argues that people forget that logical rules were originally developed to apply to limited situations and that it cannot be assumed that the rules apply to all situations without qualification.

---

* L. E. J. Brouwer, "De onbetrouwbaarheid der logische principes", *Tijdschrift voor wijsbegeerte*, Vol. 2, pp. 152–58.

In any event, let us now see what sort of a logic we would have if we dropped the law $\vdash p \vee \sim p$ from our logic. We know that $\vdash p \vee \sim p$ can be proved in the system of Chapter Two. The schema runs as follows in *reductio ad absurdum* form:

1. $\sim(p \vee \sim p)$	
2. p	
3. $p \vee \sim p$	2, vI
4. $(p \vee \sim p) \& \sim(p \vee \sim p)$	3, 1, &I
5. $\sim p$	2–4, $\sim$I
6. $p \vee \sim p$	5, vI
7. $(p \vee \sim p) \& \sim(p \vee \sim p)$	6, 1, &I
8. $\sim\sim(p \vee \sim p)$	1–7, $\sim$I
9. $p \vee \sim p$	8, $\sim\sim$E

This proof suggests that if we eliminate the rule of $\sim\sim$E the logic remaining would fail to have the law of excluded middle. Since $\sim\sim$I can be derived as follows:

1. p	
2. $\sim p$	
3. $p \& \sim p$	1, 2, &I
4. $\sim\sim p$	2–3, $\sim$I,

it is convenient to think of this logic as having no basic double negation rules. It is thus made up of the rules in Table 2.2 plus Repeat and minus $\sim\sim$E and $\sim\sim$I.

Perhaps the lack of $\sim\sim$E, together with the proof of $\sim\sim$I as a derived rule, suggests that long strings of negations could pile up without our being able to get rid of them. This is not the case as we may see from the following considerations. First, we can still prove that $(p \supset q) \supset (\sim q \supset \sim p)$:

4.1

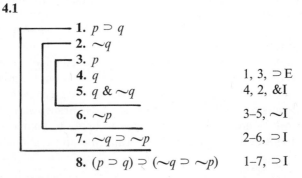

1. $p \supset q$	
2. $\sim q$	
3. p	
4. q	1, 3, $\supset$E
5. $q \& \sim q$	4, 2, &I
6. $\sim p$	3–5, $\sim$I
7. $\sim q \supset \sim p$	2–6, $\supset$I
8. $(p \supset q) \supset (\sim q \supset \sim p)$	1–7, $\supset$I

The converse (which holds in classical logic) does not hold in intuitionist logic, as we can see* from the proof of it in the non-intuitionist logic of Chapter Two:

$$
\begin{array}{lll}
1. & \sim q \supset \sim p & \\
2. & p & \\
3. & \sim q & \\
4. & \sim p & 1, 3, \supset E \\
5. & p \,\&\, \sim p & 2, 4, \&I \\
6. & \sim\!\sim q & 3\text{–}5, \sim I \\
7. & q & 6, \sim\!\sim E \\
8. & p \supset q & 2\text{–}7, \supset I \\
9. & (\sim q \supset \sim p) \supset (p \supset q) & 1\text{–}8, \supset I
\end{array}
$$

In the logic of intuitionism, however, step 7 fails, and with it the whole deduction.

On the other hand, the following proof holds within intuitionism:

4.2

$$
\begin{array}{lll}
1. & p & \\
2. & \sim\!\sim p & 1, \sim\!\sim I \\
3. & p \supset \sim\!\sim p & 1\text{–}2, \supset I
\end{array}
$$

By 4.1, we can infer from line 3 here that $\sim\!\sim\!\sim p \supset \sim p$. And by $\sim\!\sim I$, $\sim p \supset \sim\!\sim\!\sim p$. Hence strings of negation signs can always be reduced to single signs or pairs of them.

In intuitionistic logic, the Law of Noncontradiction does hold as we see from direct application of the rule of $\sim I$. If we wish, we can formalize this as follows:

$$
\begin{array}{lll}
1. & p \,\&\, \sim p & \\
2. & p \,\&\, \sim p & 1, \text{Repeat} \\
3. & \sim(p \,\&\, \sim p) & 1\text{–}2, \sim I
\end{array}
$$

In PL, as we have presented it in Chapters One, Two, and Three, the law of noncontradiction is equivalent to the law of excluded middle. This is because De Morgan's laws hold. In intuitionistic logic, on the other hand, De Morgan's laws are only partially true, and the relationship between noncontradiction and the excluded middle is more complicated. Thus, in classical logic, we could add to the above proof:

$$
\begin{array}{lll}
4. & \sim p \vee p & 3, \text{DM}
\end{array}
$$

The appeal to DM here is actually a reference to $\vdash \sim(p \,\&\, q) \supset (\sim p \vee \sim q)$.

---

* It should be emphasized that we do not claim to have *demonstrated* that

$$\vdash (\sim q \supset \sim p) \supset (p \supset q)$$

cannot be proved in intuitionistic logic. We are at most offering a suggestion as to why the latter cannot be proved.

Let us prove this in classical logic.

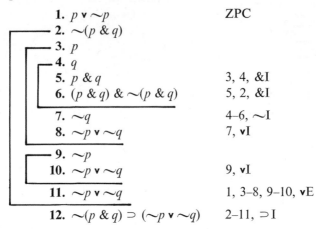

1. $p \lor \sim p$		ZPC
2. $\sim(p \& q)$		
3. p		
4. q		
5. $p \& q$		3, 4, &I
6. $(p \& q) \& \sim(p \& q)$		5, 2, &I
7. $\sim q$		4–6, $\sim$I
8. $\sim p \lor \sim q$		7, $\lor$I
9. $\sim p$		
10. $\sim p \lor \sim q$		9, $\lor$I
11. $\sim p \lor \sim q$		1, 3–8, 9–10, $\lor$E
12. $\sim(p \& q) \supset (\sim p \lor \sim q)$		2–11, $\supset$I

The only step in the whole of this extended proof that is inadmissible in intuitionistic logic is 1. Without this step we cannot get the result—hence this one of De Morgan's Laws does not hold in intuitionism, and, conversely, without it, we cannot prove the law of the excluded middle.

There are many reasons for studying variations in propositional logic. A good enough reason is simply the curiosity we have to see what will happen if we make modifications of a certain kind. Thus, if it occurs to us that it is possible to construct a three-valued truth table, this possibility can lead us on to the consideration of the resulting logic. Our motivation may, on the other hand, be more fundamental than this.

From this point of view we might observe that no completely satisfactory interpretation for three-valued and *n*-valued logics is available. Note, however, that non-Euclidian geometry was studied before a satisfactory interpretation was known.

Intuitionistic logic, on the other hand, is claimed by its developers and advocates to be the basis of a type of reasoning which occurs frequently in mathematics.

EXERCISE 4.2

I. Heyting, an intuitionist, has given a formulation of the propositional calculus which may be described as the system of Chapter Two less the principle of double-negation elimination plus Repeat. By using only the introduction and elimination rules of Chapter Two, prove the following formulas and then decide which portions of these proofs would be rejected by Heyting and the intuitionists.

1. $\sim\sim p \equiv p$ 3. $(p \lor q) \equiv \sim(\sim p \& \sim q)$

2. $(p \lor \sim q) \equiv \sim(\sim p \& q)$ 4. $(p \& q) \equiv \sim(\sim p \lor \sim q)$

5. $(p \supset q) \equiv (\sim p \vee q)$ 8. $(\sim p \, \& \, \sim q) \equiv \sim (p \vee q)$

6. $(p \vee q) \equiv (\sim p \supset q)$ 9. $(p \supset q) \equiv (\sim q \supset \sim p)$

7. $\sim (p \, \& \, q) \equiv (\sim p \vee \sim q)$ 10. $(\sim p \vee q) \equiv \sim (p \, \& \, \sim q)$

II. Which of the three-valued tautologies of Exercise 4.1, parts II and III, are provable as ZPC's in intuitionistic logic?

III. Which of the formulas in Exercise 4.1, part III, that are *not* three-valued tautologies are provable as ZPC's in intuitionistic logic?

IV. Fitch has given a formulation of the propositional calculus in which the rule of negation introduction is replaced by a restricted rule of negation introduction that demands that $p \vee \sim p$ be assumed before the rule can be applied. Which of the formulas of part I above are valid in Fitch's system?

V. Heyting's system shows that it is possible to construct a system in which $p \vee \sim p$, the law of excluded middle, is absent while its dual, $\sim (p \, \& \, \sim p)$, the Law of Noncontradiction, is present. Would it be possible to construct a system in which the Law of Noncontradiction were absent, and the law of excluded middle were present? Could one construct a system in which both were absent? (Hint: remember that logical systems can be axiomatic systems.)

VI. The laws of contradiction and excluded middle are traditionally known as laws of thought. If either or both can be absent from a system of logic, is their status as laws of thought destroyed?

VII. We have seen that the law of excluded middle is not a law of either Heyting's, Fitch's, or a three-valued system of logic. Does this mean that the law is not universally true? Discuss the validity of this law in connection with logics with more than three values.

VIII. In intuitionistic logic, proof by *reductio* is not acceptable in general. In Fitch's logic, such proofs are acceptable only upon the assumption of the law of excluded middle. Does this necessarily mean that those laws derived by such proofs are not acceptable to the intuitionists and Fitch? Under what circumstances can these laws be proven in other ways, *e.g.*?

IX. If $\sim\sim\sim p \supset \sim p$ belongs to intuitionistic logic, why can't we substitute p for $\sim p$, getting $\sim\sim p \supset p$?

4.3 Modal Logic

Intuitionistic logic, as we have seen, exemplifies the possibility of a logic in which the law of excluded middle does not occur. In three-valued logic, the absence of the law of excluded middle is combined with an interest in such properties of statements as possibility and necessity. It is also possible to formulate these properties in a logic based upon the rules of PL given in Chapter Two and therefore including the law of excluded middle. Since the properties and relations exemplified in such assertions as

> A is possible
>
> A is necessary
>
> A strictly implies B
>
> A and B are consistent

are sometimes referred to as *modal* properties and relations, the logic that formulates them is called *modal logic* when it is based upon the ordinary rules of PL. The modal logics most commonly studied are those introduced by C. I. Lewis.* The system presented here is equivalent to the one designated by Lewis as S4.

One motive for the study of modal logic is the desire to focus attention upon a certain class of implications—namely, those that are *strict implications*. The restriction on implications that yields the class of strict implications is suggested by the following examples. Since $A \supset (B \supset A)$ is a ZPC of PL, the modal logician takes the position that A strictly implies that $B \supset A$, but he denies that A strictly implies that B *strictly implies* A. Again, $\sim A \supset (A \supset B)$ is a ZPC of PL; and accordingly, $\sim A$ strictly implies that $A \supset B$. But $\sim A$ does *not* strictly imply that A *strictly implies* B.

The restriction can readily be made precise. Let us use $p \prec q$ to symbolize p strictly implies q. We now state a *rule of strict implication introduction* ($\prec$ I):

where no step within the scope of the assumption p makes any use of any other undischarged assumption, except that any lines of the form $r \prec s$ may be used.

It is obvious that this formulation of $\prec$ I permits the deduction of $A \prec (B \supset A)$ but not of $A \prec (B \prec A)$, and of $\sim A \prec (A \supset B)$ but not of $\sim A \prec (A \prec B)$. Consider the former case. We can proceed

---

* See Lewis and Langford, *Symbolic Logic* (New York: The Century Co., 1932. Reprinted New York: Dover Publications, 1951), Ch. VI and Appendix II ; and F. B. Fitch, *Symbolic Logic* (New York: The Ronald Press Company, 1952), Ch. 3.

but we cannot write

$$
\begin{array}{lll}
\text{1'.} & A & \\
\text{2'.} & B & \\
\text{3'.} & A & \text{1', Repeat} \\
\text{4'.} & B \prec A & \text{2', –3', erroneous } \prec \text{ introduction,}
\end{array}
$$

because step 3', within the scope of B, makes use of (in fact, repeats) the undischarged assumption A. We can go on now, if we like, to finish the sequence 1–4, obtaining

$$
\begin{array}{lll}
\text{1.} & A & \\
\text{2.} & B & \\
\text{3.} & A & \text{1, Repeat} \\
\text{4.} & B \supset A & \text{2–3, } \supset \text{I} \\
\text{5.} & A \prec (B \supset A) & \text{1–4, } \prec \text{I,}
\end{array}
$$

which the modal logician accepts and which conforms to the rule of $\prec$ I as stated above.

We now state a rule for eliminating $\prec$:

$$
\prec \text{E} \qquad\qquad\qquad
\begin{array}{l}
p \prec q \\
p \\
\therefore\ q
\end{array}
$$

Using this and $\prec$ I together, we can derive such results as the principle of the hypothetical syllogism for modal logic:

4.3   ⊢ $[(p \prec q)\ \&\ (q \prec r)] \prec (p \prec r)$
Proof:

$$
\begin{array}{lll}
\text{1.} & (p \prec q)\ \&\ (q \prec r) & \\
\text{2.} & p & \\
\text{3.} & p \prec q & \text{1, \&E} \\
\text{4.} & q & \text{2, 3, } \prec \text{E} \\
\text{5.} & q \prec r & \text{1, \&E} \\
\text{6.} & r & \text{5, 4, } \prec \text{E} \\
\text{7.} & p \prec r & \text{2–6, } \prec \text{I} \\
\text{8.} & [(p \prec q)\ \&\ (q \prec r)] \prec (p \prec r) & \text{1–8, } \prec \text{I}
\end{array}
$$

Here we use an undischarged assumption in the course of the deduction (steps 3 and 5) but this is permissible since the undischarged assumption is used in the manner prescribed by the conditions upon the rule $\prec$ I.

Another example of the use of these rules may be found in the following deduction:

$$
\begin{array}{lll}
\quad\ 1.\ p & & \\
\quad\ 2.\ {\sim}{\sim}p & & 1,\ {\sim}{\sim}I \\
\quad\ 3.\ p \prec {\sim}{\sim}p & & 1\text{-}2,\ \prec I \\
\quad\ 4.\ {\sim}{\sim}p & & \\
\quad\ 5.\ p & & 4,\ {\sim}{\sim}E \\
\quad\ 6.\ {\sim}{\sim}p \prec p & & 4\text{-}5,\ \prec I \\
\quad\ 7.\ (p \prec {\sim}{\sim}p)\ \&\ ({\sim}{\sim}p \prec p) & & 3,\ 6,\ \&I \\
\quad\ 8.\ p \equiv q & & 7,\ {\equiv}I \\
\quad\ 9.\ (p \prec {\sim}{\sim}p)\ \&\ ({\sim}{\sim}p \prec p) & & 8,\ {\equiv}E
\end{array}
$$

Here we obtain line 8 by the use of a new rule of *strict equivalence introduction*, symbolized $\equiv I$. The rule of *strict equivalence elimination*, $\equiv E$, justifies the inference to line 9. We summarize these two rules in the convenient form of a strict equivalence, in analogy with the formulations in Chapter Two, Table 2.3.

4.4 $\vdash (p \equiv q) \equiv [(p \prec q)\ \&\ (q \prec p)]$

The distinction of strict implications within implications permits us to deal with the modal properties such as necessity and possibility and the modal relation of consistency. We first introduce the property of necessity. Any ZPC of PL is necessarily true in the sense that it does not depend upon any assumptions. Further, as we noted in Chapter Three, any ZPC is a tautology. In consequence, if $\vdash p$, then ${\sim}p$ is a contradiction and equivalent to $q\ \&\ {\sim}q$, as a check by truth tables will establish.* This equivalence enables us to establish the following deduction schema:

$$
\begin{array}{lll}
\quad\ 1.\ {\sim}p & \text{where } p \text{ is ZPC.} \\
\quad\ 2.\ {\sim}p \equiv (q\ \&\ {\sim}q) & \text{ZPC} \\
\quad\ 3.\ q\ \&\ {\sim}q & 1,\ 2,\ {\equiv}E,\ \&E,\ {\supset}E \\
\quad\ 4.\ p & 3,\ {\sim}E \\
\quad\ 5.\ {\sim}p \prec p & 1\text{-}4,\ \prec I
\end{array}
$$

Line 5 suggests a formulation of the necessity of p in terms of $\prec$, and we use $\Box p$ as an abbreviation for it. The rules of *necessity introduction* and *necessity elimination* are conveniently summarized as a strict equivalence.

4.5 $\vdash \Box p \equiv ({\sim}p \prec p)$

The availability of the operation $\Box$ enables us to write $\Box{\sim}p$; that is, to assert that p is impossible; and to write ${\sim}\Box p$; that is, to assert that p is possibly false. Further, we may now establish some interesting truths concerning necessity. First we prove that p is strictly implied by the necessity of p.

---

* This is proved rigorously in Chapter Nine, Section Five.

4.6. $\vdash \Box p \prec p$

Proof:

1. $\Box p$		
2. $\sim p \prec p$	1, 4.5, 4.2, &E, $\prec$ E	
3. $\sim p$		
4. p	2, 3, $\prec$ E	
5. $p \,\&\, \sim p$	3, 4, & I	
6. $\sim\sim p$	3–5, $\sim$I	
7. p	6, $\sim\sim$E	
8. $\Box p \prec p$	1–7, $\prec$ I	

Since we can also prove $\Box p \prec \Box\Box p$, it follows that $\Box\Box p \equiv \Box p$. We may now state the relation between $\prec$ and $\supset$. As it happens $p \prec q$ is strictly equivalent to $\Box(p \supset q)$. We establish this fact in the following deduction schemas:

4.7 $\vdash (p \prec q) \prec \Box(p \supset q)$

Proof:

1. $p \prec q$	
2. $\sim(p \supset q)$	
3. $p \prec q$	1, Repeat
4. p	
5. q	3, 4, $\prec$ E
6. $p \supset q$	4–5, $\supset$I
7. $\sim(p \supset q) \prec (p \supset q)$	2–6, $\prec$ I
8. $\Box(p \supset q)$	7, 4.5, etc.
9. $(p \prec q) \prec \Box(p \supset q)$	1–9, $\prec$ I

4.8 $\vdash \Box(p \supset q) \prec (p \prec q)$

Proof:

1. $\Box(p \supset q)$	
2. $\sim(p \supset q) \prec (p \supset q)$	1, 4.5, etc.
3. p	
4. $\sim(p \supset q)$	
5. $p \supset q$	2, 4, $\prec$ E
6. $(p \supset q) \,\&\, \sim(p \supset q)$	5, 4, &I
7. $\sim\sim(p \supset q)$	4–6, $\sim$I
8. $p \supset q$	7, $\sim\sim$E
9. q	8, 3, $\supset$E
10. $p \prec q$	3–9, $\prec$ I
11. $\Box(p \supset q) \prec (p \prec q)$	1–10, $\prec$ I

And by 4.2, 4.5, and 4.6, we have

4.9 $(p \prec q) \equiv \Box(p \supset q)$

Further truths concern the distribution of $\Box$ over conjunctions, alternations

and so on. In the following two schemas, for example, we establish that
$\Box(p \& q) \equiv (\Box p \& \Box q)$.

4.10 $\vdash \Box(p \& q) \prec (\Box p \& \Box q)$

Proof:

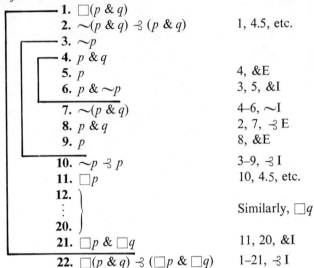

1. $\Box(p \& q)$	
2. $\sim(p \& q) \prec (p \& q)$	1, 4.5, etc.
3. $\sim p$	
4. $p \& q$	
5. p	4, &E
6. $p \& \sim p$	3, 5, &I
7. $\sim(p \& q)$	4–6, $\sim$I
8. $p \& q$	2, 7, $\prec$ E
9. p	8, &E
10. $\sim p \prec p$	3–9, $\prec$ I
11. $\Box p$	10, 4.5, etc.
12.	
$\vdots$	Similarly, $\Box q$
20.	
21. $\Box p \& \Box q$	11, 20, &I
22. $\Box(p \& q) \prec (\Box p \& \Box q)$	1–21, $\prec$ I

4.11 $\vdash (\Box p \& \Box q) \prec \Box(p \& q)$

Proof:

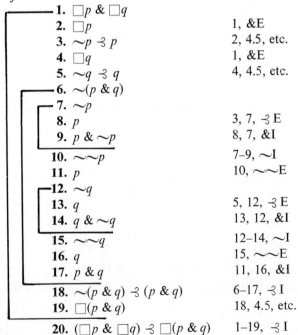

1. $\Box p \& \Box q$	
2. $\Box p$	1, &E
3. $\sim p \prec p$	2, 4.5, etc.
4. $\Box q$	1, &E
5. $\sim q \prec q$	4, 4.5, etc.
6. $\sim(p \& q)$	
7. $\sim p$	
8. p	3, 7, $\prec$ E
9. $p \& \sim p$	8, 7, &I
10. $\sim\sim p$	7–9, $\sim$I
11. p	10, $\sim\sim$E
12. $\sim q$	
13. q	5, 12, $\prec$ E
14. $q \& \sim q$	13, 12, &I
15. $\sim\sim q$	12–14, $\sim$I
16. q	15, $\sim\sim$E
17. $p \& q$	11, 16, &I
18. $\sim(p \& q) \prec (p \& q)$	6–17, $\prec$ I
19. $\Box(p \& q)$	18, 4.5, etc.
20. $(\Box p \& \Box q) \prec \Box(p \& q)$	1–19, $\prec$ I

As for necessity, we may introduce an operation of *possibility*, symbolized ◇. We summarize the rules of introduction and elimination in the following strict equivalence:

4.12 $\vdash ◇p \equiv \sim(p \dashv3 \sim p)$

Since $\sim(p \dashv3 \sim p) \equiv \sim\square\sim p$ we also have

4.13 $\vdash ◇p \equiv \sim\square\sim p$

With these principles we can prove both that $p \dashv3 ◇ p$ and that $◇◇p \dashv3 ◇p$. The proof of the latter runs as follows:

4.14 $\vdash ◇◇p \dashv3 ◇p$

Proof:

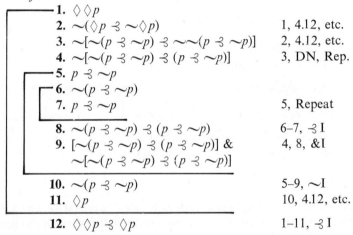

1. ◇◇p	
2. ~(◇p -3 ~◇p)	1, 4.12, etc.
3. ~[~(p -3 ~p) -3 ~~(p -3 ~p)]	2, 4.12, etc.
4. ~[~(p -3 ~p) -3 (p -3 ~p)]	3, DN, Rep.
5. p -3 ~p	
6. ~(p -3 ~p)	
7. p -3 ~p	5, Repeat
8. ~(p -3 ~p) -3 (p -3 ~p)	6–7, -3 I
9. [~(p -3 ~p) -3 (p -3 ~p)] & ~[~(p -3 ~p) -3 (p -3 ~p)]	4, 8, &I
10. ~(p -3 ~p)	5–9, ~I
11. ◇p	10, 4.12, etc.
12. ◇◇p -3 ◇p	1–11, -3 I

Since $◇p \dashv3 ◇◇p$, iterated diamonds can always be replaced by a single diamond, just as iterated squares are reducible to a single one.

Truths concerning the distribution of ◇ over alternations, conjunctions, etc., can be proved. In particular, $(◇p \vee ◇q) \dashv3 ◇(p \vee q)$ is demonstrable. Another such distribution is $\vdash [(p \dashv3 q) \& ◇p] \dashv3 ◇q$. This, and the corresponding statement $\vdash [(p \dashv3 q) \& \square p] \dashv3 \square q$, may be regarded as special forms of -3 E.

One further modal idea worth mentioning is that of *consistency*. When p is consistent with q, the conjunction of p with q is possible; symbolically,

4.15 $\vdash p \triangle q \equiv ◇(p \& q)$

We mention some of the truths which can be established about consistency. To say that p is possible is to say that it is self-consistent; $\vdash ◇p \equiv p \triangle p$. If p is consistent with any other statement, it is self-consistent;

$$\vdash p \triangle p \dashv3 (p \triangle p).$$

As with $\square$ and ◇, there are distribution principles for $\triangle$. For example, $\vdash p \triangle (q \& r) \dashv3 [(q \triangle r) \& (p \triangle r)]$. The converse does not hold.

The system of modal logic sketched here is but one of a variety of such systems which attempt to deal with modal operations and to narrow the conception of implication to a stricter implication than the $\supset$ of PL. Although they are interesting, a great deal of work remains to be done on these logics before they achieve their goals.

EXERCISE 4.3

I. Prove:

1. $\Box p \prec \Box \Box p$

2. $p \prec \Diamond p$

3. $(\Diamond p \lor \Diamond q) \prec \Diamond (p \lor q)$

4. $(p \prec q) \prec (\sim q \prec \sim p)$

5. $[(p \prec q) \,\&\, \Box p] \prec \Box q$

6. $[(p \prec q) \,\&\, \Diamond p] \prec \Diamond q$

7. $\Diamond (p \,\&\, q) \prec \Diamond p$

8. $\Box p \prec \Box (p \lor q)$

9. $[p \prec (q \prec r)] \prec [(p \,\&\, q) \prec r]$

10. $p \triangle (q \,\&\, r) \prec [(p \triangle q) \,\&\, (p \triangle r) \,\&\, (q \triangle r)]$

11. $[(p \prec r) \,\&\, (q \prec s) \,\&\, \sim (r \triangle s)] \prec \sim (p \triangle q)$

II. Taking $\prec$ as $\rightarrow$, $\Diamond$ as M, $\lor$ as $\circ$, $\sim$ as N, $\&$ as $\wedge$, $\Box p$ as NMNp, and $p \triangle q$ as M($p \wedge q$), use truth tables to determine which of the statements in part I above are three-valued tautologies.

III. Explain why $\sim$A $\prec$ (A $\prec$ B) is not derivable in the system of modal logic developed in this section. Explain also why

$$[(A \,\&\, B) \prec C] \prec [A \prec (B \prec C)]$$

is not derivable.

IV. 1. $\Diamond \Box p \prec \Box p$ is not derivable in the modal logic developed in Section 4.13. How would the rule of $\prec$ I have to be relaxed in order to permit its proof?

2. Assuming $\Diamond \Box p \prec \Box p$ already proved, prove

(a) $\Diamond \Box p \equiv \Box p$
(b) $\Diamond p \prec \Box \Diamond p$
(c) $\Diamond p \equiv \Box \Diamond p$

SUGGESTED READINGS

1. F. B. Fitch, *Symbolic Logic* (New York: The Ronald Press Co., 1952), Ch. III.

2. A. Heyting, *Intuitionism, An Introduction* (Amsterdam: North Holland Pub. Co., 1956).

3. C. I. Lewis and C. H. Langford, *Symbolic Logic* (New York and London: The Century Co., 1932, Reprinted 1951), Ch. VI, X.

4. A. N. Prior, *Formal Logic* (Oxford: The Clarendon Press, 1955), Part III.

5. J. B. Rosser and A. R. Turquette, *Many-Valued Logics* (Amsterdam: North Holland Pub. Co., 1952).

6. G. H. von Wright, *An Essay on Modal Logic* (Amsterdam: North Holland Pub. Co., 1951).

Chapter 5

Introduction to Predicate Logic

5.1 Individual Variables

One of the most evident characteristics of modern mathematics is its use
of symbols. Among the most important symbols used in mathematics are
those associated with variables. Although in principle we might be able to
replace them with words, in practice such a replacement would result in a
breakdown in communication. Even so simple an expression as

$$(x + 1)^2 = (x^2 + 2x + 1)$$

becomes quite lengthy and unmanageable when rephrased without symbols
for variables: The square of the sum of a given number and one equals the
sum of the square of the number, the double of the number, and one. The
use of symbols for variables in mathematics, however, is relatively recent.
Perhaps the first systematic use of them dates from the end of the sixteenth
century, when the French mathematician Vieta contributed much to their
popularity.

Like many ideas which greatly simplify the solution of difficult problems,
the conception of variables involves complicated distinctions. Perhaps the
distinction most important to our study of the axiomatic method is the difference between the rules of inference required when variables are used within
axioms, and the rules that suffice when they are not so used. In order to deal
effectively with axioms involving variables, we shall find that we must add to
the list of rules so far given.

An example of some kinds of inference required in cases where variables occur within axioms is to be found in Th. 1.1. The proof of Th. 1.1 was based on Axiom 2 of the system for simple order and is written

1. If $x < y$ then x and y are distinct   Ax. 2
2. If $x < x$ then x and x are distinct
3. $\sim(x$ and x are distinct$)$
4. $\sim(x < x)$ 2, 3, MT

The step in this deduction that interests us at the moment is line 2. Here we have introduced x for y in line 1. This seems plausible enough, but let us expand upon our line of reasoning. As an axiom, line 1 is clearly true for any and every instance of its variables x and y; it is therefore true when the variables have the same value. In essence, this is the justification for line 2 above. As before we then proceed by the rules of PL to line 4. A rule like MT, as used in the preceding chapters, refers to statements, and if we formulate it as a schema,

$$p \supset q$$
$$\sim q$$
$$\therefore \ \sim p,$$

we see that p and q may stand for any statements at all. Yet its use in the deduction above does not involve statements, for neither "$x < x$" nor "x and x are distinct" is, for reasons that we shall soon point out, a statement. Thus not only does the use of variables require new rules of inference, but it requires the application of the rules of PL to formulas that are not statements.

In ordinary language, the use of pronouns and indefinite nouns is much like the occurrence of variables in mathematical expressions. Thus we use "He is a man" and "The former is less than the latter". Perhaps we think of "He is a man" as a sentence; yet it is not a statement in the sense of being true or false. Indeed, we cannot determine its truth or falsity until we know what "he" refers to; which is to say that "He is a man" becomes a statement only when we introduce a *value* (or the name of a value) for the pronoun. For example,

Tom is a man

or

Joe Smith is a man.

The truth or falsity of *these* statements depends upon the individuals named. Similarly "The former is less than the latter" becomes a statement (true or false) if we introduce values, as in

1 is less than 2
5 is less than 3

But these two statements might also have been arrived at by introducing values into $x < y$. Similarly "He is a man" could be expressed as $M(x)$.

Although in the preceding pages we have sometimes used variables, we have discussed their nature only once before. In Chapter Two, Section 5, we observed that A, B, C, ... were variables. There we noted also that they ranged over any particular sentences as values. We have used *these* variables as a means of developing a logic of statements. Like the variables A, B, C, ... the variables $x, y, z, \ldots$ have a range of values. Their range is over the individuals which (or the names of which) may be introduced into expressions in place of them, thus making these expressions true or false and hence statements. Such variables are referred to as *individual* variables because they take individuals as substituents.

In practice these variables occur in specific deductions in forms like $M(x)$, $x < y$, and $G(x,y)$. Such expressions can be made into statements by introducing appropriate substituents in place of the variables. For this reason such expressions are called *statement functions*; that is, they determine statements corresponding to the various values of these variables.

EXERCISE 5.1

I. Which of the following are statements? Statement functions?

   1. Roses are red.

   2. They are red.

   3. $x^2 + 27x = 0$.

   4. $(x + 1)^2 = x^2 + 2x + 1$.

   5. Whatever number n you choose, $n^2 - 1 = (n + 1)(n - 1)$.

   6. There is at least one number x such that $x/2 = 2/x$.

   7. $x = \sin y$.

   8. Columbus discovered America.

   9. Columbus discovered it.

   10. He discovered it.

II. Change any statements in part I of this exercise into statement functions by introducing variables where appropriate, or by other means.

5.2 Quantification

There are many instances of statement functions in both ordinary English and in mathematics. The use of variables to represent unspecified objects has its counterpart in ordinary language, since sentences involving pronouns may often be symbolized as statement functions. Thus

He is a philosopher

becomes

$$P(x)$$

while

He is a Greek or they are Turks

can be symbolized

$$G(x) \lor T(y)$$

(Note that the (x) here need not be regarded as necessarily either singular or plural; and the same for the (y)). In mathematics the equations of ordinary algebra often use variables to represent unspecified objects in the form of *unknowns*. Thus consider

$$6x = 12$$

or, as we shall now write it,

$$N(x)$$

which can be read: x is a number obtained by dividing the number twelve by the number six. We may introduce values of x to get statements. Thus

$$N(2)$$

is a true statement. However,

$$N(7)$$

is a false statement since $6 \cdot 7 \neq 12$.

Many mathematical equations are of this type, although some involve more than one variable. Thus

$$x^2 + y^2 = 8$$

would be symbolized

$$N(x,y)$$

On the other hand, there are expressions involving variables in mathematics that have a different meaning. Thus trigonometric identities such as

$$\sin^2 \varphi + \cos^2 \varphi = 1$$

have the peculiarity that every value of φ makes them true. In this they differ from the usual equation, which is true only for some values of the variable. This difference is sometimes noted in trigonometry by the use of $\equiv$ as in

$$\sin^2 \varphi + \cos^2 \varphi \equiv 1$$

There are other examples of expressions which are true for all values of their variables. In fact, many axioms make this claim. The well-known axiom that things equal to the same thing are equal to each other is such an instance. We may take explicit account of this by writing

For all x, y, and z $[(x = y \,\&\, x = z) \supset y = z]$

Or, in more technical symbols that we shall explain shortly,

$$\textstyle\prod_x(\prod_y\{\prod_z[(x = y \ \& \ x = z) \supset y = z]\})$$

Under this condition the axiom is a statement, for, so conceived, it is capable of being true or false, and in this case is true. Similarly, the expression

$$x = x$$

is tacitly accepted as a statement because we see at once that it holds for all values of the variables, that is,

$$\textstyle\prod_x(x = x)$$

The axioms in the system for simple order in Chapter One claim to be true for all values of their variables and can be rewritten in such a way as to make this fact explicit.

The symbol $\prod$ is called a *universal quantifier* and asserts (rightly or wrongly) that the expression following it holds for all values of the variables designated by its index. Note that such an assertion need not actually be true. Thus

$$\textstyle\prod_x\{\prod_y[(x < y) \supset (y < x)]\}$$

is patently false. The point is just that the universal quantifier explicitly indicates that the variables here are to range over all values rather than to represent unspecified objects.

The use of the symbol $\prod$ is not accidental and an understanding of its choice will aid in an understanding of its function.* Consider the statement "For all integers x, $x > 0 \supset 0 \not> x$".† This means

$$[(1 > 0) \supset (0 \not> 1)] \ \& \ [(2 > 0) \supset (0 \not> 2)] \ \& \ [(3 > 0) \supset (0 \not> 3)] \ \& \dots$$

This infinite expression is the conjunction of all statements of the form $(x > 0) \supset (0 \not> x)$, where x assumes all integral values in turn. Now, conjunctions are sometimes called *logical products* because of the resemblance between conjunction and multiplication. Thus this conjunction can be called the logical product with respect to x of $(x > 0) \supset (0 \not> x)$. It may be written $\prod_x[(x > 0) \supset (0 \not> x)]$, for the capital Greek letter *Pi* is used in mathematics to represent a *product*, and we use it in a similar fashion here. Using this notation, we may write the statement "For all integers x and y, $(x > y) \supset (y \not> x)$" like this:

$$\textstyle\prod_x[(x > 0) \supset (0 \not> x)] \ \& \ \prod_x[(x > 1) \supset (1 \not> x)] \ \& \ \prod_x[(x > 2) \supset$$
$$(2 \not> x)] \ \& \dots$$

or, more simply, as

$$\textstyle\prod_y\{\prod_x[(x > y) \supset (y \not> x)]\}$$

---

* Other symbols in common use for this purpose are found in the following statements: $\mathsf{V}_x\mathrm{M}(x)$ and $(x)\mathrm{M}(x)$, which are read the same as $\Pi_x\mathrm{M}(x)$.

† We are using $y \not> x$ here as an abbreviation for $\sim(y > x)$.

$\prod_x$, $\prod_y$, and so on, are spoken of as *universal quantifiers*. There are other ways as well of turning statement functions into statements, but the only additional operator needed for our present purposes is known as the *existential quantifier*. This is tacitly used in such statements as:

> Some numbers are smaller than others.
> There is at least one man.
> There exists a number greater than zero.

Using obvious abbreviations, these statements are symbolized as

$$\sum_x [\sum_y (x < y)]$$
$$\sum_x M(x)$$
$$\sum_x (x > 0)$$

The symbol $\sum$ is used to change the statement functions $x < y$, $M(x)$, and $x > 0$ to statements which in these three instances are true. However, the statement

$$\sum_x \sim (x = x)$$

is false, as are many other existentially quantified statements.

We use the symbol $\sum$ because of the reference of the operator to disjunction and the analogy between disjunction and addition in certain kinds of algebra. When we say

$$\sum_x (x < 99)$$

we mean that

$$(1 < 99) \vee (2 < 99) \vee \ldots \vee (99 < 99) \vee (100 < 99) \vee \ldots$$

The whole of what we mean is a disjunction of statements of this form. Just as conjunction resembles multiplication, disjunction resembles addition, and since the Greek letter *Sigma* is used often in mathematics to represent a *sum*, we use it here.

EXERCISE 5.2

I. Express each of the following as logical sums and logical products.

1. $\prod_x A(x)$

2. $\sum_x A(x)$

3. $\prod_x [A(x) \vee B(x)]$

4. $\prod_x A(x) \vee \prod_x B(x)$

5. $\prod_x [A(x) \,\&\, B(x)]$

6. $\prod_x A(x) \,\&\, \prod_x B(x)$

7. $\prod_x [A(x) \supset B(x)]$

8. $\prod_x [A(x) \supset \prod_y B(y)]$

9. $\sum_x [A(x) \supset \prod_y B(y)]$

10. $\sum_x A(x) \vee \sum_x B(x)$

11. $\sum_x [A(x) \,\&\, B(x)]$

12. $\sum_x A(x) \,\&\, \sum_x B(x)$

13. $\sim\prod_x A(x)$ 19. $\prod_x\prod_y \varphi(x,y)$*

14. $\prod_x \sim A(x)$ 20. $\prod_y\prod_x \varphi(x,y)$

15. $\sim\sum_x A(x)$ 21. $\sum_x\sum_y \varphi(x,y)$

16. $\sum_x \sim A(x)$ 22. $\sum_y\sum_x \varphi(x,y)$

17. $\sim\sum_x \sim A(x)$ 23. $\prod_x\sum_y \varphi(x,y)$

18. $\sim\prod_x \sim A(x)$ 24. $\sum_y\prod_x \varphi(x,y)$

II. Which of the above are equivalent to one another?

5.3 Notes on Symbolizing Ordinary Language

In this section we shall consider how a number of statements in English must be translated into quantificational language, and how various quantificational expressions ought to be translated into English. This task is not too difficult, but a study of some of the problems it presents will clarify the symbolism of quantification and fix its meaning as determining a range of values of a variable. We shall proceed by considering a number of examples loosely grouped into analogous forms.

It is sometimes helpful to restate an English sentence before symbolizing it. Thus "Every prime number greater than two is odd" can be rephrased as "Every number is such that if it is a prime greater than two, then it is odd." This should be symbolized $\prod_x[P(x) \supset O(x)]$ where $P(x)$ means x is a prime greater than two. Other sentences that have the same meaning (and so the same symbolism) are:

Each prime number greater than 2 is odd.

All prime numbers greater than 2 are odd.

Given a prime number greater than 2, it is odd.

Whatever prime number greater than 2 you choose, it is odd.

Prime numbers greater than 2 are always odd.

Any prime number greater than 2 is odd.

It thus appears that "every", "each", "all", "whatever", and "any" are all symbolized in the same way. This is, in fact, true of all of these expressions except "any", which requires careful consideration in practice. For example, notice that whereas

Not every number is factorable.

Not all numbers are factorable.

It is not the case that whatever number you choose, it is factorable, *etc.*,

---

* Note that parentheses between successive quantifiers are often omitted when no ambiguity would result.

all have the same meaning, the statement "Not any number is factorable" differs in meaning from these. While the meaning common to the list above could be symbolized as

$$(1) \quad {\sim}\textstyle\prod_x F(x)$$

that of "Not any number is factorable" would require instead

$$(2) \quad \textstyle\prod_x {\sim}F(x)$$

(1) is the denial of a conjunction; *i.e.,*

$$(1') \quad {\sim}[F(1) \ \& \ F(2) \ \& \ F(3) \ \& \ldots]$$

whereas (2) is the conjunction of a series of negative statements:

$$(2') \quad {\sim}F(1) \ \& \ {\sim}F(2) \ \& \ {\sim}F(3) \ \& \ldots$$

If we apply DeMorgan's Laws to each of these conjunctions we obtain

$$(1'') \quad {\sim}F(1) \ \textbf{v} \ {\sim}F(2) \ \textbf{v} \ {\sim}F(3) \ \textbf{v} \ldots ; \ i.e., \ \textstyle\sum_x {\sim}F(x)$$

and

$$(2'') \quad {\sim}[F(1) \ \textbf{v} \ F(2) \ \textbf{v} \ F(3) \ \textbf{v} \ldots]; \ i.e., \ {\sim}\textstyle\sum_x F(x)$$

To conclude that $\vdash {\sim}\prod_x F(x) \equiv \sum_x {\sim}F(x)$ and $\prod_x {\sim}F(x) \equiv {\sim}\sum_x F(x)$ is, in fact, correct, but certain risks are taken whenever an operation defined only for a finite set of elements is extended to cover an infinite set of them. A rigorous proof of the equivalence in question, not depending upon any assumptions regarding the behavior of $\sim$, &, or **v** in infinite situations, will be given later.

If we interpret $S(x)$ as "The sum of the digits of x is divisible by 9" and $N(x)$ as "x is divisible by 9", the difference in meaning between $\prod_x [S(x) \supset N(x)]$ and $\prod_x S(x) \supset \prod_x N(x)$ is suggested. While the former translates as "Every number is such that if the sum of its digits is divisible by 9, the number itself is divisible by 9", the latter must be read "If every number is such that the sum of its digits is divisible by 9, then every number is divisible by 9". The difference, then, is the difference between "Every x is such that if ..." and "If every x is such that ...".

Another example of the care that must be paid to the word "any", when we symbolize sentences involving it, is illustrated by comparing

> If every number greater than k is factorable, then the number of primes is finite.

with

> If any number greater than k is factorable, then the number of primes is finite.

The first of these statements is vacuously true, since it is false that there is a number k such that every number greater than it is factorable. The second, however, is false; the mere existence of some factorable number greater than k would be no evidence that the number of primes was finite. The first statement must be symbolized as

$$\textstyle\prod_x[x > k \supset F(x)] \supset N$$

(where N stands for the statement "The number of primes is finite"). The second has the symbolic structure

$$\textstyle\prod_x\{[x > k \mathbin{\&} F(x)] \supset N\};$$

i.e., whatever number you choose, if it is greater than k and factorable, then the number of primes is finite. In other words, from the fact that there *existed* such a number it would follow that the number of primes was finite. Thus we could alternatively symbolize this sentence using an existential quantifier:

$$\textstyle\sum_x[x > k \mathbin{\&} F(x)] \supset N$$

i.e., if there exists a number greater than k and factorable, then the number of primes is finite. In general, "If for every x $G(x)$ then p" should be symbolized as $\prod_x G(x) \supset p$, whereas "If for any x $G(x)$ then p" should be symbolized as $\prod_x[G(x) \supset p]$ or as $\sum_x G(x) \supset p$.

When we use the universal quantifier, $\prod$, in a formula involving two predicates, we usually quantify a conditional, as in $\prod_x[x > k \supset F(x)]$. However, when we use the existential quantifier, $\sum$, we usually quantify a conjunction, as in $\sum_x[x > k \mathbin{\&} F(x)]$. The first of these symbolizes "Every number greater than k is factorable," and the second, "Some number greater than k is factorable". A natural question is why one of the expressions in parentheses must be a conditional while the other is a conjunction. One part of the answer is obvious: certainly we could not adequately represent "Every number greater than k is factorable" by $\prod_x[x > k \mathbin{\&} F(x)]$; for this would mean that every number *is* greater than k *and* is factorable, which is false if only because not every number can be greater than k. (The sentence $\prod_x[x > k \supset F(x)]$ is, of course, false, too, but for entirely different reasons.)

Likewise, "There exists a number greater than k and factorable" cannot be symbolized as $\sum_x[x > k \supset F(x)]$. In order to make this statement come out true, we need pay no attention to arithmetic. We need only pick a u such that $u < k$. For this u, then, $u > k \supset F(u)$ will be trivially true. But when we use "There exists a number greater than k and factorable" we do not intend to state a trivial truth. We intend to state a truth of arithmetic, whose verification would require at least some consultation of arithmetical facts. (We might reason, for example, that if k is odd, then $k + 1$ is factorable, and if k is even, $k + 2$ is factorable.)

We can schematize this discussion by saying that "Every φ is ψ" should be translated into quantificational language as $\prod_\alpha[\varphi(\alpha) \supset \psi(\alpha)]$, while "There exists a φ that is ψ" should be translated as $\sum_{\alpha}[\varphi(\alpha) \,\&\, \psi(\alpha)]$. The following sentences all should be symbolized according to this latter schema:

> There exists a number equal to the sum of its factors.
>
> At least one number is equal to the sum of its factors.
>
> Some number (or other) is equal to the sum of its factors.
>
> Numbers are sometimes equal to the sum of their factors.

Let us turn to a different problem in translation. Consider the statement "All squares and circles are plane figures." How should we symbolize this? $\prod_x\{[S(x) \,\&\, C(x)] \supset P(x)\}$ clearly will not do; because there can be no u that is both square and circular, each of the conditionals $[S(u) \,\&\, C(u)] \supset P(u)$ whose conjunction is represented by the product will be vacuously true. Surely the intention of anyone who uses "Squares and circles are plane figures", however, must be to assert that if anything is a square *or* a circle, it is a plane figure; *i.e.*, $\prod_x\{[S(x) \vee C(x)] \supset P(x)\}$. On the other hand, "All ellipses are plane and curved" would be correctly represented by $\prod_x\{E(x) \supset [P(x) \,\&\, C(x)]\}$. There are cases in which the antecedent of each conditional must be a conjunction rather than an alternation, as in the correct translation of "If any number greater than k is factorable, then the number of primes is finite". For this consequent follows when a number x fulfills two conditions simultaneously: it is greater than k, and it is factorable. Similarly, "Every even number greater than two is the sum of two primes" is symbolized as $\prod_x\{[E(x) \,\&\, x > 2] \supset S(x)\}$.

It is possible in some cases to simplify symbolism by suppressing explicit account of the reference of the variables where such account is not essential to the argument. We have, in fact, done this in the last example, since the sentence might have been symbolized to refer to the fact that x is a number. We could have written

$$\prod_x\{[N(x) \,\&\, E(x) \,\&\, x > 2] \supset S(x)\};$$

i.e., everything *that is a number*, and is even, and is greater than 2 is the sum of two primes. Again, "Every prime number greater than 2 is odd" need not have been translated precisely as it was. The recommended translation, it will be recalled, was $\prod_x[P(x) \supset O(x)]$ where $P(x)$ stood for "x is a prime number greater than 2". We could take $P(x)$ to stand for "x is a prime number", and write

$$\prod_x\{[P(x) \,\&\, x > 2] \supset O(x)\}$$

or, taking $P(x)$ as standing for "x is prime", we might set down

$$\prod_x\{[N(x) \,\&\, P(x) \,\&\, x > 2] \supset O(x)\}$$

How do we decide which of these courses to adopt? One important factor is the deduction in which a given sentence occurs as a premise or conclusion.

Consider the following argument:

All prime numbers greater than 2 are odd.

All numbers of the form $n^2 - n + 41$ {$n < 41$} are prime numbers greater than 2.

Hence, all numbers of the form $n^2 - n + 41$ {$n < 41$} are odd.

This argument could be translated as

$$\prod_x \{[N(x) \text{ \& } P(x) \text{ \& } x > 2] \supset O(x)\}$$
$$\prod_x \{[N(x) \text{ \& } F(x)] \supset [N(x) \text{ \& } P(x) \text{ \& } x > 2]\}$$
$$\therefore \ \prod_x \{[N(x) \text{ \& } F(x)] \supset O(x)\}$$

But, since the conjunctions $[N(x) \text{ \& } P(x) \text{ \& } x > 2]$ and $[N(x) \text{ \& } F(x)]$ are preserved intact throughout the argument, we might as well write, much more simply,

$$\prod_x [P(x) \supset O(x)]$$
$$\prod_x [F(x) \supset P(x)]$$
$$\therefore \ \prod_x [F(x) \supset O(x)]$$

On the other hand, the following deduction presents a different situation:

All prime numbers greater than 2 are odd.

No odd numbers are even.

Hence any even number is either not prime or not greater than 2.

Here the association of prime numbers and numbers greater than 2 is not preserved throughout the argument; so we shall have to write

$$\prod_x [(P(x) \text{ \& } x > 2) \supset O(x)]$$
$$\prod_x [O(x) \supset \sim E(x)]$$
$$\therefore \ \prod_x [E(x) \supset (\sim P(x) \text{ v } x \not> 2)]$$

It is usually possible to take for granted the fact that we are dealing with the universe of things of which all the predicates occurring in the argument are subclasses. For example, most arithmetical arguments and proofs will be concerned with numbers. Thus we can take it for granted that if $\prod_x [(P(x) \text{ \& } x > 2) \supset O(x)]$ is a premise or conclusion of an arithmetical argument, the x's will be numbers. This idea can be expressed by saying that the *range* of x is numbers. Other possible ranges of individual variables include points, lines, forces, voltages, persons, times, and—in the most general case—entities. The range of the variables occurring in any argument rarely needs to be explicitly symbolized. Thus, in an arithmetical argument, it is usually unnecessary to impose the condition that the entities with which the argument deals are numbers. For instance, in the argument symbolized at the end of the last paragraph, there is no harm in letting $P(x)$ stand for "x is prime" rather than "x is a prime number".

EXERCISE 5.3

I. Translate the following statements into quantificational form, using the suggested symbols. Note that lower-case symbols stand for *individuals*; "Homer is blind" might be written B(h), for example.

1. All integers are either even or odd. [I(x), E(x), O(x)]

2. No integers are both odd and even. [I(x), O(x), E(x)]

3. All gases are combustible. [G(x), C(x)]

4. Some gases are not combustible. [G(x), C(x)]

5. Hydrogen is explosive, but neon is not. [E(x); h, n]

6. Everything is real. [R(x)]

7. Some things are not real. [R(x)]

8. Each fox is a mammal. [F(x), M(x)]

9. Some mammals are not foxes. [M(x), F(x)]

10. No fox is not a mammal. [F(x), M(x)]

11. Nothing which is not a number is an integer. [N(x), I(x)]

12. If all integers are numbers, then any given integer will be a number. [I(x), N(x)]

13. If all swans are white, then some things are white. [S(x), W(x)]

14. If some swans are white, then it is false that nothing is white. [S(x), W(x)]

15. If there is a red fox, then something is red and something is a fox. [R(x), F(x)]

16. If nothing is white, then no swans are white. [W(x), S(x)]

17. If all men are featherless bipeds, then if Socrates is a man he must be featherless. [M(x), F(x), B(x); s]

18. If Socrates is not honest, then no man is. [H(x), M(x); s]

19. If anything has property P, individual *a* has. [P(x); *a*]

20. If Pegasus is a horse, then either some horses are winged or Pegasus has no wings after all. [H(x), W(x); p]

21. It is not the case that if an animal is a horse, and some horses have wings, then that animal has wings. [A(x), H(x), W(x)]

22. No insurance company will pay unless all suspicions have been allayed. [I(x), P(x), S(x), A(x)]

23. If all suspicions had been allayed, any insurance company would have paid. [S(x), A(x), I(x), P(x)]

24. Some insurance companies would not pay whether or not all suspicions had vanished. [I(x), P(x), S(x), V(x)]

25. If something is constructive, then if every person sacrifices, it will be accomplished. [C(x), P(x), S(x), A(x)]

26. Only if every person sacrifices will anything constructive be accomplished. [P(x), S(x), C(x), A(x)]

27. If all of the thieves were observed, then some of the observed were guilty, but Slim is not guilty if he was not observed. [T(x), O(x), G(x); s]

28. If any species has a biological liability, then, if there exists a species without that liability, the first species will vanish. [S(x), L(x), V(x)]

29. Unless some person is very talented, a difficult job will be accomplished only if some person drives himself. [P(x), T(x), D(x), J(x), A(x), H(x)]

30. Every man is a son, but only some men are fathers. [M(x), S(x), F(x)]

II. 1. For each of your translations in the first part of this exercise, find another translation which has the same meaning, but which has an existential quantifier for each universal quantifier of your first symbolization, and a universal quantifier for each existential one. (Note that "all x are . . ." means the same as "there are not some x which are not . . .", etc.)

  2. Do the same for all of the quantified expressions in the first part of Exercise 5.2 above.

III. Translate the following into quantificational notation.

  1. All men are mortal.

  2. No men are immortal.

  3. No men are gods.

  4. Sons are male.

  5. Each octagon has eight sides.

  6. Given an event, one can find its cause.

  7. Whatever number you choose between zero and one, you can find a smaller number.

  8. Any natural born citizen, thirty-five years old or more, who has lived in the United States fourteen or more years, can be elected president.

  9. Something is colored.

  10. Some stars are colored.

  11. Some stars are not colored.

12. At least one planet has no moons.

13. There are no prime squares.

14. There exist numbers x and y such that x is the square root of y.

15. Only plane triangles have an angular sum of 180°.

16. Some numbers are factorable only if one is a factor.

17. There are non-washable fabrics.

18. There is something eternal.

19. Nothing is eternal.

20. Everything is identical with itself.

21. Nothing is identical with itself.

22. Everything is identical with nothing.

23. Nothing is identical with everything.

24. Nothing is identical with nothing.

25. Everything is identical with everything.

26. Anything is identical with nothing.

27. Anything is identical with everything.

28. Anything is identical with anything.

29. Nothing is identical with anything.

30. Everything is identical with anything.

IV. Translate the following into idiomatic English, supplying interpretations of predicate symbols where necessary.

1. $\prod_x$[Male (x) **v** Female (x)]

2. $\prod_x$[Gr$(x,3)$ $\supset$ Gr$(x,2)$]

3. $\sum_x$[Prime (x) & Gr$(x,5)$]

4. $\sum_x$[Sq$(x,3)$]

5. $\prod_x[\sum_y$Hus(y,x) $\supset$ Fml(x)]

6. $\sim\sum_x$[Sq$(3,x)$]

7. $\prod_x$[Prime(x) & Gr$(x,2)$ $\supset$ $\sim$Even(x)]

8. $\prod_x\{$F(x) $\supset$ [G(x) $\supset$ T]$\}$

9. $\prod_x\{$[F(x) $\supset$ G(x)] $\supset$ T$\}$

10. $\prod_x$[F(x) $\supset$ G(x)] $\supset$ T

5.4 Formulas, Scopes, Bound and Free Variables

In analyzing the nature of deductions involving statements, we found it advisable to give a formal definition of a statement. But we delayed stating the definition until an intuitive background for it had been developed, so that it does not occur until Chapter Two, Section Five. The extension of our analysis of deductions to those involving individual variables introduces other kinds of expressions than statements, such as statement functions. These expressions must be incorporated in the definition of a *formula*, which follows.

As a means for talking about statements such as A, B, C, . . . we have used the schematic variables p, q, r, . . . , which may stand for any statement. Because we now need to refer to statement functions such as F(x), G(x), . . . F(y), G(y), . . . as well as F(x,y), G(x,y), . . . and still more complex instances, we shall need new schematic variables for this purpose. We introduce $\varphi(\alpha)$, $\psi(\alpha)$, . . . to stand for statement functions of one variable; $\varphi(\alpha,\beta)$, $\psi(\alpha,\beta)$, . . . to stand for statement functions of two variables; and so on. $\varphi(\alpha)$ may stand for F(x), F(y), G(z), H(x), or any one-place statement function regardless of the variable occurring in it. $\psi(\alpha, \beta)$ may stand for J(x,y), H(z,y), H(x,y), or any two-place statement function. It is well to observe also that F(x), G(z), etc., symbolize statement functions with one free* variable. They are called *monadic* statement functions. However, H(x,z), J(x,y), etc., are symbolizations of expressions involving two variables, and are called *dyadic* statement functions. Similarly, there exist *triadic, tetradic*, and in general *n-adic* statement functions. In each case, the F, G, H, J, etc., are referred to as monadic, dyadic, triadic, and in general *n*-adic *predicates*, since they translate such phrases as "— is red", "— is less than —", "— lies between — and —".

Each of α, β, γ, . . . refers to any of the variables x, y, z, ... In addition, φ, ψ, χ, . . . standing alone can refer to statements such as A, B, C, . . . , and $\prod_x$F(x), $\prod_x \sum_y$[F(y) $\supset$ H(x,y)], as well as to statement functions when it is not essential to take explicit account of variables.

We now express these ideas more formally in a definition of a formula.

Formula: (1) Statements are formulas.
  (2) Statement functions are formulas.
  (3) If φ is a formula, then $\sim\varphi$ is a formula.
  (4) If φ and ψ are formulas, then (φ & ψ), ($\varphi \supset \psi$), (φ v ψ), and ($\varphi \equiv \psi$) are formulas.
  (5) If $\varphi(\alpha)$ is a formula, then $\prod_\alpha[\varphi(\alpha)]$ and $\sum_\alpha[\varphi(\alpha)]$ are formulas.
  (6) The only formulas are given by (1)–(5).

Notice that the formulas following the universal and existential quantifiers appear in brackets. These brackets are to be regarded as a part of the quantifier-symbol itself: $\prod_\alpha[\square]$ and $\sum_\alpha[\square]$ are quantificational symbols. We often

---

* For a discussion of what it means to call a variable free, see pp. 154–155.

simplify notation by dropping these brackets in practice wherever no ambiguity would result. It is permissible to write $\sum_x E(x)$ instead of $\sum_x[E(x)]$. But we ought not to write $\sum_x E(x) \supset A(x)$ when we mean $\sum_x[E(x) \supset A(x)]$. The procedure just described corresponds precisely to what we have been doing already.

The following expressions are formulas, as we can see from (1)–(6) above:

$$A$$
$$A \lor B$$
$$A \lor F(x)$$
$$\sim[A \supset F(x)]$$
$$A \mathbin{\&} \sum_x[F(x)]$$
$$\sim\{A \mathbin{\&} \prod_x[\sim F(x)]\}$$
$$F(x) \equiv \sim\prod_y[G(y)]$$
$$\prod_x\{\sum_y[H(x,y)]\}$$

A second concept necessary for the analysis of deductions involving variables is that of the scope of the occurrence of a quantifier. The *scope* of the occurrence of a quantifier is defined as the formula occurring in the brackets that constitute the right-hand part of the occurrence of the quantifier. Thus, the scopes of $\prod_x$ in

(1) $\prod_x[A(x)]$

(2) $\prod_x[A(x) \mathbin{\&} B(x,y)] \lor C(z)$

(3) $\prod_x[\sim D(z) \supset T(x,z)]$

are

(1′) $A(x)$

(2′) $A(x) \mathbin{\&} B(x,y)$

(3′) $\sim D(z) \supset T(x,z)$

Similarly, the scope of the first occurrence of $\prod_x$ in

(4) $\prod_x[A(x) \supset B] \equiv \sim\prod_x[A(x)] \supset B$

is

$$A(x) \supset B$$

and the scope of the second occurrence of $\prod_x$ is the formula

$$A(x)$$

on the right.

Any occurrence of a variable within the scope of a quantifier having that variable as a subscript is called a *bound* occurrence. All other occurrences are *free*. For the sake of completeness, we say that the subscripts of a quantifier are bound. Thus, in (1) above, the x in $A(x)$ is bound—as is the x in $\prod_x$. In

(2) above, the x in [A(x) & B(x,y)] is bound, but the y is free. In (3) above, the x in [∼D(z) ⊃ T(x,z)] is bound, but the z is free. In (4) above, the x in the first A(x) is bound by the first occurrence of the quantifier $\prod_x$, whereas in its second occurrence it is bound by the second occurrence of the quantifier $\prod_x$.

A literal formulation of bound variables can be given by drawing binding lines.

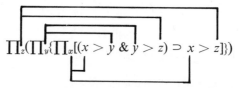

Here each solid line connects the quantifier to the variables which are bound by it, and in this case all variables are bound. But consider

$$\Sigma_x[\prod_y(y > x \,\&\, z > y)]$$

Here z is free while x and y are bound by the quantifiers Σ_x and $\prod_y$ respectively, which govern them.

Returning our attention to the two kinds of variables we have been discussing—those that represent unspecified objects and those that range over certain values—we note that the former are free while the latter are bound. Statement functions may contain either free or bound variables, depending on whether they are quantified and how. If all the variables are bound, however, the expression in question is a statement rather than a statement function.

With these technical terms at our command, we may proceed to consider the more difficult problems of the nature of the rules of inference required in dealing with statement functions and universally or existentially quantified statement functions.

EXERCISE 5.4

  I. Decide which of the following are formulas, and which are not.

    1. p

    2. F

    3. F v G(x)

    4. F & (x)

    5. G(x)

    6. $\prod_x(x)$

    7. $\prod_x$F

  8. $\prod_x \supset F(x)$

  9. $\prod_x \sum_y [F(x) \supset G(y)]$

10. $\prod_x \sum_x [F(x) \supset G(x)]$

11. $\prod_x \sum_y [F(x) \supset G(z)]$

12. $\prod_x \& \sum_x [F(x)]$

13. $\prod_x [G(x) \supset \sum_x F(x)]$

14. $\prod_x \{F(y) \supset \sum_x [F(x) \& G(x)]\}$

15. $\prod_x F(x) \supset \sum_x [F(x) \& G(x)]$

II. (1) Decide which of the variables in the first part of this exercise are bound, and which are free.

   (2) Do the same for each of the variables in the following formulas.

    1. $F(x)$

    2. $\sum_x F(x) \lor A$

    3. $\prod_x F(x) \lor G(x)$

    4. $\prod_x F(x)$

    5. $\prod_x F(x) \supset G(x)$

    6. $\sum_x [F(x) \& G(x)]$

    7. $\prod_x F(x) \equiv \sum_y F(x,y)$

    8. $\prod_x F(x) \& \sum_y [G(y) \& F(x)]$

    9. $\prod_x \{F(x) \supset \sum_y [G(y) \& F(x)]\}$

  10. $\sum_x F(x) \supset \sum_x [G(x) \& F(x)]$

  11. $\prod_x \sum_y \{[F(x) \supset G(y)] \& [G(y) \supset F(x)]\}$

  12. $\sum_x \{F(x) \& G(y) \& \prod_y [G(x) \supset F(y)]\}$

  13. $\prod_x ([F(x) \& G(x)] \supset \{\sum_y [H(y) \& G(y)] \supset [F(y) \& H(x)]\})$

  14. $\prod_x \prod_y \prod_z \{[F(x,y) \& F(y,z)] \supset [F(x,z) \& \sim F(z,x)]\}$

  15. $\prod_x \prod_y \prod_z [F(x,y) \& F(y,z)] \supset [F(x,z) \& \sim F(z,x)]$

III. Delineate the scopes in the following formulas.

    1. $\prod_x [B(x) \& A(x)] \supset \{\sum_y [D(y) \& C(y)] \supset E(x)\}$

    2. $\{\sum_x F(x) \supset \sum_x [F(x) \lor G(x)]\} \& \{\sum_x G(x) \supset \sum_x [F(x) \lor G(x)]\}$

    3. $\prod_x A$

    4. $\sum_x [A \lor H(x)]$

    5. $\sum_x \prod_y \sum_z [H(y,z) \lor H(x,z) \lor H(x,y)]$

    6. $\prod_x [F(x) \supset \sum_y Q(x,y)]$

7. $\prod_x\{A(x) \supset \prod_y[B(y) \supset C(y,x)]\}$

8. $\prod_x\{A(x) \supset [B(d,j,x) \supset C(d,j,x)]\}$

IV. Which variables in the following formulas are bound? Which are free?

1. $\prod_x\prod_y\prod_z\{[F(x,y) \ \& \ F(y,z)] \supset F(x,z)\}$

2. $\prod_x\prod_y\{[F(x,y) \ \& \ F(y,z)] \supset F(x,z)\}$

3. $\prod_x[F(x,y) \ \& \ F(y,z)] \supset F(x,z)$

4. $\prod_z[F(x,y) \ \& \ F(y,u)] \supset F(x,u)$

5. $\sum_x\{A(x) \ \& \ B(x) \ \& \ \prod_y[H(x,y) \supset A(y)]\}$

6. $\sum_x\{A(y) \ \& \ B(y) \ \& \ \prod_y[H(x,y) \supset A(y)]\}$

V. Which of the following predicates are monadic? Dyadic? Triadic?

$Q(x)$	$V(x,x,x)$
$R(x,x)$	$W(x,y,z)$
$S(x,y)$	$N(x,x,y,z)$
$T(x,y,x)$	____ is equal to ____
$U(x,y,y)$	x times y is equal to z

5.5 Statement Functions and Propositional Rules of Inference

In Chapter Two we stated some conditions for correct deductions. We observed that a line in a deduction must be either

(A) A premise,

(B) Any arbitrary assumption, discharged at a succeeding line,

(C) A line inferred by a rule from a preceding line not in the scope of a discharged assumption, or

(D) A zero-premise conclusion.

Implicitly, however, we were presupposing that every line must be a statement and that rules of inference applied to statements only. In Section One of this chapter we applied the rule of MT to statement functions as if they were statements. Our question now is whether we were justified in doing this, and whether we would be justified in extending the use of the rules of PL to lines in deductions including statement functions.

The rules of PL apply to statements. In consequence, they apply to the statements

$$P(1)$$

where P means

____ is a prime

and

$$\sim D(1,2)$$

where D means

____ is divisible by ____.

Thus we may argue

    —— **1.** $P(1) \supset \sim D(1,2)$
    —— **2.** $P(1)$
        3. $\sim D(1,2)$ 1, 2, $\supset$E

If we consider the case of statement functions, we see that they introduce no complications. We write

    —— **1.** $P(x) \supset \sim D(x,y)$
    —— **2.** $P(x)$
        3. $\sim D(x,y)$ 1, 2, $\supset$E

The free variables in these lines stand as place-holders for individual substituents. If we replace the variable by any such substituent, the statement function becomes a statement in every case, and the statement function may be dealt with by the rule $\supset$E.

A similar analysis applies to any statement function and any rule of PL. Thus we may extend the rules of PL to include lines in a deduction containing free variables, that is, containing statement functions. One consequence of this extension is the inference of statement functions from statements:

    —— **1.** A
        2. A ∨ $F(x,y)$ 1, ∨I,

and the inference of statements from statement functions:

    —— **1.** $P(1)$ & $\sim D(x,y)$
        2. $P(1)$ 1, &E

This analysis does not require a reformulation of the conditions of a deduction, but it does demand that we reinterpret such words as "premise", "assumption", and "conclusion" to include a reference to the occurrence of free variables in statement functions and the word "rule" to include the extension to such functions. This is easy enough. More difficult, as we shall see, is the analysis required by the occurrence of bound variables in statements.

EXERCISE 5.5

Prove each of the following:

1. $[\sim M(x) \vee \sim N(x)] \supset \sim[M(x) \& N(x)]$
2. $[B \& Q(x)] \equiv [Q(x) \& B]$
3. $\{[R(x) \supset S(x)] \supset R(x)\} \supset R(x)$
4. $T(x) \vee \sim T(x)$
5. $\{[K(x) \supset Q(x,y)] \& [L(x) \supset \sim Q(x,y)] \& [K(x) \supset L(x)] \& K(x)\} \supset W(z)$
6. $[(p \supset q) \& p] \supset [q \vee \varphi(\alpha)]$
7. $\{[H(x) \equiv I(x)] \equiv \sim I(x)\} \equiv \sim H(x)$
8. $\{[A \vee G(x)] \& \sim G(x)\} \supset A$

5.6   Rules of Inference for Monadic Predicate Logic

As long as quantified expressions (in which variables are bound) are treated as unanalyzed units, they occur in deductions as statements and require no attention beyond that accorded any other statement. We argue

> 1. $\prod_x[H(x) \supset G(x)]$
> 2. $\prod_x[H(x) \supset G(x)] \vee A$ 1, ∨I
>
> 3. $\prod_x[H(x) \supset G(x)] \supset \{\prod_x[H(x) \supset G(x)] \vee A\}$ 1–2, ⊃I

and so on.

As in Section One, however, we often reason from universally quantified expressions to instances of them. Thus, to take another example, we argue

> 1. $\prod_y[\prod_x(x < y \supset y \not< x)]$
> 2. $_x\prod(x < 2 \supset 2 \not< x)$
> 3. $0 < 2 \supset 2 \not< 0$

In each step after line 1 above we instantiate the preceding line; that is, we select one of the values for which the universal statement holds and replace the variable by it. Certainly, if the statement is true for all values of the variable, it will be true for (any) one of them.

Since we could have replaced y in line 1 by any other value of the variable, it is correct to replace it by a free variable, which serves as a place-holder for these values. Similarly, we could have replaced x in line 2 by a free variable. On this basis, we argue

> 1. $\prod_y[\prod_x(x < y \supset y \not< x)]$
> 2. $\prod_x(x < w \supset w \not< x)$
> 3. $(u < w) \supset (w \not< u)$

THE RULE OF $\prod$E

The rule to which we have implicitly appealed is often called *the Rule of Universal Instantiation* for the reasons just reviewed. It can also be viewed as a rule that eliminates $\prod$, as the successive lines of the deduction testify; and in keeping with the names of the rules of PL we shall call it *Universal Quantifier Elimination*, symbolized by $\prod$E.

In order to introduce the simplest form of this rule and of the three others needed for elimination and introduction of quantifiers, we restrict our discussion for the balance of this chapter to *monadic formulas*; that is, formulas in which the only statement functions are monadic (see p. 153). We state the schema of such inferences as

$$\prod_\alpha \varphi(\alpha)$$
$$\therefore \; \varphi(\beta)$$

In using this schema, however, we must observe certain precautions in order to avoid error. The introduction of β for α in φ usually produces no difficulties; occasionally, however, this introduction of a different variable may result in the accidental binding of a variable that should be free. For example, let E(x) mean x is even and O(x) mean x is odd; then the following is a justifiable inference:

$$\text{———} \quad \textbf{1.} \ \prod_x \sum_y [E(x) \equiv O(y)]$$
$$\textbf{2.} \ \sum_y [E(x) \equiv O(y)]$$

We might also have inferred

$$\textbf{2'.} \ \sum_y [E(z) \equiv O(y)]$$

or

$$\textbf{2''.} \ \sum_y [E(u) \equiv O(y)]$$

but *not*

$$\textbf{2'''.} \ \sum_y [E(y) \equiv O(y)] \qquad \text{error}$$

We may see that this is in error if we treat line 1 as "Given any number x, there is at least one number y such that x is even if and only if y is odd". Line 2''' is definitely false, since there is no number that is even if and only if it is odd. In line 2''' we have inadvertently bound a variable that was free in the corresponding statement function in line 1. When this kind of thing happens, we speak of a *confusion of bound variables.** It is necessary that such confusion be avoided, if error in inference is to be avoided. Hence, in stating the rule we add a restriction that has this function.

$\prod$E: $\quad \prod_\alpha \varphi(\alpha)$
$\quad \therefore \ \varphi(\beta)$

      Where $\varphi(\beta)$ is like $\varphi(\alpha)$ except for containing free occurrences of β wherever $\varphi(\alpha)$ contains free occurrences of α.

This restriction ensures that the inadvertent and erroneous binding of β does not occur.

    It is this rule that justifies the inferences that we have been discussing, and we note its use in a deduction by mentioning it to the right of the step in question; for example,

$$\text{———} \quad \textbf{1.} \ \prod_x M(x)$$
$$\textbf{2.} \ M(u) \qquad\qquad 1, \prod E$$

Notice that given a universally quantified premise we use $\prod$E to infer a conclusion concerning a definite individual if we wish—we are not required to infer a statement function, since we may replace the individual variables with the names of individuals. Given "All U.S. Presidents have been male", for instance, which we can symbolize

$$\prod_x [P(x) \supset M(x)],$$

we can use $\prod$E to deduce not only

$$P(u) \supset M(u),$$

---

* Another phrase sometimes used is *collision of variables.*

for an unspecified u, but also

$$P(\text{Coolidge}) \supset M(\text{Coolidge}).$$

THE RULE OF $\sum$I

Another example of a rule of inference involving variables, which may be formulated and understood readily, is implicit in the following argument.

Every natural number of the form $n^2 - n + 41$ (where $n < 41$) is prime. At least one number is of this form. Thus at least one number is prime.

Symbolically this argument is

$$
\begin{array}{ll}
\text{\underline{\hspace{1em}}} \text{1. } \prod_x[F(x) \supset P(x)] & \\
\text{\underline{\hspace{1em}}} \text{2. } \sum_x F(x) & \\
\text{3. } F(u) & 2, ? \\
\text{4. } F(u) \supset P(u) & 1, \prod E \\
\text{5. } P(u) & 4, 3, \supset E \\
\text{6. } \sum_x P(x) & 5, ? \\
\end{array}
$$

For the moment we disregard the problem of justifying line 3, although it is evident that the rule used will be called *Existential Quantifier Elimination* and abbreviated $\sum$E. What concerns us at the moment is the rule justifying line 6, which is called *Existential Quantifier Introduction*, abbreviated $\sum$I.

That the inference from line 5 to line 6 is acceptable is clear if we observe that $P(u)$ is a monadic predicate containing a free variable; that is, a variable that refers to an unspecified object. Thus $P(u)$ is true of at least one individual; but this is what we mean when we bind the variable in $P(x)$ with an existential quantifier, saying $\sum_x P(x)$. We state the schema of such inferences as

$$\varphi(\beta)$$
$$\therefore \sum_\alpha \varphi(\alpha)$$

As in the case of $\prod$E, the use of this schema requires precautions to avoid error due to confusion of variables. The introduction of α for β may result in errors. For example, we are justified in arguing

$$
\begin{array}{ll}
\text{\underline{\hspace{1em}}} \text{1. } E(x) \equiv O(y) & \\
\text{2. } \sum_z[E(z) \equiv O(y)] & 1, \sum I \\
\end{array}
$$

as well as in concluding

$$
\text{2'. } \sum_w[E(w) \equiv O(y)] \qquad 1, \sum I
$$

Nevertheless, we would be wrong to conclude

$$
\text{2''. } \sum_y[E(y) \equiv O(y)] \qquad \text{error}
$$

Here, as before, we inadvertently bind a variable that was free in line 1 and the result is a falsehood. Line 1, in which both x and y are free and so serve to represent unspecified objects, may be true, but line 2″, where y is bound, cannot be true. To avoid this sort of error we restrict the introduction of the existential quantifier in stating the rule.

$\sum$**I:** $\varphi(\beta)$

$\therefore \sum_\alpha \varphi(\alpha)$

Where $\varphi(\beta)$ is like $\varphi(\alpha)$ except for containing free occurrences of β wherever $\varphi(\alpha)$ contains free occurrences of α.

As in the case of $\prod$E, β may name a specific individual. Suppose T means "is over 25,000 feet tall". Then from

$$T(\text{Mount Everest})$$

we can use $\sum$I to infer

$$\sum_x T(x).$$

Heuristically, the reader may notice that $\prod$E is a sort of generalization of the propositional rule of &E, since it authorizes the move from a conjunction of many conjuncts to one of the conjuncts. Similarly, $\sum$I is a sort of generalization of **v**I.

THE RULE OF $\prod$I

We now turn to the first of the remaining two rules, both of which require careful formulation. The first is the rule of *Universal Quantifier Introduction*, which states the conditions under which free variables in a predicate may be bound by a universal quantifier. The rule of $\prod$I tells us when an inference from a statement function to a universal statement is permitted. One can see intuitively that such an inference is permitted when the free variables have no conditions imposed upon them.

We begin with an illustration of a tacit use of this rule from plane geometry. Euclid states and proves one of the theorems of his geometry somewhat as follows:

Proposition 13: If a straight line set upon a straight line makes angles, it will make either two right angles or angles equal to two right angles.

Proof:

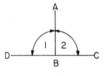

If angle 1 is equal to angle 2, each of them is a right angle. (Definition 10 of Euclid's *Elements*.)

If not, then from the point B, draw BE at right angles to CD. (This is possible by Proposition 11 of Euclid's *Elements*.) Thus angles 3 and 4 are right angles.

Now, angle 4 = angle 2 + angle 5.

Therefore, angle 4 + angle 3 = angle 2 + angle 5 + angle 3.
(This follows by Euclid's axiom 3—that equals added to equals are equal.)

Also, angle 1 = angle 3 + angle 5.

Therefore, angle 1 + angle 2 = angle 3 + angle 5 + angle 2.

So, angle 1 + angle 2 = angle 3 + angle 4.
(This follows by Euclid's axiom 1—that things equal to the same thing are equal.)

But, angle 3 and angle 4 are right angles; therefore, angles 1 and 2 together are equal to two right angles.

This proof is discussed as a whole in Chapter Eight. Here we note only that the theorem is a general statement holding for all angles, while the proof is carried out in terms of two diagrams which are particular and refer to specific angles. Thus the argument is from the specific to the general. This is possible in this case because, although the argument is carried out in terms of a particular set of angles, *it could have been carried out for any other set of angles just as well.*

Let us consider a more explicit example of the use of this rule. We begin with an argument in English that does not use this rule, in order to contrast it with one that does.

Any number, the sum of whose digits is divisible by 9, is itself divisible by 9.

The sum of the digits of 5,437,629 is divisible by 9. Hence 5,437,629 is divisible by 9.

Using symbols adopted earlier, we formalize the argument in the following way:

$$\text{1. } \textstyle\prod_x [S(x) \supset N(x)]$$

2. $S(5,437,629) \supset N(5,437,629)$ 1, $\prod$E

—— 3. $S(5,437,629)$

4. $N(5,437,629)$ 2, 3, $\supset$E

We now contrast this argument with the following one, which introduces a universal quantifier:

Any number, the sum of whose digits is divisible by 9, is itself divisible by 9.

Any number divisible by 9 is divisible by 3.

Therefore any number, the sum of whose digits is divisible by 9, is divisible by 3.

Using $T(x)$ to mean x is divisible by 3, we can write

—— 1. $\prod_x [S(x) \supset N(x)]$

—— 2. $\prod_x [N(x) \supset T(x)]$ $/\therefore \prod_x [S(x) \supset T(x)]$

In order to exhibit this argument as a justified deduction, we must use the rule of $\prod$E. Let us use $\prod$E to infer not that $S(1) \supset N(1)$ or that $S(5{,}437{,}629) \supset N(5{,}437{,}629)$ but that $S(u) \supset N(u)$, where u is any arbitrary number. We shall then obtain

$$
\begin{array}{lll}
\rule{1em}{0.4pt}\;\textbf{1.} & \prod_x[S(x) \supset N(x)] & \\
\textbf{2.} & S(u) \supset N(u) & 1,\ \prod\text{E} \\
\rule{1em}{0.4pt}\;\textbf{3.} & \prod_x[N(x) \supset T(x)] & \\
\textbf{4.} & N(u) \supset T(u) & 3,\ \prod\text{E} \\
\textbf{5.} & S(u) \supset T(u) & 2,\ 4,\ \text{HS}
\end{array}
$$

The fifth line, of course, is not yet the desired conclusion. To derive $\prod_x[S(x) \supset T(x)]$ from line 5, we need a further rule of inference. This is the rule that was exemplified in Proposition 13 of Euclid's geometry. We argued that if a statement is true of a diagram, but its truth does not depend upon any of the peculiarities of the diagram, then the statement will be true of any diagram that is essentially the same. (What we mean by "peculiarities" and "essentially" here will, of course, depend upon the type of problem we are trying to solve.) Similarly, if a statement is true of the number u, but its truth does not depend upon any of the peculiarities of this number (like its oddness or evenness, or the fact that it lies between 10^7 and 10^8), then the statement will be true of any number. This is the principle that we previously called universal quantifier introduction or $\prod$I. This rule enables us to reach the conclusion in the present argument:

$$
\textbf{6.}\quad \prod_x[S(x) \supset T(x)] \qquad 5,\ \prod\text{I}
$$

As these examples show, the use of the rule of $\prod$I requires that the free variables universalized shall be perfectly arbitrary. Our task is to state the rule in a form that will ensure that this requirement is met. We must analyze the nature of possible lines in a deduction to see where and how it might *not* be met.

For purposes of exposition, let us begin this analysis by restricting the nature of the lines in a deduction to a point at which we know that the requirements will be met. Thus our materials of proof are, for the moment, described by the following modifications of the list A–D:

(A″) Premises must be statements without individual variables, or universally quantified statement functions.

(B″) Arbitrary assumptions must be statements without individual variables, or universally quantified statement functions.

(C″) A line can be inferred only by a rule of PL or by $\prod$E or $\prod$I from preceding lines that are not in the scope of a discharged assumption.

(D″) No ZPC containing individual variables will be allowed.

These restrictions allow us deductions such as

———— 1. $\prod_x[G(x) \supset H(x)]$
———— 2. $\prod_x[H(x) \supset F(x)]$
     3. $G(u) \supset H(u)$ 1, $\prod$E
     4. $H(u) \supset F(u)$ 2, $\prod$E
     5. $G(u) \supset F(u)$ 3, 4, HS
     6. $\prod_x[G(x) \supset F(x)]$ 5, $\prod$I

In these cases, since we know that the free variable u is obtained in a deduction in every case by $\prod$E, we know that it is perfectly arbitrary and that it may be universally quantified without error.

Suppose next we relax our restrictions in (B″) *only* to

(B′) Arbitrary assumptions must be statements without individual variables, statement functions or universally quantified statement functions.

Because arbitrary assumptions (by definition) are all eventually discharged in a deduction, we must be sure that the lines discharging them (resulting from the use of the rules of $\supset$ I, **v**E, and $\sim$I) do not introduce free variables that are not perfectly arbitrary. If any free variables with conditions imposed on them were introduced, they would have to come from the arbitrary assumption of a statement function in which these variables first appeared. We can avoid error if we *never use $\prod$I on a free variable introduced in an arbitrary assumption.*

Let us illustrate this point.

———— 1. $R(u)$
———— 2. $S(u)$
     3. $R(u) \,\&\, S(u)$ 1, 2, &I
     4. $\prod_x[R(x) \,\&\, S(x)]$ 3, erroneous $\prod$ introduction

If we interpret $R(u)$ as u is rigid and $S(u)$ as u is square we see the difficulty in line 4. Clearly in lines 1 and 2, u, as a free variable, represents an unspecified object, and so is not arbitrary. Thus universalization is not permissible.

Finally, if we relax our restrictions in (B′) to include assumptions of the form $\sum_\alpha \varphi(\alpha)$ we have a general formulation

(B) Any arbitrary assumptions (statements without individual variables, statement functions, or universally or existentially quantified statement functions) are permissible.

This relaxation will not, of itself, occasion errors in the use of $\prod$I, since it does not introduce any free variables on which $\prod$I might be used.

We may now relax our restrictions in (A″) also to

(A′) Premises must be statements without individual variables, *statement functions*, or universally quantified functions.

Since this makes the introduction of free variables subject to imposed conditions possible in a premise, we avoid error *by not using the rule of* $\prod$I *on any free variable introduced in a premise.* Having agreed to this, however, we may relax our restrictions on (A′) to a general formulation

> (A) Any premises (statements without individual variables, statement functions, universally or existentially quantified statement functions) are permissible.

The occurrence of a statement of the form $\sum_{\alpha}\varphi(\alpha)$ as a premise does not introduce any free variables that can give trouble.

We may now relax our restriction on (D″) to

> (D) A ZPC containing variables may be a line in a deduction.

Since all ZPC's are arrived at *under the agreement not to use* $\prod$I *on free variables in premises and assumptions,* their introduction in a line of a proof will not be in error. Finally, we may relax the restriction of (C″) to

> (C′) A line may be inferred from a preceding line by a rule of PL, $\prod$E, $\prod$I, or $\sum$I.

The use of $\sum$I will not introduce free variables with conditions imposed, since it is used only to bind variables.

We now have a formulation of the nature of a deduction which does not yet take into account the use of the rule of $\sum$E (which has not so far been discussed). This rule requires special consideration in its own right, but we may observe here that it is a rule that introduces free variables. Thus it permits an inference beginning like

$$\text{———}1.\ \sum_{x}F(x)$$
$$\Gamma\text{———}2.\ F(u)$$

Here the $F(u)$ contains a free u, and the unknown to which u refers is not arbitrary, for it has the condition that it must be the individual (or possibly one of the several individuals) that makes $F(u)$ true.

In view of the rule of $\prod$I, then, we see that the use of the rule of $\sum$E will produce complications. In fact, we see that the rule of $\prod$I must never be used on a free variable that has been introduced by $\sum$E, for such a variable may have a condition upon it. Hence, we shall formulate $\sum$E in such a way as to introduce this variable only in an assumption. With this stipulation, however, we can relax the condition on (C′) to a general formulation

> (C) A line may be inferred from a preceding line by a rule of PL, $\prod$E, $\prod$I, $\sum$E, or $\sum$I.

The rule for $\prod$I is, then, the following:

$\prod$I: $\varphi(\beta)$
∴ $\prod_\alpha\varphi(\alpha)$

Where β does not occur free in any premise or undischarged assumption of the deduction, and where $\varphi(\beta)$ is like $\varphi(\alpha)$ except for containing free occurrences of β where, and only where, $\varphi(\alpha)$ contains free occurrences of α.

The qualification concerning $\varphi(\alpha)$ and $\varphi(\beta)$ is introduced to avoid the possibility of a "deduction" like the following:

1. $\prod_x[E(x) \supset E(x)]$ ZPC
2. $E(u) \supset E(u)$ 1, $\prod$E
3. $\prod_x[E(x) \supset E(u)]$ 2, $\prod$I (erroneous)
4. $\prod_y\prod_x[E(x) \supset E(y)]$ 3, $\prod$I

In line 2 we have permitted $\varphi(\beta)$ to include a free β in a place where no free occurrence of α occurs in the $\varphi(\alpha)$ of line 3. It is clear that line 4 is not ZPC, because, in general, if x is even, y need not be even.

THE RULE OF $\sum$E

We now have rules that permit us to introduce and eliminate the universal quantifier—that is, $\prod$I and $\prod$E—and a rule for introducing the existential quantifier, that is, $\sum$I. However, we have not completely discussed the rule for eliminating the existential quantifier.

Let us return to the deduction we used in illustrating the rule $\sum$I. It was

Every natural number of the form $n^2 - n + 41$ (where $n < 41$) is prime. At least one number is of this form. Thus at least one number is prime.

We symbolized the deduction as

1. $\prod_x[F(x) \supset P(x)]$
2. $\sum_xF(x)$
3. $F(u)$ 2, ?
4. $F(u) \supset P(u)$ 1, $\prod$E
5. $P(u)$ 4, 3, $\supset$E
6. $\sum_xP(x)$ 5, $\sum$I

In line 3 we choose the name of at least one individual guaranteed by $\sum_xF(x)$ in line 2. Clearly $\sum_xF(x)$ does guarantee that there is such an individual; *i.e.*, that at least one prime number has this form. On the other hand, $\sum_xF(x)$ does not tell us how this number exists. Thus when we write $F(u)$ we are choosing this number in principle rather than in fact, and u is not the actual name of an individual.

The first point to be emphasized in this choice is that in making it we impose conditions on the free variable. The u is not arbitrary, for it is restricted to the unspecified object, or those unspecified objects, having the property in question, F.

The second point to be emphasized in this choice is that the condition imposed on u of satisfying the property *prevents the use of a variable that has previously had a condition imposed upon it*—that is, of any free variable previously appearing in the deduction. We must, then, never use $\sum$E on a variable occurring free in an assumption or premise. To make the mistake of using a free variable, say w, previously occurring in the deduction would be to claim that the condition imposed on w and that imposed on u could be jointly met. That this cannot always be done is illustrated in the following example where F(x) is as above and E(x) means x is even:

$$\text{———1. } \sum_x E(x)$$
$$\text{———2. } \sum_x F(x)$$

3.	E(w)	1, $\sum$E
4.	F(w)	2, (error)

Clearly, since 2 is the only even prime, both conditions cannot be satisfied by the same number. Line 4 should read

$$\textbf{4}'. \ F(u)$$

The third point to be emphasized in this choice is that even though we write F(u), there is no way to be sure that the unspecified u that makes F true can actually be chosen. This point can be illustrated by recalling Euclid's proof that there is no greatest prime number. If, then, we say

There is a prime number greater than the largest known prime.

we have a true statement. Symbolically,

$$\sum_x [P(x) \ \& \ G(x)]$$

where P(x) means "x is a prime" and G(x) means "x is greater than the largest known prime". If we eliminate $\sum$ we have

$$\text{———1. } \sum_x [P(x) \ \& \ G(x)]$$
$$\text{2. } P(u) \ \& \ G(u)$$

But we have no way of actually choosing the unknown to which u refers.

The significance of this is that the rule of $\sum$E represents our claim to be able to make a choice in principle but *not* our claim to have chosen in fact. Hence, we must never leave a line justified by $\sum$E as a last line in a deduction, since this would leave the deduction up in the air. We must proceed from this line to some conclusion in which the variable u does not appear; that is, our conclusions must be based on the ability to make the choice in principle, but not the actual choice. Thus we proceed to a line in which the free variable introduced through $\sum$E is lacking. Hence, in the deduction with which our discussion of $\sum$E opened, having obtained F(u) in line 3, we proceed to deduce $\sum_x P(x)$ in line 6 on the assumption of F(u).

To take explicit account of this situation we rewrite deductions like the one above as follows:

$$\begin{array}{ll}
\text{1.} & \prod_x[F(x) \supset P(x)] \\
\text{2.} & \sum_x F(x) \\
\text{3.} & F(u) \\
\text{4.} & F(u) \supset P(u) \qquad\qquad 1, \prod E \\
\text{5.} & P(u) \qquad\qquad\qquad\quad 4, 3, \supset E \\
\text{6.} & \sum_x P(x) \qquad\qquad\quad\;\; 5, \sum I \\
\text{7.} & \sum_x P(x) \qquad\qquad\quad\;\; 2, 3\text{-}6, \sum E
\end{array}$$

This notation takes explicit account of the fact that we are not entitled to $F(u)$ until a deduction has been completed with a line in which u does not occur free. The rule of $\sum E$ discharges the $F(u)$, but it also requires—thus differing from the discharge of an assumption by means of $\supset I$—the $\sum_x F(x)$ of line 2.

We may now state the rule

$\sum E$: $\sum_\alpha \varphi(\alpha)$
$\quad\varphi(\beta)$
$\quad\;\vdots$
$\quad\;\psi$
$\quad\psi$

where there is no free β in ψ; where β does not occur free in any premise or previous undischarged assumption; and where $\varphi(\beta)$ is like $\varphi(\alpha)$ except for containing free occurrences of β where and only where $\varphi(\alpha)$ contains free occurrences of α.

The qualification concerning $\varphi(\alpha)$ and $\varphi(\beta)$ is introduced to forbid the ambiguous usage of variables that results in "deductions" like

$$\begin{array}{ll}
\text{1.} & \prod_x \sum_y [E(x) \equiv O(y)] \\
\text{2.} & \sum_y [E(u) \equiv O(y)] \qquad\quad 1, \prod E \\
\text{3.} & E(u) \equiv O(u) \\
\text{4.} & \sum_x [E(x) \equiv O(x)] \qquad\quad 3, \sum I \\
\text{5.} & \sum_x [E(x) \equiv O(x)] \qquad\quad 2, 3\text{-}4, \sum E \text{ (erroneous)}
\end{array}$$

In line 3 where we introduce $\varphi(\beta)$ we erroneously permit the free occurrence of β in a place where no free occurrence of α occurs in $\varphi(\alpha)$. This results in a conclusion which is not sound, as we see if we interpret E as even and O as odd.

Notice that when the rule is stated in this way, part of the danger involved in using $\prod I$ in a deduction in which $\sum E$ has already been used vanishes; there is clearly no inherent difficulty in the application of $\prod I$ once the assumption $\varphi(\beta)$ has been discharged. But it would be entirely wrong to use $\prod I$ within the scope of $\varphi(\beta)$, as the following erroneous deduction shows:

1. $\sum_x E(x)$
2. $E(u)$
3. $\prod_x E(x)$ 2, erroneous $\prod$ introduction
4. $\prod_x E(x)$ 1, 2–3, $\sum E$

The rules for quantifier introduction and elimination are grouped together in Table 5.1.

TABLE 5.1

INTRODUCTION	ELIMINATION
$\prod I$ $\varphi(\beta)$ $\therefore \prod_\alpha \varphi(\alpha)$ Where β does not occur free in any premise or undischarged assumption, and where $\varphi(\beta)$ is like $\varphi(\alpha)$ except for containing free occurrences of β where, and only where, $\varphi(\alpha)$ contains free occurrences of α.	$\prod E$ $\prod_\alpha \varphi(\alpha)$ $\therefore \varphi(\beta)$ Where $\varphi(\beta)$ is like $\varphi(\alpha)$ except for containing free occurrences of β wherever $\varphi(\alpha)$ contains free occurrences of α.
$\sum I$ $\varphi(\beta)$ $\therefore \sum_\alpha \varphi(\alpha)$ Where $\varphi(\beta)$ is like $\varphi(\alpha)$ except for containing free occurrences of β wherever $\varphi(\alpha)$ contains free occurrences of α.	$\sum E$ $\sum_\alpha \varphi(\alpha)$ $\varphi(\beta)$ $\vdots$ ψ $\therefore \psi$ Where there is no free β in ψ; where β does not occur free in any premise or undischarged assumption; and where $\varphi(\beta)$ is like $\varphi(\alpha)$ except for containing free occurrences of β where, and only where, $\varphi(\alpha)$ contains free occurrences of α.

EXERCISE 5.6

Which of the following inferences are erroneous?

1. $\sum_x[A(x) \ \& \ B(x)]$
   $\sum_x[A(x) \ \& \ C(x)]$
   ┌── $A(a) \ \& \ C(a)$
   │ ┌── $A(a) \ \& \ B(a)$
   │ │ $C(a)$
   │ │ $B(a)$
   │ │ $B(a) \ \& \ C(a)$
   │ └── $\sum_x[B(x) \ \& \ C(x)]$
   │ $\sum_x[B(x) \ \& \ C(x)]$
   └── $\sum_x[B(x) \ \& \ C(x)]$

2. $\prod_x\sum_y[F(x) \equiv \sim F(y)]$
   $\sum_y[F(w) \equiv \sim F(y)]$
   ┌── $F(w) \equiv \sim F(z)$
   │ $\prod_x[F(x) \equiv \sim F(z)]$
   └── $\sum_y\prod_x[F(x) \equiv \sim F(y)]$
       $\sum_y\prod_x[F(x) \equiv \sim F(y)]$

3. $\sum_x F(x)$
   $F(y)$
   $\prod_x F(x)$

4. $\sum_x[P(x) \ \& \ Q(x)]$
   $\sum_x[P(x) \ \& \ R(x)]$
   ┌── $P(a) \ \& \ Q(a)$
   │ ┌── $P(b) \ \& \ R(b)$
   │ │ $Q(a)$
   │ │ $R(b)$
   │ │ $Q(a) \ \& \ R(b)$
   │ └── $\sum_x[Q(x) \ \& \ R(b)]$
   │ $\sum_x[Q(x) \ \& \ R(b)]$
   └── $\sum_y\sum_x[Q(x) \ \& \ R(y)]$
       $\sum_y\sum_x[Q(x) \ \& \ R(y)]$

5. $\sum_x F(x) \ \& \ \sum_x G(x)$
   $\sum_x F(x)$
   ┌── $F(y)$
   │ $\sum_x G(x)$
   │ ┌── $G(y)$
   │ │ $F(y) \ \& \ G(y)$
   │ └── $\sum_x[F(x) \ \& \ G(x)]$
   └── $\sum_x[F(x) \ \& \ G(x)]$
       $\sum_x[F(x) \ \& \ G(x)]$

6. $\sum_x F(x)$
   $\sum_y \sim F(y)$
   ┌──── $F(w)$
   │ ┌── $\sim F(u)$
   │ │ $F(w)$ & $\sim F(u)$
   │ │ $\sum_z[F(z)$ & $\sim F(u)]$
   │ └─────────────────────
   │ $\sum_z[F(z)$ & $\sim F(u)]$
   │ $\sum_x\sum_z[F(z)$ & $\sim F(x)]$
   └──────────────────────────
         $\sum_x\sum_z[F(z)$ & $\sim F(x)]$

5.7 Deductions in Monadic Predicate Logic

In this section we shall discuss some deductions of a simple type in MPL. We begin with an argument cited in Section 5.3 (on p. 149).

1. $\prod_x\{[P(x)$ & $x > 2] \supset O(x)\}$

2. $\prod_x[O(x) \supset \sim E(x)]$ $/\therefore$ $\prod_x\{E(x) \supset [\sim P(x) \vee x \not> 2]\}$

This can be shown as a deduction as follows:

──**1.** $\prod_x\{[P(x)$ & $x > 2] \supset O(x)\}$	
2. $[P(u)$ & $u > 2] \supset O(u)$	1, $\prod$E
──**3.** $\prod_x[O(x) \supset \sim E(x)]$	
4. $O(u) \supset \sim E(u)$	3, $\prod$E
5. $[P(u)$ & $u > 2] \supset \sim E(u)$	2, 4, HS
┌─**6.** $E(u)$	
│ **7.** $\sim[P(u)$ & $u > 2]$	5, 6, MT
│ **8.** $\sim P(u) \vee u \not> 2$	7, DM
9. $E(u) \supset [\sim P(u) \vee u \not> 2]$	6–8, $\supset$I
10. $\prod_x\{E(x) \supset [\sim P(x) \vee x \not> 2]\}$	9, $\prod$I

It is possible to use $\supset$I to introduce a quantified assumption as well as one which, like $E(u)$ in step 6 above, lacks quantifiers. To illustrate this point, let us prove that from

> Every even number is divisible by 2

we can deduce

> If every number is even, then every number is divisible by 2.

The proof is:

──**1.** $\prod_x[E(x) \supset D(x)]$	
2. $E(u) \supset D(u)$	1, $\prod$E
┌─**3.** $\prod_x E(x)$	
│ **4.** $E(u)$	3, $\prod$E
│ **5.** $D(u)$	2, 4, $\supset$E
│ **6.** $\prod_x D(x)$	5, $\prod$I
7. $\prod_x E(x) \supset \prod_x D(x)$	3–6, $\supset$I

In a similar manner, it can be shown that "Every number is even or every number is odd" entails "Every number is either even or odd". (The reader should be sure that he notes the difference between the premise and the conclusion here.)

1.	$\prod_x E(x) \vee \prod_x O(x)$	
2.	$\prod_x E(x)$	
3.	$E(u)$	2, $\prod$E
4.	$E(u) \vee O(u)$	3, vI
5.	$\prod_x O(x)$	
6.	$O(u)$	5, $\prod$E
7.	$E(u) \vee O(u)$	6, vI
8.	$E(u) \vee O(u)$	1, 2–7, vE
9.	$\prod_x [E(x) \vee O(x)]$	8, $\prod$I

Let us now turn to cases in which the existential quantifier occurs. Suppose we argue

No prime number is a perfect square.

At least one prime number is even.

Therefore, at least one even number is not a perfect square.

The premises can be symbolized as

1.	$\prod_x [P(x) \supset \sim S(x)]$	
2.	$\sum_x [P(x) \mathbin{\&} E(x)]$	
3.	$P(u) \mathbin{\&} E(u)$	
4.	$P(u)$	3, &E
5.	$P(u) \supset \sim S(u)$	1, $\prod$E
6.	$\sim S(u)$	5, 4, $\supset$E
7.	$E(u)$	3, &E
8.	$E(u) \mathbin{\&} \sim S(u)$	7, 6, &I
9.	$\sum_x [E(x) \mathbin{\&} \sim S(x)]$	8, $\sum$I
10.	$\sum_x [E(x) \mathbin{\&} \sim S(x)]$	2, 3–9, $\sum$E

We have seen that $\prod$I cannot be used within the scope of $\sum$E. But $\sum$I can perfectly well be applied to expressions that result from $\prod$E. The simplest case of this sort is the proof that $\prod_x \varphi(x) \supset \sum_x \varphi(x)$:

1.	$\prod_x \varphi(x)$	
2.	$\varphi(u)$	1, $\prod$E
3.	$\sum_x \varphi(x)$	2, $\sum$I
4.	$\prod_x \varphi(x) \supset \sum_x \varphi(x)$	1–3, $\supset$I

Incidentally, step 4 contains the first quantificational ZPC that we have had occasion to write down. A number of others will be proved later.

Let us conclude with an illustrative argument in which we can bring together many of the techniques of deduction introduced in this section:

> All parallelograms are trapezoids, but some trapezoids are not parallelograms. Rectangles exist. All rectangles are parallelograms. Hence some trapezoids are rectangles, but some trapezoids are not rectangles.

Using obvious abbreviations, we obtain

— 1. $\prod_x[P(x) \supset T(x)]$ & $\sum_x[T(x)$ & $\sim P(x)]$
— 2. $\sum_x R(x)$
— 3. $\prod_x[R(x) \supset P(x)]$ /∴ $\sum_x[T(x)$ & $R(x)]$ & $\sum_x[T(x)$ & $\sim R(x)]$

4. $R(u)$		
5. $R(u) \supset P(u)$	3, $\prod$E	
6. $P(u)$	5, 4, $\supset$E	
7. $\prod_x[P(x) \supset T(x)]$	1, &E	
8. $P(u) \supset T(u)$	7, $\prod$E	
9. $T(u)$	8, 6, $\supset$E	
10. $T(u)$ & $R(u)$	9, 4, &I	
11. $\sum_x[T(x)$ & $R(x)]$	10, $\sum$I	
12. $\sum_x[T(x)$ & $R(x)]$	2, 4–11, $\sum$E	
13. $\sum_x[T(x)$ & $\sim P(x)]$	1, &E	
14. $T(u)$ & $\sim P(u)$		
15. $\sim P(u)$	14, &E	
16. $R(u) \supset P(u)$	3, $\prod$E	
17. $\sim R(u)$	16, 15, MT	
18. $T(u)$	14, &E	
19. $T(u)$ & $\sim R(u)$	18, 17, &I	
20. $\sum_x[T(x)$ & $\sim R(x)]$	19, $\sum$I	
21. $\sum_x[T(x)$ & $\sim R(x)]$	13, 14–20, $\sum$E	
22. $\sum_x[T(x)$ & $R(x)]$ & $\sum_x[T(x)$ & $\sim R(x)]$	12, 21, &I	

EXERCISE 5.7

I. Justify each of the following inferences by providing and justifying each of the steps required to deduce the conclusion from the premises. When translating (symbolizing), use the suggested symbols.

1. I am not a monkey's uncle. If the pooka exists, then I am a monkey's uncle. Therefore, there is no pooka. [U(x), P(x), i]

2. Some swans are white; so it is false that nothing is white. [S(x), W(x)]

3. There are no unicorns. Therefore, all unicorns have three horns. [U(x), T(x)]

4. Anything is dead if and only if it is not alive. Thus, vinegar is a salt if something is both dead and alive. [D(x), A(x), V(x), S(x)]

5. All drugs are impure, and all poisons are noxious. So all drugs are noxious if all impurities are poisons. [D(x), I(x), P(x), N(x)]

6. Some integers are odd. Nothing is both odd and even. Thus, it is not the case that all integers are even. [I(x), O(x), E(x)]

7. Some intelligent women exist; so it is therefore not the case that no women are intelligent. [I(x), W(x)]

8. All irrational numbers are real numbers. Therefore, if some irrational number is the square root of two, then some real number is the square root of two. [I(x), N(x), R(x), S(x)]

9. All isosceles triangles have two equal sides. All triangles with two equal sides are isosceles. Therefore, any triangle is isosceles if and only if it has two equal sides. [I(x), T(x), E(x)]

10. Any number either is periodic or terminates (in decimal form) if it is rational. If a number is the square root of two, then it is neither periodic nor does it terminate. Thus, if it is a number, the square root of two is not rational. [N(x), P(x), T(x), R(x), S(x)]

11. No integer is both odd and even. Therefore, an entity is an odd integer only if it is not an even integer. [I(x), O(x), E(x)]

12. No integer is both odd and even. Any integer which is not odd must be even. Therefore, anything is an odd integer if and only if it is an integer which is not even. [I(x), O(x), E(x)]

13. There are no intelligent machines. The ideal machine is an intelligent machine. So the ideal machine does not exist. [I(x), M(x), D(x)]

14. A number is rational if and only if it can be expressed as the quotient of two integers. Every integer can be expressed as such a quotient. Thus no number which is not rational is an integer. [N(x), R(x), O(x), I(x)]

15. Either all cartographers are myopic or no observers are truthful. Thus, if some observers are cartographers, then some cartographers are either myopic or untruthful. [C(x), M(x), O(x), T(x)]

16. If it is rational, any number is either periodic or terminating (in decimal form); but if it is irrational (not rational), it is neither periodic nor terminating. Therefore, any number is rational if and only if it is either periodic or terminating. [N(x), R(x), P(x), T(x)]

17. Only rectangles are square, and all rectangles are plane figures. But some rectangles are not squares. Thus some plane figures are not squares. [R(x), S(x), F(x)]

18. All preachers believe in God. No one who believes in God is an atheist. All Marxists are atheists. Hence, any Marxist preacher is the Devil in disguise. [P(x), B(x), A(x), M(x), D(x)]

19. If some conceited person is a fraud, then no beautiful persons are conceited. All beautiful persons must be attractive, and all attractive persons are conceited. Therefore, if some fraud is an attractive person, then there are no beautiful persons. [C(x), P(x), F(x), B(x), A(x)]

20. Either all gases have expanded, or some gases have been cooled. No gases which have been heated have been cooled. Therefore, if some gases have not expanded, then some gases were not heated. [G(x), E(x), C(x), H(x)]

21. All Franklin stoves are pot-bellied, but not all pot-bellied stoves are Franklin stoves. Consequently, it is not the case that a stove is pot-bellied if and only if it is a Franklin stove. [F(x), S(x), P(x)]

22. No angle is both acute and obtuse. It is not the case that every angle is acute if and only if it is not obtuse. So some angles must be neither acute nor obtuse. [L(x), A(x), O(x)]

23. Some angles are neither acute nor obtuse. Therefore, it is not the case that every angle is acute if and only if it is obtuse. [L(x), A(x), O(x)]

24. If any food is not tasty then some negligent cook is guilty. All cooks are people, and all negligent people are guilty. No unsalted food is tasty. Thus, if there are no guilty people, then all food is salted. [F(x), T(x), N(x), C(x), G(x), P(x), S(x)]

II. Construct deductions for the following arguments. Use your own symbols.

1. Complexes are composed of parts, and everything that exists is complex. Now this book exists and is a unity, so at least one unity is composed of parts.

2. But if complexes are composed of parts, and if everything that exists is complex, it follows that all unities that exist are complex; and since nothing can be a unity and not exist, all unities are complex and are composed of parts.

3. Every exhibit in a museum of art is an art object, and all art is beautiful. But some paintings that are ugly are exhibited in museums of art. Thus, either it is not the case that all art is beautiful, or every exhibit in a museum of art is not an art object.

4. In 1895, the Supreme Court argued that taxes on income from property were tantamount to property taxes and, since property taxes were direct taxes, and since according to Article I, sec. 2, par. 3, of the Constitution, direct taxes had to be apportioned to the states in proportion to the population of each state, an income tax on income from property was unconstitutional because income does not vary proportionately with population; and since an income tax *per se* is a tax on income from property, income taxes were unconstitutional.

5. Anything that contradicts a law of nature is incredible, for, since laws of nature are universally true, anything that contradicts a law of nature must be false, and that which must be false is incredible. But there are events related in the Bible that both are believed and contradict laws of nature. Thus, some events which are believed are incredible. But what is incredible cannot be believed; so some things are believed which cannot be believed, and since that which cannot be believed is not believed, some things are both believed and not believed together.

III. Construct deductions for the following arguments.

1. $\prod_x[M(x) \supset P(x)]$, $\prod_x[S(x) \supset M(x)]$
   /∴ $\prod_x[S(x) \supset P(x)]$ Barbara

2. $\prod_x[M(x) \supset \sim P(x)]$, $\prod_x[S(x) \supset M(x)]$
   /∴ $\prod_x[S(x) \supset \sim P(x)]$ Celarent

3. $\prod_x[P(x) \supset \sim M(x)]$, $\prod_x[S(x) \supset M(x)]$
   /∴ $\prod_x[S(x) \supset \sim P(x)]$ Cesare

4. $\prod_x[P(x) \supset M(x)]$, $\prod_x[M(x) \supset \sim M(x)]$
   /∴ $\prod_x[S(x) \supset \sim P(x)]$ Camestres

5. $\prod_x[P(x) \supset M(x)]$, $\prod_x[M(x) \supset \sim S(x)]$
   /∴ $\prod_x[S(x) \supset \sim P(x)]$ Camenes

6. $\prod_x[M(x) \supset P(x)]$, $\sum_x[S(x) \,\&\, M(x)]$
   /∴ $\sum_x[S(x) \,\&\, P(x)]$ Darii

7. $\prod_x[M(x) \supset \sim P(x)]$, $\sum_x[S(x) \,\&\, M(x)]$
   /∴ $\sum_x[S(x) \,\&\, \sim P(x)]$ Ferio

8. $\prod_x[P(x) \supset \sim M(x)]$, $\sum_x[S(x) \,\&\, M(x)]$
   /∴ $\sum_x[S(x) \,\&\, \sim P(x)]$ Festino

9. $\prod_x[P(x) \supset M(x)]$, $\sum_x[S(x) \,\&\, \sim M(x)]$
   /∴ $\sum_x[S(x) \,\&\, \sim P(x)]$ Baroco

10. $\prod_x[M(x) \supset P(x)]$, $\sum_x[M(x) \,\&\, S(x)]$
    /∴ $\sum_x[S(x) \,\&\, P(x)]$ Datisi

11. $\prod_x[M(x) \supset \sim P(x)]$, $\sum_x[M(x) \,\&\, S(x)]$
    /∴ $\sum_x[S(x) \,\&\, \sim P(x)]$ Ferison

12. $\sum_x[M(x) \,\&\, P(x)]$, $\prod_x[M(x) \supset S(x)]$
    /∴ $\sum_x[S(x) \,\&\, P(x)]$ Disamis

13. $\sum_x[M(x) \,\&\, \sim P(x)]$, $\prod_x[M(x) \supset S(x)]$
    /∴ $\sum_x[S(x) \,\&\, \sim P(x)]$ Bocardo

14. $\prod_x[P(x) \supset \sim M(x)], \sum_x[M(x) \ \& \ S(x)]$
$/\therefore \sum_x[S(x) \ \& \ \sim P(x)]$ Fresison

15. $\sum_x[P(x) \ \& \ M(x)], \prod_x[M(x) \supset S(x)]$
$/\therefore \sum_x[S(x) \ \& \ P(x)]$ Dimatis

Having thus done the last fifteen problems, you have been shown that all the "syllogisms" of Aristotelian logic except Darapti, Felapton, Bramantip, and Fesapo are valid in the restricted predicate calculus. (For these missing syllogisms see, for example, Cohen and Nagel, *An Introduction to Logic and Scientific Method*, New York, 1934, Ch. IV.)

IV. **1.** By symbolizing the traditional categorical propositions as: A—All A is B; E—No A is B; I—Some A is B; O—Some A is not B, as $\prod_x[A(x) \supset B(x)]$; $\prod_x[A(x) \supset \sim B(x)]$; $\sum_x[A(x) \ \& \ B(x)]$; $\sum_x[A(x) \ \& \ \sim B(x)]$, respectively, one can show that the immediate inferences of conversion are valid for E and I, and invalid for A and O propositions respectively, and that contraposition is valid for A and O, and invalid for E and I propositions respectively. Show that this is so when one forms the converse proposition by simply interchanging subject and predicate terms and the contrapositive proposition by substituting the negation of the predicate for the subject and the negation of the subject for the predicate.

2. Let $\overline{A}$, the *complement* of A, be read non-A. Then $\prod_x[A(x) \supset \overline{B}(x)]$ and $\prod_x[A(x) \supset \sim B(x)]$ mean the same. Symbolizing the traditional categorical propositions as above, show that the immediate inference called obversion holds with all four categorical propositions where obversion is defined as forming one proposition from another by (1) changing the quality of the original proposition—*i.e.*, affirmative to negative or vice versa—and (2) replacing the predicate of the original proposition by its complement.

3. It is well known that in symbolizing the traditional categorical propositions as above, certain portions of Aristotelian logic do not hold. These portions are (1) some of the inferences of the so-called square of opposition; (2) the immediate inferences of conversion and contraposition by limitation on A and E propositions respectively; and (3) nine syllogistic forms. By resymbolizing the traditional categorical propositions as follows:

$$A—\prod_x[A(x) \supset B(x)] \ \& \ \sum_x A(x) \ \& \ \sum_x \sim B(x),$$
$$E—\prod_x[A(x) \supset \sim B(x)] \ \& \ \sum_x A(x) \ \& \ \sum_x B(x),$$
$$I—\sum_x[A(x) \ \& \ B(x)] \ \mathbf{v} \ \sim\sum_x A(x) \ \mathbf{v} \ \sim\sum_x B(x),$$
$$O—\sum_x[A(x) \ \& \ \sim B(x)] \ \mathbf{v} \ \sim\sum_x A(x) \ \mathbf{v} \ \sim\sum_x \sim B(x)$$

these inferences may be saved.

(A) Show that the inferences of the square of opposition hold; *i.e.*,
   (a) show that A $\equiv$ $\sim$O; O $\equiv$ $\sim$A; I $\equiv$ $\sim$E. (Contradictories)
   (b) show that A $\supset$ I; E $\supset$ O. (Subalternation)
   (c) show that A $\supset$ $\sim$E; E $\supset$ $\sim$A. (Contraries) (Hint: combine parts of (a) and (b).)
   (d) show that $\sim$I $\supset$ O; $\sim$O $\supset$ I. (Subcontraries) (Hint: combine parts of (a) and (c).)

(B) Show that conversion by limitation of the A proposition holds; *i.e.*, show that

$$\{\textstyle\prod_x[A(x) \supset B(x)] \& \sum_x A(x) \& \sum_x \sim B(x)\} \supset$$
$$\{\textstyle\sum_x[B(x) \& A(x)] \vee \sim\sum_x B(x) \vee \sim\sum_x A(x)\}$$

(Hint: First use the result of subalternation.)

(C) Since contraposition can be achieved by first obverting, then converting, and then obverting again, it can now be shown that the A proposition can be contraposed by limitation. How is this possible?

(D) Show that the following nine syllogistic forms are valid.

   (a) AAI-1. (Hint: use Barbara and subalternation.)
   (b) EAO-1. (Hint: use Celarent and subalternation.)
   (c) EAO-2. (Hint: use Cesare and subalternation.)
   (d) AEO-2. (Hint: use Camestres and subalternation.)
   (e) AEO-4. (Hint: use Camenes and subalternation.)
   (f) Darapti, AAI-3.
   (g) Felapton, EAO-3.
   (h) Bramantip, AAI-4.
   (i) Fesapo, EAO-4.

   In this problem the designations AAI-1, etc., indicate the mood and figure of the syllogism: the first letter stands for the major premise, the premise which contains the predicate of the conclusion; the second letter for the minor premise, the premise which contains the subject of the conclusion; and the third letter stands for the conclusion. The numerals indicate the position of the middle term—the remaining term in the premises: first figure being that which contains the middle term as subject of the major premise and predicate of the minor premise; second figure being that which contains the middle term as predicate of both premises; third figure being that which contains the middle term as subject of both premises; and fourth figure being that which contains the middle term as subject of the minor premise and predicate of the major premise.

Parts III and IV of this exercise give a treatment of much of traditional logic.

5.8   Derived Rules

As in PL, it is often convenient to have additional rules for use in deduction, that is, derived rules. The status of the derived rules of MPL is the same as that for PL. They are established by deduction schemata representing all instances of a kind of deduction (cf. Chapter Two, Section Two). As before, we use derived rules as abbreviations. They serve to indicate that at any line in a deduction we could find a deduction that would give the succeeding line.

Perhaps the most useful derived rules in MPL are those that state relations holding between universally and existentially quantified statements.

5.1 $\prod_\alpha \varphi(\alpha)$

$\therefore \sim\sum_\alpha \sim \varphi(\alpha)$

Deduction Schema

```
──── 1. ∏ₐφ(α)
┌─── 2. Σₐ ∼ φ(α)
│ ┌─ 3. ∼φ(β)
│ │   4. φ(β)                    1, ∏E
│ │   5. φ(β) & ∼φ(β)            3, 4, &I
│ │   6. p                       5, ∼E
│ │   7. ∼p                      5, ∼E
│ │   8. p & ∼p                  6, 7, &I
│ └──────────────
│     9. p & ∼p                  3, 4–8, ΣE
└──────────────
     10. ∼Σₐ ∼ φ(α)              3–9, ∼I
```

Notice how $p \mathbin{\&} \sim p$ may be derived from $\sim\varphi(\beta)$. This permits us to obtain a conclusion using $\sum$E in which β does not occur free.

5.2 $\sim\sum_\alpha \sim \varphi(\alpha)$

$\therefore \prod_\alpha \varphi(\alpha)$

Deduction Schema

```
──── 1. ∼Σₐ ∼φ(α)
┌─── 2. ∼φ(β)
│    3. Σₐ ∼φ(α)                 2, ΣI
└──────────────
     4. ∼φ(β) ⊃ Σₐ ∼φ(α)         2–3, ⊃I
     5. φ(β)                      4, 1, MT, DN
     6. ∏ₐφ(α)                    5, ∏I
```

The two derived rules can be summarized as a biconditional.

5.3 $\vdash \prod_\alpha \varphi(\alpha) \equiv \sim\sum_\alpha \sim\varphi(\alpha)$

Similarly, we can give proofs of six other useful derived rules relating existential and universal quantifiers, which can be summarized as three biconditionals.

5.4 $\vdash \sum_\alpha \varphi(\alpha) \equiv \sim\prod_\alpha \sim \varphi(\alpha)$

5.5 $\vdash \prod_\alpha \sim \varphi(\alpha) \equiv \sim\sum_\alpha \varphi(\alpha)$

5.6 $\vdash \sum_\alpha \sim \varphi(\alpha) \equiv \sim\prod_\alpha \varphi(\alpha)$

The deduction schemata establishing these biconditionals are left as exercises for the reader. From now on, we shall often justify inferences by referring to QEq. This abbreviation stands for *quantifier equivalence* and is henceforth used to refer in deductions to any of 5.3, 5.4, 5.5, and 5.6. Since these are biconditionals, their use is fundamentally in replacements based upon the biconditional, in the manner discussed in Chapter Two, Section Six. This rule authorizing replacements was there abbreviated as Rep.

We shall defer the proof of Rep for predicate logic until Chapter Six, where we can prove it for general predicate logic as well as for monadic predicate logic.

There are other useful derived rules that distribute quantifiers; for example,

5.7 $\quad \sum_\alpha[\varphi(\alpha) \vee \chi(\alpha)]$

$\quad \therefore \; \sum_\alpha \varphi(\alpha) \vee \sum_\alpha \chi(\alpha)$

The deduction schema for this is:

1. $\sum_\alpha[\varphi(\alpha) \vee \chi(\alpha)]$		
2. $\varphi(\beta) \vee \chi(\beta)$		
3. $\varphi(\beta)$		
4. $\sum_\alpha \varphi(\alpha)$	3, $\sum$I	
5. $\sum_\alpha \varphi(\alpha) \vee \sum_\alpha \chi(\alpha)$	4, vI	
6. $\chi(\beta)$		
7. $\sum_\alpha \chi(\alpha)$	6, $\sum$I	
8. $\sum_\alpha \varphi(\alpha) \vee \sum_\alpha \chi(\alpha)$	7, vI	
9. $\sum_\alpha \varphi(\alpha) \vee \sum_\alpha \chi(\alpha)$	2, 3–5, 6–8, vE	
10. $\sum_\alpha \varphi(\alpha) \vee \sum_\alpha \chi(\alpha)$	1, 2–9, $\sum$E	

5.8 $\quad \sum_\alpha \varphi(\alpha) \vee \sum_\alpha \chi(\alpha)$

$\quad \therefore \; \sum_\alpha[\varphi(\alpha) \vee \chi(\alpha)]$

The deduction schema for this is

$$
\begin{array}{ll}
\text{1. } \sum_\alpha \varphi(\alpha) \vee \sum_\alpha \chi(\alpha) & \\
\text{2. } \sum_\alpha \varphi(\alpha) & \\
\quad \text{3. } \varphi(\beta) & \\
\quad \text{4. } \varphi(\beta) \vee \chi(\beta) & \text{3, vI} \\
\quad \text{5. } \sum_\alpha [\varphi(\alpha) \vee \chi(\alpha)] & \text{4, } \sum\text{I} \\
\quad \text{6. } \sum_\alpha [\varphi(\alpha) \vee \chi(\alpha)] & \text{2, 3–5, } \sum\text{E} \\
\text{7. } \sum_\alpha \chi(\alpha) & \\
\quad \text{8. } \chi(\beta) & \\
\quad \text{9. } \varphi(\beta) \vee \chi(\beta) & \text{8, vI} \\
\quad \text{10. } \sum_\alpha [\varphi(\alpha) \vee \chi(\alpha)] & \text{9, } \sum\text{I} \\
\quad \text{11. } \sum_\alpha [\varphi(\alpha) \vee \chi(\alpha)] & \text{7, 8–10, } \sum\text{E} \\
\text{12. } \sum_\alpha [\varphi(\alpha) \vee \chi(\alpha)] & \text{1, 2–6, 7–11, vE}
\end{array}
$$

The last two rules can be summarized as a biconditional.

5.9 $\vdash [\sum_\alpha \varphi(\alpha) \vee \sum_\alpha \chi(\alpha)] \equiv \sum_\alpha [\varphi(\alpha) \vee \chi(\alpha)]$

Several other important theorems of monadic quantification theory that take the form of biconditionals will be given as exercises at the end of this section. Meanwhile, we note that not all distributions of quantifiers take the form of biconditionals. When a universal quantifier is distributed over an alternation, for example, the most that we can obtain is the following derived rule:

5.10 $\prod_\alpha \varphi(\alpha) \vee \prod_\alpha \chi(\alpha)$
$\therefore \ \prod_\alpha [\varphi(\alpha) \vee \chi(\alpha)]$

The deduction schema is:

$$
\begin{array}{ll}
\text{1. } \prod_\alpha \varphi(\alpha) \vee \prod_\alpha \chi(\alpha) & \\
\text{2. } \prod_\alpha \varphi(\alpha) & \\
\quad \text{3. } \varphi(\beta) & \text{2, } \prod\text{E} \\
\quad \text{4. } \varphi(\beta) \vee \chi(\beta) & \text{3, vI} \\
\quad \text{5. } \prod_\alpha [\varphi(\alpha) \vee \chi(\alpha)] & \text{4, } \prod\text{I} \\
\text{6. } \prod_\alpha \chi(\alpha) & \\
\quad \text{7. } \chi(\beta) & \text{6, } \prod\text{E} \\
\quad \text{8. } \varphi(\beta) \vee \chi(\beta) & \text{7, vI} \\
\quad \text{9. } \prod_\alpha [\varphi(\alpha) \vee \chi(\alpha)] & \text{8, } \prod\text{I} \\
\text{10. } \prod_\alpha [\varphi(\alpha) \vee \chi(\alpha)] & \text{1, 2–5, 6–9, vE}
\end{array}
$$

Any attempt to move in the opposite direction, however, is hopelessly blocked. The following three steps are the only ones possible:

$$
\begin{array}{ll}
\text{1. } \prod_\alpha [\varphi(\alpha) \vee \chi(\alpha)] & \\
\text{2. } \varphi(\beta) \vee \chi(\beta) & \text{1, } \prod\text{E} \\
\text{3. } \varphi(\beta) &
\end{array}
$$

The difficulty here is that it is impossible to infer $\varphi(\beta)$ from the second line in order to use $\prod$I on it. If the second line were a conjunction rather than an alternation, this would be possible, for then we could infer $\varphi(\beta)$ by the rule of &E, and so derive it as a conclusion from the first line. This suggests that we might have better luck with

$$\vdash \prod_\alpha[\varphi(\alpha) \,\&\, \chi(\alpha)] \supset [\prod_\alpha\varphi(\alpha) \,\&\, \prod_\alpha\chi(\alpha)]$$

(See Exercise 5.8.)

Among the important derived rules including quantification of conditionals are those arising when α is not free in the antecedent or in the consequent:

5.11 If α is not free in χ, $\quad \vdash \prod_\alpha[\varphi(\alpha) \supset \chi] \equiv [\sum_\alpha\varphi(\alpha) \supset \chi]$

This equivalence, like the others, naturally breaks up into two rules.

5.12 If α is not free in χ, $\prod_\alpha[\varphi(\alpha) \supset \chi]$

$$\therefore \sum_\alpha\varphi(\alpha) \supset \chi$$

Proof:

$$
\begin{array}{lll}
\text{1.} & \prod_\alpha[\varphi(\alpha) \supset \chi] & \\
\text{2.} & \varphi(\alpha) \supset \chi & \text{1, } \prod\text{E}
\end{array}
$$

(We substitute α for itself here in order to make use of the hypothesis that α is not free in χ. It would be a mistake to substitute β for α, since we have no assurance that β is not free in χ.)

$$
\begin{array}{lll}
\text{3.} & \sum_\alpha\varphi(\alpha) & \\
\text{4.} & \varphi(\alpha) & \\
\text{5.} & \chi & \text{2, 4, } \supset\text{E} \\
\text{6.} & \chi & \text{3, 4–5, } \sum\text{E} \\
\text{7.} & \sum_\alpha\varphi(\alpha) \supset \chi & \text{3–6, } \supset\text{I}
\end{array}
$$

5.13 If α is not free in χ, $\sum_\alpha[\varphi(\alpha)] \supset \chi$

$$\therefore \prod_\alpha[\varphi(\alpha) \supset \chi]$$

Proof:

$$
\begin{array}{lll}
\text{1.} & \sum_\alpha\varphi(\alpha) \supset \chi & \\
\text{2.} & \varphi(\beta) & \\
\text{3.} & \sum_\alpha\varphi(\alpha) & \text{2, } \sum\text{I} \\
\text{4.} & \chi & \text{1, 3, } \supset\text{F} \\
\text{5.} & \varphi(\beta) \supset \chi & \text{2–4, } \supset \\
\text{6.} & \prod_\alpha[\varphi(\alpha) \supset \chi] & \text{5. } \prod\text{I}
\end{array}
$$

EXERCISE 5.8

I. 1. Demonstrate that each of the biconditionals 5.4, 5.5, and 5.6 are ZPC's.

2. Can you demonstrate $\vdash \prod_\alpha[\varphi(\alpha) \ \& \ \chi(\alpha)] \supset [\prod_\alpha\varphi(\alpha) \ \& \ \prod_\alpha\chi(\alpha)]$ as suggested on page 183? Its converse?

II. Prove that the following are ZPC's of MPL:

1. $[\chi \ \mathbf{v} \ \sum_\alpha\varphi(\alpha)] \equiv \sum_\alpha[\chi \ \mathbf{v} \ \varphi(\alpha)]$ if α is not free in χ

2. $[\chi \ \mathbf{v} \ \prod_\alpha\varphi(\alpha)] \equiv \prod_\alpha[\chi \ \mathbf{v} \ \varphi(\alpha)]$ if α is not free in χ

3. $[\chi \ \& \ \sum_\alpha\varphi(\alpha)] \equiv \sum_\alpha[\chi \ \& \ \varphi(\alpha)]$ if α is not free in χ

4. $[\chi \ \& \ \prod_\alpha\varphi(\alpha)] \equiv \prod_\alpha[\chi \ \& \ \varphi(\alpha)]$ if α is not free in χ

5. $\prod_\alpha[\chi \supset \varphi(\alpha)] \equiv [\chi \supset \prod_\alpha\varphi(\alpha)]$ if α is not free in χ

6. $\sum_\alpha[\varphi(\alpha) \supset \psi(\alpha)] \supset [\prod_\alpha\varphi(\alpha) \supset \sum_\alpha\psi(\alpha)]$

7. $\sum_\alpha[\varphi(\alpha) \supset \chi] \equiv [\prod_\alpha\varphi(\alpha) \supset \chi]$ if α is not free in χ

8. $\prod_\alpha[\varphi(\alpha) \equiv \psi(\alpha)] \supset [\sum_\alpha\varphi(\alpha) \equiv \sum_\alpha\psi(\alpha)]$

In 1–5 and 7 assume that α is not free in χ.

III. Prove:

1. $\vdash \prod_x F(x) \supset \sum_x F(x)$

2. $\vdash \prod_x[A \ \mathbf{v} \ F(x)] \equiv A \ \mathbf{v} \ \prod_x F(x)$

3. $\vdash \prod_x[A \ \& \ F(x)] \equiv A \ \& \ \prod_x F(x)$

4. $\vdash \prod_x[A \supset F(x)] \equiv A \supset \prod_x F(x)$

5. $\vdash \prod_x[F(x) \ \mathbf{v} \ G(x)] \supset [\prod_x F(x) \ \mathbf{v} \sum_x G(x)]$

6. $\vdash [\prod_x F(x) \ \mathbf{v} \ \prod_x G(x)] \supset \prod_x[F(x) \ \mathbf{v} \ G(x)]$

7. $\vdash \prod_x[F(x) \ \& \ G(x)] \equiv [\prod_x F(x) \ \& \ \prod_x G(x)]$

8. $\vdash \prod_x[F(x) \equiv G(x)] \supset [\prod_x F(x) \equiv \prod_x G(x)]$

9. $\vdash \prod_x[F(x) \supset A] \equiv [\sum_x F(x) \supset A]$

10. $\vdash \sum_x[F(x) \ \& \ G(x)] \equiv [\sum_x F(x) \ \mathbf{v} \sum_x G(x)]$

11. $\vdash \sum_x[F(x) \ \& \ G(x)] \supset [\sum_x F(x) \ \& \sum_x G(x)]$

12. $\vdash [\sum_x F(x) \supset \sum_x G(x)] \supset \sum_x[F(x) \supset G(x)]$

13. $\vdash \sum_x[A \supset F(x)] \equiv [A \supset \sum_x F(x)]$

14. $\vdash \sum_x[F(x) \ \& \ A] \equiv \sum_x F(x) \ \& \ A$

15. $\vdash \sum_x[F(x) \ \mathbf{v} \ A] \equiv \sum_x F(x) \ \mathbf{v} \ A$

16. $\vdash \sum_x[F(x) \supset A] \equiv \prod_x F(x) \supset A$

17. $\vdash \sum_x[A \supset F(x)] \equiv [A \supset \sum_x F(x)]$

SUGGESTED READINGS

1. I. M. Copi, *Symbolic Logic* (New York: The Macmillan Co., 1954), Ch. IV.

2. Robert M. Exner and Myron F. Rosskopf, *Logic in Elementary Mathematics* (New York: McGraw-Hill Book Co., 1959), Ch. V.

3. Gerhard Gentzen, "Untersuchungen über das logische Schliessen", *Mathematische Zeitschrift*, vol. 39 (1934–5), pp. 176–210, 405–431. [Translated into French by R. Feys and J. Ladrière as *Recherches sur la Déduction Logique* (Paris: Presses Universitaires de France, 1955)].

4. W. V. Quine, *Methods of Logic*, rev. ed. (New York: Holt, Rinehart and Winston, Inc., 1959), Part II.

5. Patrick Suppes, *Introduction to Logic* (Princeton, N.J.: P. Van Nostrand Co., 1957), Ch. IV and V.

Chapter 6

General Predicate Logic
—First Order

6.1 Introduction

The deduction patterns of MPL are sufficient to analyze many common types of argument and proof. Indeed, all the types of argument and proof that, prior to the advent of symbolic logic, were held to fall within the scope of logic can be adequately analyzed within propositional logic and monadic predicate logic. But there are many types of argument and proof that, in fact, fall beyond logic so conceived. One of the reasons why DeMorgan, Peirce, and other investigators of the nineteenth century began to develop symbolic logic was that they wished to overcome this limitation. Thus DeMorgan's pioneering work on the logic of relations was at least partly a response to the fact that in traditional logic there is no way of analyzing the validity of even so simple an argument as

> Horses are animals; therefore, the heads of horses are the heads of animals.

Symbolically, we write

$$\prod_x[P(x) \supset A(x)] \quad /\therefore \quad \prod_x\prod_y\{[P(y) \ \& \ H(x,y)] \supset [A(y) \ \& \ H(x,y)]\}$$

where P is used for "is a horse", A for "is an animal", $H(x,y)$ for "x is a head of y". An even more obvious gap in the logic that preceded symbolic logic was its failure to make explicit the logic of most mathematical proofs. Some of these, as we have seen, can satisfactorily be analyzed by propositional logic. But the vast majority cannot be treated in this way. In order to make statements about the natural numbers, for example, we almost invariably need to use polyadic predicates. The statement that each number (of the natural numbers) has one and only one immediate successor becomes

$$\prod_x(\sum_y\{S(x,y) \;\&\; \prod_z[S(x,z) \supset z = y]\})$$

Here $S(x,y)$ means y is the immediate successor of x. Again, we can state the truth that the relation $>$ is transitive as

$$\prod_x\prod_y\prod_z[(x > y \;\&\; y > z) \supset x > z]$$

Because such statements involve predicates with more than one individual variable, such as "successor of", "is greater than", and "equals", arguments involving them do not fall within the scope of monadic predicate logic. Only in *general predicate logic*, which we abbreviate as GPL, can such proofs be analyzed. GPL did not exist, however, before the advent of symbolic logic.

A simple mathematical deduction will serve as a further example of the need for more powerful tools. From the premise

(1)   If $x > y$, then $y \not> x$

we can deduce

(2)   If $x > x$, then $x \not> x$,

whence via *reductio* (*i.e.*, the rule of $\sim$I), we can conclude that $x \not> x$. Suppose we try to handle the transition from line (1) to line (2) as a monadic deduction. We may treat "$>y$" as one predicate, say F, and "$>x$" as another, say G. Line (1) then becomes

(1′)   If F(x), then $\sim$G(y),

and line (2) translates as

(2′)   If G(x), then $\sim$G(x).

Search as we may, however, we shall find no logical rule that justifies inferring line (2′) from (1′). Exactly similar results would be obtained, furthermore, if "$x >$" were to be F and "$y >$" were to be G. No translation into monadic expressions is faithful to the logic of the deduction. The predicate $>$, as it functions in this deduction, is irreducibly dyadic.

Deductions involving dyadic, triadic, and, in general, n-adic predicates, are analyzed in general predicate logic. Notice that deductions involving monadic predicates are included as well. MPL is a special case of GPL. The latter also includes deductions that cannot be subsumed under monadic predicate logic even though monadic predicates are involved, because more complex predicates are also involved. Thus an important difference between monadic predicate logic and general predicate logic, first-order* (abbreviated GPL-1), is to be found in the nature of the predicates occurring in GPL-1.

There is nothing unusual about polyadic predicates. They are often called *relational predicates* because they represent relations. Thus, when we say that Jefferson was a contemporary of Washington, we can symbolize this as

$$C(j,w)$$

and "x is the contemporary of y" becomes

$$C(x,y)$$

and "x is related to y" is

$$R(x,y).$$

An instance of a *triadic* relation is *between*. We say that New York is between Chicago and Paris.

$$B(n,c,p)$$

Arithmetical formulas represent relations between two or more individuals. Thus $3 = 3$ can be stated as

$$= (3,3),$$

and

$$= (x,y)$$

is, of course, $x = y$. Similarly, $2 + 3 = 5$ can be stated as

$$S(2,3,5)$$

and, generally,

$$S(x,y,z)$$

is $x + y = z$. These are examples of statement functions with two and three unknowns, or of statements with two and three names.

If, now, we add quantifiers to polyadic statement functions, we bind variables. Since there are multiple variables, binding can occur in more complex ways than it occurs in the case of monadic statement functions. For example, from

$$S(x,y,z)$$

we might obtain

$$\prod_x \prod_y \prod_z [S(x,y,z)]$$

This is clearly false, for it says that $x + y = z$ for all triples of x, y, and z. On the other hand,

$$\sum_x \sum_y (x > y)$$

---

* The meaning of the adjective "first-order", as it qualifies "General Predicate Logic", will be explained in Section 4 of this chapter.

is true, for it means that there is at least one number greater than one other number, supposing that we allow x and y to range over numbers.

The complexity of the quantification of polyadic statement functions is indicated by a contrast such as that between

$$(1) \quad \prod_x \sum_y (y > x)$$

and

$$(2) \quad \sum_y \prod_x (y > x).$$

(1) means that whatever x we select, we can find at least one y that is greater, which is clearly true when x and y are integers. $\sum_y \prod_x (y > x)$, on the other hand, is clearly false of the integers. For one thing, if at least one of y is greater than any x you choose, then it must be greater than itself, which is absurd. But even if, in order to avoid this difficulty, we amend (2) to read $\sum_y \prod_x (y \neq x \supset y > x)$, it is still false; for no integer is greater than all the others. On the other hand, if there *were* at least one integer greater than all the others, it would follow that whatever integer x you select there is at least one other integer y greater than it, since as a last resort the *greatest y* could be pointed to as greater than each of the x's. Thus (2) $\supset$ (1).

It is also helpful to recall that a universally quantified statement is, in a sense, a conjunction, whereas an existentially quantified statement has the force of a disjunction. Thus $\sum_x \prod_y [F(x,y)]$ means $\sum_x [F(x,1) \& F(x,2) \& \ldots]$; *i.e.*,

$$(3) \quad [F(1,1) \& F(1,2) \& \ldots] \lor [F(2,1) \& F(2,2) \ldots] \lor \ldots$$

while $\prod_y \sum_x [F(x,y)]$ means

$$(4) \quad [F(1,1) \lor F(2,1) \lor \ldots] \& [F(1,2) \lor F(2,2) \lor \ldots] \& \ldots.$$

(3), then, is a disjunction of conjunctions. If it is true, at least one of the conjunctions will be true; which is to say that every member of the conjunction or conjunctions in question will be true. But consider any one of the conjunctions disjoined in (3), and notice that one of its members occurs in each of the disjunctions conjoined in (4). So far as the first conjunction of (3) is concerned, for example, the conjunct $F(1,1)$ occurs in the first disjunction of (4), the conjunct $F(3,1)$ would occur in the third disjunction of (4), and so on. Thus, if every member of any given conjunction in (3) is true, then every disjunction conjoined in (4) will have at least one true member. But this is sufficient to make each disjunction true, from which it follows that (4) as a whole is true. So the truth of (3) ensures the truth of (4). But the converse of this does not hold, because it would be easy to make one member of each disjunction in (4) true without making any complete conjunction in (3) true. For this purpose, it would be enough to suppose that $F(m,n)$ is true when and only when $m = n$. Thus $F(1,1)$, $F(2,2)$, etc., are true, but $F(1,2)$, $F(2,1)$, etc., are false. It is obvious that under these circumstances (4) will be true and (3) false.

In addition to complexities in quantifying variables, there are also complexities in deduction—although these are not great, as we may begin to see from the following theorem, which formalizes the discussion above.

6.1 $\vdash \sum_\alpha \prod_\beta [\varphi(\alpha,\beta)] \supset \prod_\beta \sum_\alpha [\varphi(\alpha,\beta)]$

Proof:

1.	$\sum_\alpha \prod_\beta [\varphi(\alpha,\beta)]$	
2.	$\prod_\beta [\varphi(\gamma,\beta)]$	
3.	$\varphi(\gamma,\delta)$	2, $\prod$E
4.	$\sum_\alpha [\varphi(\alpha,\delta)]$	3, $\sum$I
5.	$\prod_\beta \sum_\alpha [\varphi(\alpha,\beta)]$	4, $\prod$I
6.	$\prod_\beta \sum_\alpha [\varphi(\alpha,\beta)]$	1, 2–5, $\sum$E
7.	$\sum_\alpha \prod_\beta [\varphi(\alpha,\beta)] \supset \prod_\beta \sum_\alpha [\varphi(\alpha,\beta)]$	1–6, $\supset$I

Note that any attempt to prove the converse of 6.1 is, however, doomed by the restrictions on $\prod$I.

Another example of a deduction requiring general predicate logic is the following:

Everything is related to everything. Therefore, everything is related to itself.

(In symbols: $\prod_y \prod_x [R(x,y)] \; /\therefore \; \prod_x [R(x,x)]$)

Schematically, what we have to prove is

6.2 $\vdash \prod_\beta \prod_\alpha [\varphi(\alpha,\beta)] \supset \prod_\alpha [\varphi(\alpha,\alpha)]$

The deduction schema is

1.	$\prod_\beta \prod_\alpha [\varphi(\alpha,\beta)]$	
2.	$\prod_\alpha \varphi(\alpha,\gamma)$	1, $\prod$E
3.	$\varphi(\gamma,\gamma)$	2, $\prod$E
4.	$\prod_\alpha [\varphi(\alpha,\alpha)]$	3, $\prod$I
5.	$\prod_\beta \prod_\alpha [\varphi(\alpha,\beta)] \supset \prod_\alpha [\varphi(\alpha,\alpha)]$	1–4, $\supset$I

From the examples given, it appears that the rules of inference used in cases involving polyadic formulas are those stated for MPL. This is correct. The development of deductions, however, is often more complicated, because rules (such as $\prod$E in the last example) may need to be repeatedly invoked to handle greater numbers of quantifiers. When we apply the rules given in

Table 5.1 to polyadic formulas, we suppose the α and β in the rules to refer to that variable with which we are dealing, so that the rule may be applied repeatedly. For example,

$$
\begin{array}{lll}
\text{———} 1. & \prod_z\prod_y\prod_x[F(x,y) \supset G(z)] & \\
2. & \prod_y\prod_x[F(x,y) \supset G(u)] & 1, \prod E \\
3. & \prod_x[F(x,v) \supset G(u)] & 2, \prod E \\
4. & F(w,v) \supset G(u) & 3, \prod E \\
5. & \sum_x[F(x,v) \supset G(u)] & 4, \sum I \\
6. & \sum_y\sum_x[F(x,y) \supset G(u)] & 3, \sum I \\
7. & \sum_z\sum_y\sum_x[F(x,y) \supset G(z)] & 6, \sum I \\
\end{array}
$$

This additional complication is a small enough price to pay for the power to deal with problems of a more involved kind than those with which PL and MPL can deal. In the next section we turn to an illustration of such power as found in the calculus of relations. This calculus turns out to be nothing more than polyadic quantification theory in disguise.

EXERCISE 6.1

I. Translate the following statements into quantified expressions of GPL:

1. Nothing is blacker than sin. [$B(x,y) = x$ is blacker than y; s = sin]

2. No truer words (than these) were ever spoken. [$W(x) = x$ is a word; $S(x) = x$ is spoken; $T(x,y) = x$ is truer than y; t = these words]

3. If Liechtenstein is wealthier than Andorra, then Monaco is wealthier than all countries which are smaller than San Marino. [$C(x) = x$ is a country; $S(x,y) = x$ is smaller than y; $W(x,y) = x$ is wealthier than y; l = Liechtenstein; a = Andorra; m = Monaco; s = San Marino]

4. All headwaiters are employed by high-toned restaurants. [$H(x) = x$ is a headwaiter; $R(x) = x$ is a restaurant; $T(x) = x$ is high-toned; $E(x,y) = x$ is employed by y]

5. All high-toned restaurants employ headwaiters. [$H(x)$; $R(x)$; $T(x)$; $E(x,y)$]

6. No high-toned restaurant employs all headwaiters. [$H(x)$; $R(x)$; $T(x)$; $E(x,y)$]

7. Brevity is the soul of wit. [$B(x)$; $W(x)$; $S(x,y)$]

8. Some tales are told by idiots. [$T(x)$; $I(x)$; $T(x,y)$]

9. No one (person) knows all of his own relatives. [$P(x)$; $R(x,y)$; $K(x,y)$]

10. Everybody knows all of his own friends. [$P(x)$; $F(x,y)$; $K(x,y)$]

11. No one knows any of his great-great grandparents. [P(x); G(x,y); K(x,y)]

12. There are some of his contemporaries whom each person does not know. [P(x); C(x,y); K(x,y)]

13. Some excuses are better than others. [E(x); B(x,y); O(x,y) = x is other than y]

14. Some people are wiser than all of those who are richer than they. [P(x); W(x,y); R(x,y)]

15. Only very young boys like toads better than they like beautiful women. [V(x); B(x); T(x); U(x) = x is beautiful; W(x); L(x,y,z) = x likes y better than z]

16. Candy
Is dandy,
But liquor
Is quicker.*
[C(x); D(x); L(x); Q(x,y)]

17. Some things have ill served a poor purpose. [P(x); R(x) = x is a purpose; I(x,y) = x has ill served y]

18. Nothing is sweeter than success. [S(x); S(x,y)]

19. Good wine needs no bread. [G(x); W(x); B(x); N(x,y)]

20. It is a wise father that knows his own child. [F(x); W(x); K(x,y); C(x,y)]

21. If no one is happier than Scrooge, then Scrooge is happier than some. [P(x); H(x,y); s]

22. There is something which is the cause of an effect. [E(x); C(x,y)]

23. A substance is (by definition) dependent on nothing. [S(x); D(x,y)]

24. Anything caused by something external to it is not independent of everything. [E(x,y); C(x,y); D(x,y)]

25. For anything to be caused by a thing internal to itself is equivalent to its being caused by itself. [I(x,y); C(x,y)]

26. None can bear the whips and scorns of time. [P(x); W(x); S(x); B(x,y); O(x,y) = x is of y; t = time]

27. For every integer there exists one which is greater. [I(x); G(x,y)]

28. There is no integer which is greater than all other integers. [I(x); G(x,y); O(x,y) = x is other than y]

---

* The authors are indebted to Ogden Nash for the poem "Reflections on Ice-Breaking" in *Many Long Years Ago* (Boston: Little, Brown and Co., 1945).

29. A true statement is implied by any statement at all. [S(*x*); T(*x*); I(*x*,*y*)]

30. A false statement logically implies any statement. [S(*x*); F(*x*); I(*x*,*y*)]

31. Some works of music are composed by computers. [W(*x*); C(*x*); C(*x*,*y*)]

32. All works of music are composed by either men or computers. [W(*x*); M(*x*); C(*x*); C(*x*,*y*)]

33. Nothing composed by a woman is really music. [W(*x*); M(*x*); C(*x*,*y*)]

34. If a given line is parallel to a second line, then the second is parallel to the first. [L(*x*); P(*x*,*y*)]

35. Given any two integers, there is some third integer which is their product. [I(*x*); P(*x*,*y*,*z*) = *x* is the product of *y* and *z*]

36. For any two integers there is some third integer such that the first is the product of the second and third. [I(*x*); P(*x*,*y*,*z*)]

37. Misery acquaints a man (who possesses it) with strange bedfellows. [M(*x*); H(*x*) = *x* is a man; S(*x*); P(*x*,*y*); B(*x*,*y*); A(*x*,*y*,*z*) = *x* acquaints *y* with *z*]

38. We are such stuff as dreams are made on. [O(*x*) = *x* is one of us; D(*x*); S(*x*,*y*) = *x* is the stuff of *y*; M(*x*,*y*) = *x* is made on *y*]

39. A point is on a given line if and only if the line is on the point. [P(*x*); L(*x*); O(*x*,*y*)]

40. If a point is the midpoint of a given line, then it is on that line. [P(*x*); L(*x*); M(*x*,*y*); O(*x*,*y*)]

41. Given any two points, there is some straight line which lies on both. [P(*x*); L(*x*); O(*x*,*y*)]

42. If a given line is perpendicular to a second, and the second likewise to a third, then the first is parallel, not perpendicular, to the third. [L(*x*); P(*x*,*y*); L(*x*,*y*) = *x* is parallel to *y*]

43. Given any three points on a straight line, if they are separate from each other, then one of them is between the other two. [P(*x*); L(*x*); S(*x*); O(*x*,*y*); S(*x*,*y*) = *x* is separate from *y*; B(*x*,*y*,*z*) = *x* is between *y* and *z*]

44. Every circle has a circumference and a point within it which is equidistant from any two points on that circumference. [C(*x*) = *x* is a circle; P(*x*); C(*x*,*y*) = *x* is the circumference of *y*; O(*x*,*y*); E(*x*,*y*,*z*) = *x* is equidistant from *y* and *z*]

45. Translate 44 again, using the following symbols this time: $C(x)$; $P(x)$; $C(x,y)$; $O(x,y)$; $D(x,y,z) = x$ is the distance from y to z; $E(x,y) = x$ equals y.

46. Here lies a man whom it is neither permissible nor proper for the irreverent or the ignorant to praise (Aristotle on Plato). [$M(x)$; $L(x) = x$ lies here; $R(x) = x$ is reverent; $I(x) = x$ is ignorant; $P(x,y) = $ it is permissible for x to praise y; $R(x,y) = $ it is proper for x to praise y]

II. 1. Apply the rule of $\prod$E to the following formulas wherever possible.

$\prod_x[M(x) \ \& \ A(x)] \supset \sum_y[F(y) \ \& \ A(y) \ \& \ W(y,x)]$
$\prod_x\{M(x) \supset \sum_y\sum_z[M(y) \ \& \ F(z) \ \& \ F(y,x) \ \& \ M(z,x)]\}$
$\prod_x\sum_y\sum_z[S(x,y) \supset V(x,z)]$
$\prod_x\prod_y[B(x,y) \supset S(y,x)]$
$\prod_x\prod_y\sum_z\{S(x,y) \supset [P(z,x) \ \& \ P(z,y)]\}$

2. Apply the rule of $\sum$I to the following formulas wherever possible.

$B(y) \supset W(x,y)$
$B(x) \supset \prod_y[B(y) \supset W(x,y)]$
$B(x) \ \& \sim B(y) \ \& \sim W(x,y)$
$R(x) \ \& \ A(x) \ \& \sum_y[C(x,y) \ \& \ G(y)]$
$\prod_y\{[P(x) \ \& \ W(y)] \supset \sim R(x,y)\}$

3. Apply the rule of $\prod$I to the following formulas wherever possible.

$F(x) \ \& \ G(x) \ \& \ G(y) \ \& \ H(y) \ \& \ G(z) \ \& \ I(z)$
$\sum_x[F(x) \supset G(y)] \ \& \ F(x)$
$\prod_x[F(y) \supset F(x)]$
$F(y) \supset G(w)$

4. Apply the rule of $\sum$E to the following formulas wherever possible.

$\prod_x\sum_y\sum_z\{[F(x) \equiv \sim F(y)] \supset G(z,x,y)\}$
$\sum_x\sum_y[F(x) \ \& \sim G(x)] \ \& \sum_z\sum_w[\sim F(x) \ \& \ G(x)]$
$\sum_x\sum_y\{[F(x) \lor F(y)] \supset \prod_z\sum_w[G(z,w,x) \lor G(z,w,y)]\}$
$H(x) \supset \sum_x\sum_y\prod_z\{G(x) \lor G(y) \lor [G(z) \supset F(x) \ \& \ F(y)]\}$

III. Which of the following deductions are erroneous?

1. $\underline{\quad\quad \prod_x\sum_y[F(x) \equiv \sim F(y)]}$
   $\sum_y[F(y) \equiv \sim F(y)]$

2. $\underline{\quad\quad \sum_y[F(z) \equiv \sim F(y)]}$
   $\overline{\quad F(z) \equiv \sim F(w)}$
   $\underline{\quad\quad \sum_z[F(z) \equiv \sim F(z)]}$
   $\sum_z[F(z) \equiv \sim F(z)]$

3. —— $\prod_x[F(x) \supset F(x)]$
   $F(z) \supset F(z)$
   $\prod_y[F(z) \supset F(y)]$
   $\prod_x\prod_y[F(x) \supset F(y)]$

4. —— $\prod_x\sum_y[F(x,y)]$
   $\sum_yF(z,y)$
   ⎡ $F(a,z)$
   ⎢ $\prod_xF(x,z)$
   ⎣ $\sum_y\prod_xF(x,y)$
   $\sum_y\prod_xF(x,y)$

5. —— $\prod_x\sum_y[F(x) \equiv \sim F(y)]$
   $\sum_y[F(x) \equiv \sim F(y)]$

6. —— $\sum_y[F(z) \equiv \sim F(y)]$
   ⎡ $F(z) \equiv \sim F(w)$
   ⎣ $\sum_w[F(z) \equiv \sim F(w)]$
   $\sum_w[F(z) \equiv \sim F(w)]$
   $\sum_z\sum_w[F(z) \equiv \sim F(w)]$

7. —— $\prod_xF(x,x)$
   $F(y,y)$
   $\prod_xF(x,y)$
   $\sum_y\prod_xF(x,y)$

8. —— $\prod_x\sum_yF(x,y)$
   $\sum_yF(x,y)$
   ⎡ $F(x,x)$
   ⎣ $\sum_xF(x,x)$
   $\sum_xF(x,x)$

9. ⎡ $F(z)$
   ⎣ $\prod_xF(x)$
   $F(z) \supset \prod_xF(x)$
   $\prod_y[F(y) \supset \prod_xF(x)]$

10. ⎡ $F(u)$
    ⎢ $\prod_xF(x)$
    ⎣ $F(w)$
    $F(u) \supset F(w)$
    $\prod_y[F(u) \supset F(y)]$
    $\prod_x\prod_y[F(x) \supset F(y)]$

IV. Given the following "vocabulary":

$E(x,y) = x$ equals y; $L(x,y) = x$ is less than y:

1. Translate the following axioms for simple order (those given in Chapter One) into quantified statements of GPL:

   Ax. 1. $\sim(a = b) \supset [(a < b) \lor (b < a)]$
   Ax. 2. $(a < b) \supset \sim(a = b)$
   Ax. 3. $[(a < b) \& (b < c)] \supset (a < c)$
   Ax. 4. $a = a$
   Ax. 5. $(a = b) \supset (b = a)$
   Ax. 6. $[(a = b) \& (b = c)] \supset (a = c)$

2. Translate the following theorems for simple order, and derive them from the axioms as translated. Where extensions of the rules are required, use common sense to extend them, as in the proofs of 6.1 and 6.2.

   Th. 1. $\sim(a < a)$
   Th. 2. $(a < b) \supset \sim(b < a)$
   Th. 3. $(a = b) \equiv [\sim(a < b) \& \sim(b < a)]$
   Th. 4. $\sim(a = b) \equiv \sim(b = a)$
   Th. 5. $[(a = b) \& \sim(b = c)] \supset \sim(a = c)$
   Th. 6. $(a < b) \supset [\sim(a = b) \& \sim(b < a)]$
   Th. 7. $\sim(a < b) \supset [(a = b) \lor (b < a)]$
   Th. 8. $[(a < b) \& (b = c)] \supset (a < c)$
   Th. 9. $[\sim(a < b) \& \sim(b < c)] \supset \sim(a < c)$

V. Consider the following axioms:

   Ax. 1. $\prod_x[P(x) \supset \sim L(x)]$
   Ax. 2. $\prod_x[P(x) \lor L(x)]$
   Ax. 3. $\prod_x\prod_y\{O(x,y) \supset [P(x) \& L(y)]\}$
   Ax. 4. $\prod_x\prod_y\prod_z\{J(x,y,z) \supset [P(x) \& P(y) \& L(z)]\}$
   Ax. 5. $\prod_x\prod_y\prod_z[J(x,y,z) \equiv J(y,x,z)]$
   Ax. 6. $\prod_x\sum_y\sum_z[P(x) \supset J(x,y,z)]$
   Ax. 7. $\prod_x\{L(x) \supset \sum_y\sum_z[P(y) \& P(z) \& J(y,z,x)]\}$
   Ax. 8. $\prod_x\prod_y\prod_z\{J(x,y,z) \supset [O(x,z) \& O(y,z)]\}$

   From these axioms, derive each of the following theorems:

   Th. 1. $\prod_x\prod_y\{O(x,y) \supset [L(y) \& \sim L(x)]\}$
   Th. 2. $\prod_x\prod_y\{[L(x) \& L(y)] \supset \sim O(x,y)\}$
   Th. 3. $\prod_x\prod_y\prod_z[J(x,y,z) \supset \sim P(z)]$
   Th. 4. $\prod_x\prod_y\prod_z\{[\sim P(x) \lor \sim P(y)] \supset \sim J(x,y,z)\}$
   Th. 5. $\prod_x\prod_y\prod_z[L(x) \supset \sim J(x,y,z)]$
   Th. 6. $\prod_x\prod_y\prod_z\{[L(x) \lor L(y) \lor P(z)] \supset \sim J(x,y,z)\}$

Th. 7. $\prod_x \sum_y \sum_z [J(x,y,z) \lor J(y,x,z) \lor J(y,z,x)]$

Th. 8. $\prod_x \prod_y [O(x,y) \supset \sim O(y,x)]$

Th. 9. $\prod_x \prod_y \prod_z [J(x,y,z) \supset \sim O(x,y)]$

Th. 10. $\prod_x \prod_y \prod_z \prod_w [J(x,y,z) \supset \sim O(x,w)]$

Th. 11. $\prod_x \prod_y \{[L(x) \lor P(y)] \supset \sim O(x,y)\}$

Th. 12. $\prod_x \prod_y [\sim J(x,y,x) \ \& \ \sim J(y,x,x)]$

Th. 13. $\prod_x \sim O(x,x)$

Th. 14. $\prod_x [P(x) \equiv \sim L(x)]$

Th. 15. $\sim \sum_x L(x) \supset \sim \sum_x P(x)$

Th. 16. $\sum_x P(x) \equiv \sum_x L(x)$

Th. 17. $\sum_x P(x) \supset \sum_x \sum_y \sum_z [P(x) \ \& \ P(y) \ \& \ L(z) \ \& \ J(x,y,z)]$

Th. 18. $\prod_x [L(x) \equiv \sim \sum_y O(x,y)]$

Th. 19. $\prod_x [P(x) \equiv \sim \sum_y O(y,x)]$

Th. 20. $\prod_x \prod_y \prod_z \{[P(x) \ \& \ P(y) \ \& \ L(z)] \supset \sim \sum_w O(w,y)\}$

VI. Translate each of the axioms and theorems of part V above into a clear English sentence, using the following set of translations:

$L(x) = x$ is a line.
$P(x) = x$ is a point.
$O(x,y) = x$ is on y.
$J(x,y,z) = x$ and y are joined by z.

VII. Translate each of the axioms and theorems of part V into a clear and idiomatic English sentence using the following translations:

x, y, z, etc. $=$ human beings.
$P(x) = x$ is male.
$L(x) = x$ is female.
$O(x,y) = x$ is the brother or sister of y.
$J(x,y,z) = x$ and y are brothers of sister z.

VIII. Can you find another such interpretation in terms of which the axioms of part V, if not true, are at least meaningful?

IX. Can you find an interpretation for the axioms in part IV above, in terms of which they are all true? Are all of the theorems true on this interpretation?

6.2 Relations

In the first section of this chapter we observed that the use of relational predicates enabled us to extend the analysis of proof to cases involving arithmetical reasoning. The capacity to use relational predicates also opens a field of enquiry concerning the properties of relational predicates as such.

This field is often called the calculus of relations. We noted in Section 6.1 that we were able to state the transitivity of $>$ in our notation as

$$\prod_z \prod_y \prod_x [(x > y \ \& \ y > z) \supset x > z]$$

We could state this as a schema

$$\prod_\gamma \prod_\beta \prod_\alpha [(\alpha R \beta \ \& \ \beta R \gamma) \supset \alpha R \gamma],$$

thus expressing the *transitivity* of a given dyadic relation R.*

Similarly, our discussion of the deduction of the conclusion "If $x > x$, then $x \not> x$" from the premise "If $x > y$, then $y \not> x$" in Section 6.1 could have been stated as a problem of deducing one property of a dyadic relation from another. Thus

———1. $\prod_\beta \prod_\alpha (\alpha R \beta \supset \sim \beta R \alpha)$
    2. $\gamma R \gamma \supset \sim \gamma R \gamma$ 1, $\prod$E (twice)
    3. $\prod_\alpha (\alpha R \alpha \supset \sim \alpha R \alpha)$ 2, $\prod$I

From here we may continue to an interesting result about dyadic relations:

———1. $\prod_\alpha (\alpha R \alpha \supset \sim \alpha R \alpha)$
    2. $\beta R \beta \supset \sim \beta R \beta$ 1, $\prod$E
 ┌─3. $\beta R \beta$
 │ 4. $\sim \beta R \beta$ 2, 3, $\supset$E
 │ 5. $\beta R \beta \ \& \sim \beta R \beta$ 3, 4, &I
    6. $\sim \beta R \beta$ 3–5, $\sim$I
    7. $\prod_\beta (\sim \beta R \beta)$ 6, $\prod$I

These deduction schemata give us a derived rule.

6.3 $\prod_\beta \prod_\alpha (\alpha R \beta \supset \sim \beta R \alpha)$
    $\therefore \ \prod_\beta (\sim \beta R \beta)$

This rule states that every *asymmetrical* relation is *irreflexive*. It demonstrates the fact that there are deductions connecting properties of relations as well as eliminations, introductions, and arrangements of quantifiers. In order to develop this idea and state additional logical truths, we begin by symbolizing various important properties of relations, which we shall then interconnect.

SYMMETRY, ASYMMETRY, AND NONSYMMETRY

To explain the use of the term *asymmetrical*, let us begin by defining symmetrical relations. We shall abbreviate "Relation R is symmetrical" as Sym(R) using a notation that we shall discuss in Section 6.4. We write

---

* Notice how we now picture the statement "α bears relation R to β" by writing R between α and β. We thus exploit a possibility available when predicates are dyadic but not otherwise. Since we shall be concerned exclusively with dyadic relations throughout this section, we shall continue to use this notation.

$$\textbf{Sym(R)} \equiv_{df} \prod_\beta \prod_\alpha (\alpha R\beta \supset \beta R\alpha)^*$$

Examples of symmetrical relations are *is next to, marries,* $=$, and *is congruent with*. But what shall we say of $\geq$, *is a brother of*, and *respects*? If $x \geq y$, it is possible that $y \geq x$ also (namely, when $x = y$), but this need not be so. If William is the brother of Lee, it is possible for Lee to be the brother of William; but Lee, for all we know, might be a girl. If Smith respects Jones, it does not follow that Jones respects Smith, although this is not impossible either. Relations of this kind are said to be *nonsymmetrical*. Thus

$$\textbf{Nonsym(R)} \equiv_{df} \sim\prod_\beta \prod_\alpha (\alpha R\beta \supset \beta R\alpha)$$

Owing to QEq, Impl, and DM, the definition may also be written

$$\textbf{Nonsym(R)} \equiv_{df} \sum_\beta \sum_\alpha (\alpha R\beta \;\&\; \sim\beta R\alpha)$$

Symmetrical and nonsymmetrical relations exhaust the possibilities, but within the class of nonsymmetrical relations there are those relations such that when $\alpha R\beta$ is true, $\beta R\alpha$ is always false. Examples are $>$, *is the father of*, and __ $+ 1 =$ __. Such relations are said to be *asymmetrical*, and are defined

$$\textbf{Asym(R)} \equiv_{df} \prod_\beta \prod_\alpha (\alpha R\beta \supset \sim\beta R\alpha).$$

REFLEXIVITY, IRREFLEXIVITY, AND NONREFLEXIVITY

Let us consider now the conclusion that we drew from the premise that $>$ is asymmetrical. This was that $\sim(x > x)$; or, by an obvious use of $\prod$I, that $\prod_x \sim (x > x)$. Relations functioning like $>$ in this respect are said to be *irreflexive*. We define the conditions under which a relation is *totally reflexive*:

$$\textbf{Totrx(R)} \equiv_{df} \prod_\alpha (\alpha R\alpha)$$

Extremely few relations satisfy this definition; perhaps the only relation that relates every x to itself is identity. A relation like *weighs the same as* does not relate every x to itself, since there are some x's (*e.g.*, numbers) to which it does not apply at all. But whenever it relates x to any y, it also relates x to itself; so that *weighs the same as* is *reflexive*. In general,

$$\textbf{Rx(R)} \equiv_{df} \prod_\beta \prod_\alpha (\alpha R\beta \supset \alpha R\alpha)$$

Among other reflexive relations are *is congruent with* and $\geq$.

Not all relations, naturally, are reflexive. Many of them, like *loves, hates, teaches French to,* and *is the dual of*, are *nonreflexive*, since they satisfy:

$$\textbf{Nonrx(R)} \equiv_{df} \sim\prod_\beta \prod_\alpha (\alpha R\beta \supset \alpha R\alpha)$$

---

* The symbol $\equiv_{df}$ may be read "is an abbreviational definition for". Thus the abbreviation given can be eliminated from any formula, and so is not an essential part of the logical notation. Alternatively we may, if we like, read $\equiv_{df}$ as a summary of (here unstated) introduction and elimination rules as in the biconditionals of Table 2.3 or in Section 4.3.

Within the class of nonreflexive relations, however, there are some that could never relate any x to itself. These are said to be *irreflexive*. Thus

$$\textbf{Irrx(R)} \equiv_{df} \textstyle\prod_\alpha \sim(\alpha R\alpha)$$

Examples are $>$, *is the father of*, $\_\_ + 1 = \_\_$, *is next to*, and *defeats at tennis*. Notice that, although most of these examples are asymmetrical, *is next to* is symmetrical. A nonsymmetrical irreflexive relation would be *is the brother of*, if we assume that no one is his own brother.

Two relations that are both irreflexive and asymmetrical can differ in still other respects. Consider $>$ and *is the father of*. If $x > y$ and $y > z$, then $x > z$. But if A is the father of B and B is the father of C, then we can conclude that A is *not* the father of C. These facts can be expressed by saying that $>$ is *transitive*, while *is the father of* is *intransitive*. Let us define both of these properties:

$$\textbf{Tr(R)} \equiv_{df} \textstyle\prod_\gamma\prod_\beta\prod_\alpha[(\alpha R\beta \,\&\, \beta R\gamma) \supset \alpha R\gamma]$$
$$\textbf{Intr(R)} \equiv_{df} \textstyle\prod_\gamma\prod_\beta\prod_\alpha[(\alpha R\beta \,\&\, \beta R\gamma) \supset \sim\alpha R\gamma]$$

Transitive and intransitive relations do not exhaust the possibilities, since given that a loves b and b loves c, we cannot infer either that a loves c or that a does not love c; and given $x + y = 4$ and $y + z = 4$, we cannot infer either that $x + z = 4$ or that $x + z \neq 4$. Relations like these are said to be *nontransitive*:

$$\textbf{Nontr(R)} \equiv_{df} \sim\textstyle\prod_\gamma\prod_\beta\prod_\alpha[(\alpha R\beta \,\&\, \beta R\gamma) \supset \alpha R\gamma]$$

Transitive and nontransitive relations, of course, exhaust the possibilities, and it is easy to show that all intransitive relations are nontransitive.

Given any two integers x and y such that $x \neq y$, it is clear that either $x > y$ or $y > x$. But given two integers x and y such that $x \neq y$, it is not necessarily true that either x is the successor of y or y is the successor of x. We express this difference between $>$ and *is the successor of* by saying that $>$ is *connected* in (or with respect to) the class of integers, whereas *is the successor of* is not. Thus, in general,

$$\textbf{Con(R)} \equiv_{df} \textstyle\prod_\beta\prod_\alpha[(\alpha \neq \beta) \supset (\alpha R\beta \lor \beta R\alpha)]$$

The definition of a nonconnected relation seems obvious. And there would be no point in defining "disconnected" relations, on the analogy of asymmetrical and intransitive relations, for the effect of putting $\sim$ in front of

($\alpha R\beta$ **v** $\beta R\alpha$) in the definition just given would be to deny that there were any individuals between which the relation held. Such a property of relations is not of interest.

Having designated certain properties of relations, we now note that there are schemata like 6.3 connecting them; that is, that derived rules of deduction involving these properties can be stated. The significance of these rules can be suggested by noting some cases where there is no necessary connection between the properties of relations. Thus, for example, an asymmetrical relation can be either transitive (*e.g.*, $<$) or intransitive (*e.g.*, *is the father of*), and a reflexive relation can be either symmetrical (*e.g.*, $=$) or nonsymmetrical (*e.g.*, $\leq$). A symmetrical relation can be intransitive (*e.g.*, *is next to*) or transitive (*e.g.*, *is congruent with*). A nonsymmetrical relation can be transitive (*e.g.*, *is the brother of*) or nontransitive (*e.g.*, *loves*). A connected relation may be either asymmetrical (*e.g.*, $>$ with respect to integers) or symmetrical (*e.g.*, *is a relative of*, with respect to a family). A transitive asymmetrical relation may be either connected (*e.g.*, $>$ with respect to integers) or nonconnected (*e.g.*, *is an ancestor of* with respect to human beings). Transitive asymmetrical connected relations are of special importance in mathematics, since they define ordering; for example, the integers are *ordered* by the relation $>$. When a relation is nonsymmetrical, transitive, and connected, it defines what is called a partial ordering.

Not every such combination, however, is possible. Any asymmetrical relation, for example, must be irreflexive. We have already proved this, in fact, in 6.3. We may also prove that every irreflexive transitive relation is asymmetrical.

6.4 $\vdash [\mathrm{Irrx}(R)\ \&\ \mathrm{Tr}(R)] \supset \mathrm{Asym}(R)$

The proof is left to the reader. Similarly we may prove that

6.5 $\vdash [\mathrm{Sym}(R)\ \&\ \mathrm{Tr}(R)] \supset \mathrm{Rx}(R)$

Two further important operations on relations are suggested by the following statements:

$$\text{If } x > y, \text{ then } y < x$$
$$\text{If } x > y, \text{ then } \sim(x < y)$$

We express the relationship between $>$ and $<$ by saying that each is the *converse* of the other. The converse of any relation R is symbolized $\breve{R}$, so that instead of $<$ we could write $\breve{>}$. A *definition* of $\breve{R}$ requires the concept of an ordered pair, which is not explained until Chapter Twelve, Section Seven (although some use of it is made in Chapter Eleven). Here we simply state the relation between R and $\breve{R}$ as an *axiom*.

Ax. $\breve{R}$: $\vdash \prod_\beta \prod_\alpha [\beta \breve{R} \alpha \equiv \alpha R \beta]$

The relationship between $>$ and $\leq$, however, is not that of converses, since when $x \leq y$ it is possible for $y > x$ to be false (namely, when $x = y$). It is rather the case that $\leq$ is the *complement* of $>$. In general,

$$\textbf{Ax. } \overline{\textbf{R}}: \; \vdash \textstyle\prod_\beta \prod_\alpha (\alpha \overline{R} \beta \equiv \mathord{\sim}\alpha R\beta),$$

where $\overline{R}$ symbolizes the complement of R. Notice that once again we formulate a concept axiomatically. One difference between $\check{R}$ and $\overline{R}$ is that $\alpha R\beta$ is inconsistent with $\alpha\check{R}\beta$ only when R is asymmetrical, while $\alpha R\beta$ and $\alpha\overline{R}\beta$ are always mutually inconsistent.

It is useful at this point to define two other ideas. One of them arises from the observation that whatever x and y we choose, if y is the successor of x, then $y > x$. Let us say that the relation *is the successor of* is *included* in the relation $>$. In general,

$$\textbf{R} \subseteq \textbf{S} \equiv_{df} \textstyle\prod_\beta \prod_\alpha (\alpha R\beta \supset \alpha S\beta)$$

Now it can happen that both R $\subseteq$ S and S $\subseteq$ R. Consider the case in which R is *marries* and S is $\underline{marries}$. Now $\prod_y \prod_x (x$ marries $y \supset x$ $\underline{marries}$ $y)$, whence *marries* $\subseteq$ $\underline{marries}$. But similarly, $\underline{marries} \subseteq$ *marries*. In view of this reciprocal inclusion, we say that *marries* $=$ $\underline{marries}$ making use now of the definition

$$\textbf{R} = \textbf{S} \equiv_{df} [(\textbf{R} \subseteq \textbf{S}) \mathbin{\&} (\textbf{S} \subseteq \textbf{R})]$$

Since the point we just made about *marries* is perfectly general, we can prove as a ZPC schema that

6.6 $\;\; \vdash \mathrm{Sym}(R) \supset (R = \check{R})$

Proof:

1.	$\mathrm{Sym}(R)$	
2.	$\prod_\beta \prod_\alpha (\alpha R\beta \supset \beta R\alpha)$	1, Definition Sym (R)
3.	$\gamma R\delta \supset \delta R\gamma$	2, $\prod$E (twice)
4.	$\gamma R\delta \equiv \delta\check{R}\gamma$	Ax. $\check{R}$, $\prod$E (twice)
5.	$\delta\check{R}\gamma \supset \gamma R\delta$	4, $\equiv$E, etc.
6.	$\delta\check{R}\gamma \supset \delta R\gamma$	5, 3, HS
7.	$\prod_\beta \prod_\alpha (\beta\check{R}\alpha \supset \beta R\alpha)$	6, $\prod$I
8.	$\check{R} \subseteq R$	7, Definition R $\subseteq$ S
9.	$R \subseteq \check{R}$	Similarly to 5–8
10.	$R = \check{R}$	8, 9, &I, Definition R = S

$\quad$**11.** $\mathrm{Sym}(R) \supset (R = \check{R})$ $\qquad\qquad$ 1–10, $\supset$I

Let us now prove something that is perhaps a little less obvious; namely, that when a relation is asymmetrical, its converse is included in its complement.

6.7 $\vdash \text{Asym}(R) \supset (\check{R} \subseteq \bar{R})$

Proof:

1.	$\text{Asym}(R)$	
2.	$\prod_\beta \prod_\alpha (\alpha R \beta \supset {\sim} \beta R \alpha)$	1, Definition Asym (R)
3.	$\gamma R \delta \supset {\sim}\delta R \gamma$	2, $\prod$E (twice)
4.	$\gamma R \delta \equiv \delta \check{R} \gamma$	Ax. $\check{R}$, $\prod$E (twice)
5.	$\delta \check{R} \gamma \supset \gamma R \delta$	4, $\equiv$E, &E
6.	$\delta \check{R} \gamma \supset {\sim}\delta R \gamma$	3, 5, HS
7.	$\delta R \gamma \equiv {\sim}\delta \bar{R} \gamma$	Ax. $\bar{R}$, $\prod$E (twice)
8.	${\sim}\delta \bar{R} \gamma \supset \delta R \gamma$	7, $\equiv$E, &E
9.	${\sim}\delta R \gamma \supset \delta \bar{R} \gamma$	8, Cp
10.	$\delta \check{R} \gamma \supset \delta \bar{R} \gamma$	6, 9, HS
11.	$\prod_\beta \prod_\alpha (\alpha \check{R} \beta \supset \alpha \bar{R} \beta)$	10, $\prod$I
12.	$\check{R} \subseteq \bar{R}$	11, Definition R $\subseteq$ S
13.	$\text{Asym}(R) \supset (\check{R} \subseteq \bar{R})$	1–12, $\supset$I

The converse of this can also readily be proved, so that a necessary and sufficient condition for the asymmetry of any relation is that the converse of the relation be included in its complement.

What of the situation in which the complement of a relation is included in its converse? When this happens, they will be connected in any class to whose members it applies. Let us present this proof in an even more sketchy form than hitherto:

6.8 $\vdash (\bar{R} \subseteq \check{R}) \supset \text{Con}(R)$

1.	$\bar{R} \subseteq \check{R}$	
2.	$\gamma \neq \delta$	
3.	${\sim}\gamma R \delta \supset \delta R \gamma$	1, Definitions R $\subseteq$ S, Ax. $\bar{R}$, Ax. $\check{R}$, $\prod$E
4.	$\gamma R \delta \vee \delta R \gamma$	
5.	$\gamma \neq \delta \supset (\gamma R \delta \vee \delta R \gamma)$	2–4, $\supset$I
6.	$\prod_\beta \prod_\alpha [(\alpha \neq \beta) \supset (\alpha R \beta \vee \beta R \alpha)]$	5, $\prod$I
7.	$\text{Con}(R)$	6, Definition Con(R)
8.	$(\bar{R} \subseteq \check{R}) \supset \text{Con}(R)$	1–7, $\supset$I

Notice that the assumption of line 2 functions vacuously, since the only conclusion drawn from it is just the result of discharging it in line 5. But this strategy is required in order to reconstitute the definiens of Con(R).

An example of an R such that $\bar{R} \subset \check{R}$ is $\leq$. But not every connected relation exhibits this property. One that does not is $<$.

Other ZPC schemata concerning converses, complements, inclusion, and identity are the following, the proofs of which will be left as exercises.

6.9 $\vdash R = \check{\check{R}}$

6.10 $\vdash R = \bar{\bar{R}}$

6.11 $\vdash \check{\bar{R}} = \bar{\check{R}}$

6.12 $\vdash (R \subseteq S) \equiv (\check{R} \subseteq \check{S})$

6.13 $\vdash (R \subseteq S) \equiv (\bar{S} \subseteq \bar{R})$

A further useful idea is that of the *relative product* of two relations. The relative product of $>$ and *is the square of* is the relation *is greater than the square of*. Obviously, the relative product does not commute; *is a teacher of a parent of* is altogether different from *is a parent of a teacher of*. We express the relative product of R and S as R/S, which we axiomatize in the following way:

$$\text{Ax. R/S:} \ \vdash \prod_\beta\prod_\alpha[\alpha R/S\beta \equiv \sum_\gamma(\alpha R\gamma \ \& \ \gamma S\beta)]$$

Let us now prove

6.14 $\vdash (R \subseteq S) \supset [(R/T) \subseteq (S/T)]$

1. $R \subseteq S$	
2. $\prod_\beta\prod_\alpha(\alpha R\beta \supset \alpha S\beta)$	1, Definition $R \subseteq S$
3. $\gamma R\delta \supset \gamma S\delta$	2, $\prod$E (twice)
4. $\gamma R/T\delta \equiv \sum_\varepsilon(\gamma R\varepsilon \ \& \ \varepsilon T\delta)$	Ax. R/S, $\prod$E (twice)
5. $\gamma R/T\delta$	
6. $\sum_\varepsilon(\gamma R\varepsilon \ \& \ \varepsilon T\delta)$	4, $\equiv$E, &E, 5, $\supset$E
7. $\sum_\varepsilon(\gamma R\varepsilon \ \& \ \varepsilon T\delta) \equiv \gamma S/T\delta$	Ax. R/S, $\prod$E (twice)
8. $\gamma S/T\delta$	7, $\equiv$E, &E, 6, $\supset$E
9. $\gamma R/T\delta \supset \gamma S/T\delta$	5–8, $\supset$I
10. $\prod_\beta\prod_\alpha(\alpha R/T\beta \supset \alpha S/T\beta)$	9, $\prod$I
11. $R/T \subseteq S/T$	10, Definition $R \subseteq S$
12. $(R \subseteq S) \supset (R/T \subseteq S/T)$	1–11, $\supset$I

Other ZPC schemata, the proofs of which are left to the reader, include:

6.15 $\vdash (R \subseteq S) \supset (T/R \subseteq T/S)$

6.16 $\vdash (R/S)/T = R/(S/T)$

Hence, the associative law holds for the relative product, even if the commutative law does not. Finally, we have

6.17 $\vdash \widecheck{R/S} = \check{S}/\check{R}$

EXERCISE 6.2

I. Consider the following uninterpreted axioms:

Ax. 1. If x/y then not y/x.
Ax. 2. If x/y and y/z, then x/z.

1. Translate the above axioms into quantified statements of GPL, symbolizing x/y as $R(x,y)$.

2. Translate the following theorems into quantified statements of GPL, and derive each of them from the axioms as translated in the preceding problem:
Th. 1. If x/y and y/z, then not z/x.
Th. 2. Not both x/y and y/x.
Th. 3. Not x/x.
Th. 4. If x/y, y/z, and z/w, then not w/x.
Th. 5. Either not x/y or not y/x.

3. Translate each of the above axioms and theorems again, this time using only the existential quantifier, $\sum$.

4. Justify each of the retranslations of the preceding problem (3) by deriving it from the corresponding original translation.

II. 1. Each of the axioms given in the first part of this exercise shows the relation / to have a peculiar property. Name that property for each axiom.

2. Do any of the theorems do the same? Name the property for each theorem that does.

3. Prove that any relation with the two properties you named in II-1 above must possess each property named in II-2.

III. Which of the axioms and theorems of Exercise 6.1, part IV, show either of the relations ___ = ___ and ___ < ___ to have some one of the particular properties discussed in the text, and which property does each define?

IV. Name for each of the following relations all of those properties, described in Section 6.2, that it may be said to possess.

1. equals

2. is greater than

3. is not less than

4. is greater than or equal to

5. is the successor of

6. is a predecessor of

7. is congruent with

8. is fond of

9. is the spouse of

10. is the wife of

11. is the uncle of

12. is the brother of

13. is the sibling of

14. is the friend of

15. is north of

16. is hungry for

17. loves the wife of

18. is next to

19. defeats

20. defeats the brother of

21. is on the right of

22. is an ancestor of

23. is the square root of

24. is as sour as

25. is compatible with

26. is incompatible with the denial of

27. is the equivalent normal form of

28. logically implies

29. is logically equivalent to

30. is logically equivalent to the denial of

V. Decide whether each of the following is true or false. If it is true, prove
   it, assuming a nonempty relation (*i.e.*, an R such that $\sum_\beta \sum_\alpha (\alpha R \beta)$). If it
   is false, give a counterexample.

   1. Every asymmetrical relation is also nonsymmetrical.

   2. Every irreflexive transitive relation is also nonsymmetrical.

   3. Every irreflexive transitive relation is also asymmetrical.

   4. All intransitive relations are nontransitive.

   5. It is not the case that all nontransitive relations are intransitive.

6. Every symmetrical transitive relation is also reflexive.

7. The converse of Theorem 6.7.

8. An asymmetrical relation can be nontransitive. (Produce such a relation.)

9. A reflexive relation cannot be asymmetrical.

10. A symmetrical relation can be nontransitive.

11. A nonsymmetrical relation cannot be intransitive.

12. It is false that a connected relation cannot be nonsymmetrical.

VI. Prove

1. Schema 6.4	**6.** Schema 6.12
2. Schema 6.5	**7.** Schema 6.13
3. Schema 6.9	**8.** Schema 6.15
4. Schema 6.10	**9.** Schema 6.16
5. Schema 6.11	**10.** Schema 6.17

VII. Symbolize the following arguments using the suggested notation. Then derive the conclusion of each from the premises, and justify each step by citing the rules that are used. (In general, symbols are explained only when not obvious.)

1. Everybody is more naive than is Socrates. If any person is more naive than another, then that other is not more naive than the first. Therefore, Socrates is more naive than no one. [$P(x) = x$ is a person; $N(x,y) = x$ is more naive than y; s = Socrates]

2. Only those (countries) which are weaker than Germany are afraid of China. Britain is weaker than none except those which are more courageous than Finland. Furthermore, none which is more courageous than the Soviet Union is excelled in courage by Germany. Therefore, if Finland is more courageous than the Soviet Union, then Britain is not afraid of China. [x, y, z, etc. = countries; $W(x,y) = x$ is weaker than y; $A(x,y) = x$ is afraid of y; $C(x,y) = x$ is more courageous than y; c = China; b = Britain; f = Finland; g = Germany; s = Soviet Union]

3. Scrooge is happier than no one. If anyone is sadder than another, then the other is not sadder than the first. Anyone is sadder than another if and only if he is not happier. So if anybody exists, then somebody is happier than Scrooge. [$P(x)$; $H(x,y)$; $S(x,y)$; s]

4. Horses are animals. Therefore, the heads of horses are the heads of animals. [$P(x)$; $A(x)$; $H(x,y)$]

5. Every number is less than some other number. Thus, it is not the case that there is a number which is not less than any other number. [N(x); L(x,y)]

6. All moose are animals. Therefore, if Eben slays a moose, he slays an animal. [M(x); A(x); S(x,y); e]

7. Some people are respected by everybody. Hence, there are some people who respect themselves. [P(x); R(x,y)]

8. Any number is either not less than any other given number, or it is not greater than that number. If a number equals seventy-nine, then it is less than eighty-seven, and if it equals ninety it is greater. There-fore, any number is either not equal to seventy-nine or not equal to ninety. [N(x); L(x,y); G(x,y); E(x,y); e; s; n]

9. Only a genius would play a musical instrument at the age of two. But a citizen of Austria once played the piano at the age of two, and the piano is a musical instrument. No citizen of Japan can be a citizen of Austria. So not all geniuses are citizens of Japan. [G(x); T(x) = x is two years old; M(x) = x is a musical instrument; P(x,y); C(x,y); a; j; p = the piano]

10. All absolutely adequate thought involves absolute certainty about something. There can be no absolute certainty about anything. Therefore, no one has ever had an absolutely adequate thought. [A(x) = x is absolutely adequate; T(x); C(x) = x is absolutely cer-tain; P(x) = x is a person; I(x,y); H(x,y)]

11. If any integer is even, the product of that integer and any other integer at all is an even integer. An integer is even if and only if it is not odd. Thus we can infer that if *m* and *n* are integers and they have a product which is an odd integer, then *m* and *n* are both odd. [I(x); E(x); O(x); P(x,y,z) = x is the product of y and z; m; n]

12. Everything done in deceit is a crime, and anybody who encourages a crime is a criminal. Someone who is very timid has encouraged certain deceitful activities. Therefore, some criminal is very timid. [D(x); C(x); V(x) = x is a criminal; P(x); T(x) = x is very timid; A(x); E(x,y)]

13. Only a cad would steal money from his grandmother. So if Jonathan is the grandson of both Mrs. Smith and Mrs. Brown and is not a cad, then he has stolen money from neither of them. [C(x); M(x); G(x,y) = x is the grandson of y; S(x,y,z) = x steals y from z; j; s; b]

14. A substance is (by definition) unlimited by anything. Any substance can be limited only by a different substance. If any two substances are different from one another, then one limits the other and is limited by the other. Consequently, if any substance exists then no substance is different from it. [S(x); L(x,y) = x limits y; D(x,y) = x is different from y]

15. Some students are bibliophiles, but, while every university is attended by some students, there is no university which is attended only by students who are bibliophiles. There is a university, however, which is attended by all those students who are bibliophiles. So there is a university at which some students are bibliophiles, and others are not. [S(x); B(x); U(x); A(x,y)]

VIII. Provide deductions for the following inferences:

1. $\prod_x[F(x) \supset G(x)]$
   /∴ $\prod_y\{\sum_x[F(x) \& H(y,x)] \supset \sum_x[G(x) \& H(y,x)]\}$

2. $\sum_y\{F(y) \& \prod_x[G(x) \supset H(x,y)]\}$
   /∴ $\prod_x\{G(x) \supset \sum_y[F(y) \& H(x,y)]\}$

3. $\sum_y\{F(y) \& \prod_x[F(x) \supset G(x,y)]\}$ /∴ $\sum_x[F(x) \& G(x,x)]$

4. $\prod_x[F(x) \supset G(x)]$
   /∴ $\prod_x\{\sum_y[F(y) \& H(x,y)] \supset \sum_y[G(y) \& H(x,y)]\}$

5. $\prod_x\{[F(x) \& \sim G(x)] \supset \sum_y[H(x,y) \& J(y)]\}$
   $\sum_x\{K(x) \& F(x) \& \prod_y[H(x,y) \supset K(y)]\}$
   $\prod_x[K(x) \supset \sim G(x)]$ /∴ $\sum_x[K(x) \& J(x)]$

6. $\prod_x[F(x) \supset \sum_y G(y,x)]$
   $\prod_x[G(x,a) \supset H(x,a)]$
   $\prod_x \sim H(x,a)$ /∴ $\sim F(a)$

7. $\prod_x\{F(x) \supset \prod_y[G(y) \supset H(x,y)]\}$
   $\sum_y\{J(y) \& \prod_z[K(z) \supset H(y,z)]\}$
   $\prod_x\prod_y\prod_z\{[H(x,y) \& H(y,z)] \supset H(x,z)\}$
   $\prod_y[J(y) \supset G(y)]$ /∴ $\prod_x\{F(x) \supset \prod_z[K(z) \supset H(x,z)]\}$

8. There is a philosopher whom all philosophers criticize; thus there is a philosopher who criticizes himself.

9. There is a man that all men admire; thus every man admires some man or other.

10. A thinking man can outwit a nonthinker. And since some philosophers are not thinkers, it follows that any thinker can outwit some philosopher or other.

11. Every student who receives a degree on a certain date has been examined before that date. Thus every student who receives a degree has been examined at one time or another.

12. Provide a deduction for the proof of Brown's citizenship of which the premises are given on the first page of Section 1.1.

6.3 Derived Rules of GPL-1

Just as it is helpful in PL and MPL to have additional rules for handling proofs, this is likewise true for GPL-1. These derived rules often permit expeditious and time-saving analysis of steps in a deduction. We present here rules for introducing and eliminating quantifiers, for changing variables, for replacement, and for duality.

GENERALIZED RULES OF INTRODUCTION AND ELIMINATION

Although most of the instances of polyadic predicates so far discussed have been dyadic or triadic, the techniques of GPL-1 apply to formulas involving *n*-adic predicates in general. In such cases the repeated use of quantificational rules—of $\prod$I, for example—is burdensome. In fact, in some of the deductions on the preceding pages, repeated use of $\prod$I has been elided and justified as one step. That such elision is permissible we see from the rule

6.18* $\varphi(\beta_n, \beta_{n-1}, \ldots, \beta_1)$
$$\therefore \prod_{\alpha_n}[\prod_{\alpha_{n-1}}(\ldots\{\prod_{\alpha_1}[\varphi(\alpha_n, \alpha_{n-1}, \ldots, \alpha_1)]\})],$$

where none of $\beta_n, \beta_{n-1}, \ldots, \beta_1$ occurs free in a premise or undischarged assumption and where $\varphi(\beta_n, \beta_{n-1}, \ldots, \beta_1)$ is like $\varphi(\alpha_n, \alpha_{n-1}, \ldots, \alpha_1)$ except for containing free occurrences of β_i where and only where $\varphi(\alpha_n, \alpha_{n-1}, \ldots, \alpha_1)$ contains free occurrences of α_i.

The deduction schema proving this rule is obtained by *n* successive applications of $\prod$I. In each case where $\prod$I is applied the restrictions on its use must be observed.

Similarly, the elision of repeated uses of $\prod$E is permissible, as we see from the rule

6.19* $\prod_{\alpha_n}[\prod_{\alpha_{n-1}}(\ldots\{\prod_{\alpha_1}[\varphi(\alpha_n, \alpha_{n-1}, \ldots, \alpha_1)]\})]$
$$\therefore \varphi(\beta_n, \beta_{n-1}, \ldots, \beta_1)$$

where $\varphi(\beta_n, \beta_{n-1}, \ldots, \beta_1)$ is like $\varphi(\alpha_n, \alpha_{n-1}, \ldots, \alpha_1)$ except for containing free occurrences of β_i wherever $\varphi(\alpha_n, \alpha_{n-1}, \ldots, \alpha_1)$ contains free occurrences of α_i.

The deduction schema proving this rule is obtained by *n* successive applications of $\prod$E. In each case where $\prod$E is applied, the restrictions on its use must be observed; hence the restriction on 6.19*.

---

* The reason these rules are starred is that they will be restated in Table 6.1 in simpler notation.

We now pause to streamline our notation, which is a bit too cumbersome for our purposes. Our modified notation involves four changes:

(a) Dropping the left-hand parentheses separating quantifiers, and, of course, the mates of these parentheses. We have, to a considerable extent, already been following this practice.

(b) Dropping the parentheses enclosing a quantified expression, unless any ambiguity results from doing this. This, too, represents a procedure already in effect.

(c) Dropping all occurrences of the same quantifier except the first in a sequence of such occurrences, and dropping the corresponding variables following the predicate letter. Thus instead of $\prod_{\alpha_n} \prod_{\alpha_{n-1}}$, $\ldots \prod_{\alpha_2} \prod_{\alpha_1} \varphi(\alpha_n,\ \alpha_{n-1},\ \ldots,\ \alpha_2,\ \alpha_1)$, we shall write simply $\prod_{\alpha_n \ldots \alpha_1} \varphi$ $(\alpha_n, \ldots, \alpha_1)$.

(d) Dropping, in some cases, the individual variables grouped together following a predicate. Thus instead of $\varphi(\alpha_n, \alpha_{n-1}, \ldots, \alpha_1)$ we shall write just φ on some occasions.

It is worth noting that (d) adds generality as well as convenience, for although the statement function $\varphi(\alpha_n, \alpha_{n-1}, \ldots, \alpha_1)$ makes clear that α_1, for example, is free in it, the formula φ does not make this explicit. Thus what we can prove of φ *simpliciter* will hold whether α_1(or α_i) is free in φ or not.

Similar to the generalized rules for $\prod$I and $\prod$E, there are generalized rules for $\sum$I and $\sum$E. We have

6.20* $\varphi(\beta_n, \ldots, \beta_1)$
∴ $\sum_{\alpha_n \ldots \alpha_1} \varphi(\alpha_n, \ldots, \alpha_1)$,

where $\varphi(\beta_n, \ldots, \beta_1)$ is like $\varphi(\alpha_n, \ldots, \alpha_1)$ except for containing free occurrences of β_i wherever $\varphi(\alpha_n, \ldots, \alpha_1)$ contains free occurrences of α_i.

The deduction schema establishing this rule is obtained by n successive uses of $\sum$I, each use involving the restriction on $\sum$I and hence requiring the restriction stated for 6.20*.

The generalized rule for $\sum$E is

6.21* $\sum_{\alpha_n \ldots \alpha_1} \varphi(\alpha_n, \ldots, \alpha_1)$
⌐— $\varphi(\beta_n, \ldots, \beta_1)$
⋮
ψ

ψ,

where none of $\beta_n, \ldots, \beta_1$ occurs free in any premise or undischarged assumption of the deduction, nor in ψ and where $\varphi(\beta_n, \ldots, \beta_1)$ is like $\varphi(\alpha_n, \ldots, \alpha_1)$ except for containing free occurrences of β_i where and only where $\varphi(\alpha_n, \ldots, \alpha_1)$ contains free occurrences of α_i.

Again, the restriction results from the fact that the deduction schema establishing this rule is obtained by n successive uses of ΣE, each use involving a restriction.

RULE OF REPLACEMENT

We proved the derived rule Rep for PL in Chapter Two and asserted in Chapter Five that this rule could be used in MPL, deferring until this point a proof of Rep for predicate logic. We are now in a position to prove Rep for GPL-1 and note that it holds for the special case of MPL. The power of the derived rule Rep is evident in that it permits us to appeal directly to ZPC biconditionals in justifying steps in a deduction. There are four lemmas required for Rep. We establish the first by means of the following deduction schema:

6.22* $\prod_{\alpha_n...\alpha_1}[\varphi(\alpha_n, \ldots, \alpha_1) \supset \psi(\alpha_n, \ldots, \alpha_1)]$
$\therefore \prod_{\alpha_n...\alpha_1}\varphi(\alpha_n, \ldots, \alpha_1) \supset \prod_{\alpha_n...\alpha_1}\psi(\alpha_n, \ldots, \alpha_1)$

> 1. $\prod_{\alpha_n...\alpha_1}[\varphi(\alpha_n, \ldots, \alpha_1) \supset \psi(\alpha_n, \ldots, \alpha_1)]$
> 2. $\varphi(\beta_n, \ldots, \beta_1) \supset \psi(\beta_n, \ldots, \beta_1)$ 1, 6.19*
> 3. $\prod_{\alpha_n...\alpha_1}\varphi(\alpha_n, \ldots, \alpha_1)$
> 4. $\varphi(\beta_n, \ldots, \beta_1)$ 3, 6.19*
> 5. $\psi(\beta_n, \ldots, \beta_1)$ 2, 4, $\supset E$
> 6. $\prod_{\alpha_n...\alpha_1}\psi(\alpha_n, \ldots, \alpha_1)$ 5, 6.18*

7. $\prod_{\alpha_n...\alpha_1}\varphi(\alpha_n, \ldots, \alpha_1) \supset$
   $\prod_{\alpha_n...\alpha_1}\psi(\alpha_n, \ldots, \alpha_1)$ 3–6, $\supset I$

We may now establish

6.23* $\prod_{\alpha_n...\alpha_1}[\varphi(\alpha_n, \ldots, \alpha_1) \equiv \psi(\alpha_n, \ldots, \alpha_1)]$
$\therefore \prod_{\alpha_n...\alpha_1}\varphi(\alpha_n, \ldots, \alpha_1) \equiv \prod_{\alpha_n...\alpha_1}\psi(\alpha_n, \ldots, \alpha_1)$

The deduction schema is

> 1. $\prod_{\alpha_n...\alpha_1}[\varphi(\alpha_n, \ldots, \alpha_1) \equiv \psi(\alpha_n, \ldots, \alpha_1)]$
> 2. $\varphi(\beta_n, \ldots, \beta_1) \equiv \psi(\beta_n, \ldots, \beta_1)$ 1, 6.19*
> 3. $[\varphi(\beta_n, \ldots, \beta_1) \supset \psi(\beta_n, \ldots, \beta_1)] \,\&$
> $[\psi(\beta_n, \ldots, \beta_1) \supset \varphi(\beta_n, \ldots, \beta_1)]$ 2, $\equiv E$
> 4. $\varphi(\beta_n, \ldots, \beta_1) \supset \psi(\beta_n, \ldots, \beta_1)$ 3, $\&E$
> 5. $\prod_{\alpha_n...\alpha_1}[\varphi(\alpha_n, \ldots, \alpha_1) \supset \psi(\alpha_n, \ldots, \alpha_1)]$ 4, 6.18*
> 6. $\prod_{\alpha_n...\alpha_1}\varphi(\alpha_n, \ldots, \alpha_1) \supset$
> $\prod_{\alpha_n}\cdots\alpha_1\psi(\alpha_n, \ldots, \alpha_1)$ 5, 6.22*
> 7. $\psi(\beta_n, \ldots, \beta_1) \supset \varphi(\beta_n, \ldots, \beta_1)$ 3, $\&E$
> 8. $\prod_{\alpha_n...\alpha_1}[\psi(\alpha_n, \ldots, \alpha_1) \supset \varphi(\alpha_n, \ldots, \alpha_1)]$ 7, 6.18*
> 9. $\prod_{\alpha_n...\alpha_1}\psi(\alpha_n, \ldots, \alpha_1) \supset$
> $\prod_{\alpha_n...\alpha_1}\varphi(\alpha_n, \ldots, \alpha_1)$ 8, 6.22*
> 10. $\prod_{\alpha_n...\alpha_1}\varphi(\alpha_n, \ldots, \alpha_1) \equiv$
> $\prod_{\alpha_n...\alpha_1}\psi(\alpha_n, \ldots, \alpha_1)$ 6, 9, $\equiv I$

We also need similar rules for Σ. That is

6.24*
$$\prod_{\alpha_n \ldots \alpha_1}[\varphi(\alpha_n, \ldots, \alpha_1) \supset \psi(\alpha_n, \ldots, \alpha_1)]$$
$$\therefore \Sigma_{\alpha_n \ldots \alpha_1}\varphi(\alpha_n, \ldots, \alpha_1) \supset \Sigma_{\alpha_n \ldots \alpha_1}\psi(\alpha_n, \ldots, \alpha_1)$$

The deduction schema is

1. $\prod_{\alpha_n \ldots \alpha_1}[\varphi(\alpha_n, \ldots, \alpha_1) \supset \psi(\alpha_n, \ldots, \alpha_1)]$
2. $\varphi(\beta_n, \ldots, \beta_1) \supset \psi(\beta_n, \ldots, \beta_1)$ — 1, 6.19*
3. $\Sigma_{\alpha_n \ldots \alpha_1}\varphi(\alpha_n, \ldots, \alpha_1)$
4. $\varphi(\beta_n, \ldots, \beta_1)$
5. $\psi(\beta_n, \ldots, \beta_1)$ — 2, 4, $\supset$E
6. $\Sigma_{\alpha_n \ldots \alpha_1}\psi(\alpha_n, \ldots, \alpha_1)$ — 5, 6.20*
7. $\Sigma_{\alpha_n \ldots \alpha_1}\psi(\alpha_n, \ldots, \alpha_1)$ — 3, 4-6, 6.21*
8. $\Sigma_{\alpha_n \ldots \alpha_1}\varphi(\alpha_n, \ldots, \alpha_1) \supset \Sigma_{\alpha_n \ldots \alpha_1}\psi(\alpha_n, \ldots, \alpha_1)$ — 3-7, $\supset$I

We also need

6.25*
$$\prod_{\alpha_n \ldots \alpha_1}[\varphi(\alpha_n, \ldots, \alpha_1) \equiv \psi(\alpha_n, \ldots, \alpha_1)]$$
$$\therefore \Sigma_{\alpha_n \ldots \alpha_1}\varphi(\alpha_n, \ldots, \alpha_1) \equiv \Sigma_{\alpha_n \ldots \alpha_1}\psi(\alpha_n. \ldots, \alpha_1)$$

The deduction schema is an analogue of that for 6.23*, using 6.24* in place of 6.22*.

We now state the rule of replacement for predicate logic in schematic form:

Rep: Let L be a line of a deduction containing $\psi(\alpha_n, \ldots, \alpha_1)$ at one place or more and let L* be like L except for containing $\varphi(\alpha_n, \ldots, \alpha_1)$ at one or more places where L contained $\psi(\alpha_n, \ldots, \alpha_1)$. If $\alpha_n, \ldots, \alpha_1$ are all the bound variables of L, then

(1) if $\prod_{\alpha_n \ldots \alpha_1}[\varphi(\alpha_n, \ldots, \alpha_1) \equiv \psi(\alpha_n, \ldots, \alpha_1)]$, then

$$L \qquad\qquad L*$$
$$\text{and}$$
$$\therefore L* \qquad \therefore L;$$

that is, $L \equiv L*$

(2) if $\vdash \prod_{\alpha_n \ldots \alpha_1}[\varphi(\alpha_n, \ldots, \alpha_1) \equiv \psi(\alpha_n, \ldots, \alpha_1)]$
then $\vdash L \equiv L*$.

As in the case of PL, we proceed by the use of mathematical induction. We show that Rep holds for all lines with no operators—this is the basis of the induction—and that if Rep holds for a line containing n operators, it holds for a line containing $n + 1$ operators—this is the induction step.

As in the case of PL, our method of considering possible lines is to arrange them in numerical order, basing this order upon the number of times any one of the logical operators for PL (*i.e.*, $\sim$, &, $\mathbf{v}$, $\supset$), or $\prod$ or $\sum$, occurs outside $\psi(\alpha_n, \ldots, \alpha_1)$ in L.

Basis: If we consider a line L having no operators outside $\psi(\alpha_n, \ldots, \alpha_1)$ then L is $\psi(\alpha_n, \ldots, \alpha_1)$. Under the conditions of the rule of Rep, $\prod_{\alpha_n \ldots \alpha_1}[\varphi(\alpha_n, \ldots, \alpha_1) \equiv \psi(\alpha_n, \ldots, \alpha_1)]$ and L* is $\varphi(\alpha_n, \ldots, \alpha_1)$. We have by 6.19* that $\varphi(\alpha_n, \ldots, \alpha_1) \equiv \psi(\alpha_n, \ldots, \alpha_1)$, and so L $\equiv$ L*. This completes the proof of the basis.

Induction Step: We want to show that if $\prod_{\alpha_n \ldots \alpha_1}[\varphi(\alpha_n, \ldots, \alpha_1) \equiv \psi(\alpha_n, \ldots, \alpha_1)] \supset$ (L $\equiv$ L*) for L of any given order of complexity, then $\prod_{\alpha_n \ldots \alpha_1}[\varphi(\alpha_n, \ldots, \alpha_1) \equiv \psi(\alpha_n, \ldots, \alpha_1)] \supset [f(L) \equiv f(L*)]$, where $f(L)$ is either $\sim$L, χ & L, χ $\mathbf{v}$ L, $\chi \supset$ L, L $\supset \chi$, $\chi \equiv$ L, $\prod_{\alpha_i}(L)$, or $\sum_{\alpha_i}(L)$. Since $\psi(\alpha_n, \ldots, \alpha_1)$ is embedded in L, the quantifiers in the last two contexts bind any α_i occurring in ψ. Since the argument that Rep holds in these cases is analogous to that in Chapter Two, Section Six, we only sketch it here.

I. *Negative Context.* $\psi(\alpha_n, \ldots, \alpha_1)$ occurs in the context $\sim$L. The deduction schema showing that $\prod_{\alpha_n \ldots \alpha_1}[\varphi(\alpha_n, \ldots, \alpha_1) \equiv \psi(\alpha_n, \ldots, \alpha_1)] \supset$ ($\sim$L $\equiv \sim$L*) is analogous to that for the negative context in Chapter Two, as are the deduction schemata for the

II.   *Conjunctive Context,*
III. *Conditional Context,*
IV. *Alternative Context,* and
V.   *Biconditional Context.*

We consider the details of the schemata for the universal context and the existential context, which are not found in the proof of Rep for PL.

VI. *Universal Context.* $\psi(\alpha_n, \ldots, \alpha_1)$ occurs in the context $\prod_{\alpha_i}$L. We give a schema showing that the inference from

$$\prod_{\alpha_n \ldots \alpha_1}[\varphi(\alpha_n, \ldots, \alpha_1) \equiv \psi(\alpha_n, \ldots, \alpha_1)] \supset (L \equiv L*)$$

to $\prod_{\alpha_n \ldots \alpha_1}[\varphi(\alpha_n, \ldots, \alpha_1) \equiv \psi(\alpha_n, \ldots, \alpha_1)] \supset (\prod_{\alpha_i}L \equiv \prod_{\alpha_i}L*)$

is justified.

—1. $\prod_{\alpha_n \ldots \alpha_1}[\varphi(\alpha_n, \ldots, \alpha_1) \equiv \psi(\alpha_n, \ldots, \alpha_1)] \supset (L \equiv L*)$		
—2. $\prod_{\alpha_n \ldots \alpha_1}[\varphi(\alpha_n, \ldots, \alpha_1) \equiv \psi(\alpha_n, \ldots, \alpha_1)]$		
3. L $\equiv$ L*		2, 1, $\supset$E
4. $\prod_{\alpha_i}(L \equiv L*)$		3, 6-18*
5. $\prod_{\alpha_i}L \equiv \prod_{\alpha_i}L*$		4, 6-23*

6. $\prod_{\alpha_n \ldots \alpha_1}[\varphi(\alpha_n, \ldots, \alpha_1) \equiv \psi(\alpha_n, \ldots, \alpha_1)]$
     $\supset (\prod_{\alpha_i}L \equiv \prod_{\alpha_i}L*)$ 2–5, $\supset$I

Finally, discharge of the hypothesis of the induction (line 1) establishes the induction step for this case. In this deduction schema we presuppose the condition of Rep that α_i does not occur free in $\prod_{\alpha_n \ldots \alpha_1}[\varphi(\alpha_n, \ldots, \alpha_1) \equiv \psi(\alpha_n, \ldots, \alpha_1)]$. It is this restriction which justifies the use of $\prod$I at line 3.

VII. *Existential Context.* $\psi(\alpha_n, \ldots, \alpha_1)$ occurs in the context $\sum_{\alpha_i}L$. We give a schema showing that the inference from

$$\prod_{\alpha_n \ldots \alpha_1}[\varphi(\alpha_n, \ldots, \alpha_1) \equiv \psi(\alpha_n, \ldots, \alpha_1)] \supset (L \equiv L^*)$$

to $\prod_{\alpha_n \ldots \alpha_1}[\varphi(\alpha_n, \ldots, \alpha_1) \equiv \psi(\alpha_n, \ldots, \alpha_1)] \supset (\sum_{\alpha_i}L \equiv \sum_{\alpha_i}L^*)$

is justified.

───1. $\prod_{\alpha_n \ldots \alpha_1}[\varphi(\alpha_n, \ldots, \alpha_1) \equiv \psi(\alpha_n, \ldots, \alpha_1)] \supset (L \equiv L^*)$

┌──2. $\prod_{\alpha_n \ldots \alpha_1}[\varphi(\alpha_n, \ldots, \alpha_1) \equiv \psi(\alpha_n, \ldots, \alpha_1)]$

3. $L \equiv L^*$	2, 1, $\supset$E
4. $\prod_{\alpha_i}(L \equiv L^*)$	3, 6-18*
5. $\sum_{\alpha_i}L \equiv \sum_{\alpha_i}L^*$	4, 6-25*

   6. $\prod_{\alpha_n \ldots \alpha_1}[\varphi(\alpha_n, \ldots, \alpha_1) \equiv \psi(\alpha_n, \ldots, \alpha_1)]$
      $\supset (\sum_{\alpha_i}L \equiv \sum_{\alpha_i}L^*)$ 2–5, $\supset$I

And, finally, discharge of the hypothesis of the induction (line 1) establishes the induction step for this case. The analysis of these seven cases establishes the induction step in general and so the first form of Rep for GPL-1. Since MPL is a special case of GPL-1, the rule holds for MPL.

The second version of Rep follows directly, since we have shown that a deduction exists of the form:

───1. $\prod_{\alpha_n \ldots \alpha_1}[\psi(\alpha_n, \ldots, \alpha_1) \equiv \varphi(\alpha_n, \ldots, \alpha_1)]$
     $\vdots$
    k. $L \equiv L^*$.

By $\supset$I, $\vdash \prod_{\alpha_n \ldots \alpha_1}[\psi(\alpha_n, \ldots, \alpha_1) \equiv \varphi(\alpha_n, \ldots, \alpha_1)]$, and $\supset$E we obtain $\vdash L \equiv L^*$.

REWRITING

Another result of the quantificational rules, of some importance, is the possibility of rewriting variables in formulas. That is, it is sometimes useful to change the variables in a formula in order to facilitate use of the formula in a deduction, as when a definition is introduced as a line. This change is quite possible, as, for example, we may rewrite

    (1) $\sum_x F(x)$

as

    (1') $\sum_y F(y)$

or

    (1'') $\sum_u F(u)$.

Similarly,

(2) $F(x) \vee \prod_x[F(x)]$

may be written as

(2') $F(x) \vee \prod_y[F(y)]$

(2'') $F(x) \vee \prod_z[F(z)]$.

We may rewrite polyadic formulas such as

(3) $\prod_x\prod_y F(x,y) \ \& \ G(z)$

in the form

(3') $\prod_z\prod_y F(z,y) \ \& \ G(z)$

or

(3'') $\prod_w\prod_u F(w,u) \ \& \ G(z)$.

In such rewriting we must preserve the structure of the binding of variables and the distinction between bound and free variables. That is, no variables that are free in the formula we rewrite can be bound as a result of the change, and no variables that were bound should become free. We cannot allow

(4) $\prod_x\prod_y[F(x,y) \vee F(x,z)]$

to become either

(4') $\prod_z\prod_w[F(z,w) \vee F(z,z)]$

or

(4'') $\prod_x\prod_z[F(x,z) \vee F(x,z)]$.

We state procedures for rewriting variables as follows:

Rewrite: Where φ is a formula having n symbols, φ may be rewritten as φ' if the two formulas have the same number of symbols and if (1) where the kth symbol of φ is not a variable, the kth symbol of φ' is the same; (2) where the kth symbol of φ is a free variable, the kth symbol of φ' is the same free variable; (3) where the kth symbol of φ is a variable bound by the lth quantifier of φ, the kth symbol of φ' is a (possibly different) variable bound by the lth quantifier of φ'.

We may establish useful equivalences between formulas and their re-writings. For example,

6.26A   (1) $\vdash \prod_\alpha\varphi(\alpha) \equiv \prod_\gamma\varphi(\gamma)$

         and

     (2) $\vdash \sum_\alpha\varphi(\alpha) \equiv \sum_\gamma\varphi(\gamma)$

     where the right side of each equivalence is a rewriting of the left side.

The deduction schema for the left-to-right implication in (1) is

$$
\begin{array}{ll}
\text{1. } \prod_\alpha \varphi(\alpha) & \\
\text{2. } \varphi(\beta) & \text{1, } \prod\text{E} \\
\text{3. } \prod_\gamma \varphi(\gamma) & \text{2, } \prod\text{I} \\
\text{4. } \prod_\alpha \varphi(\alpha) \supset \prod_\gamma \varphi(\gamma) & \text{1–3, } \supset\text{I}
\end{array}
$$

Note that the restriction on the use of $\prod$E in line 2 ensures that β is free wherever α is free and, hence, β is not bound accidentally by some quantifier in φ. Also, the restrictions on the use of $\prod$I in line 3 ensure that β was not free in $\prod_\alpha\varphi(\alpha)$, and that β occurs free in $\varphi(\beta)$ where and only where γ occurs free in $\varphi(\alpha)$. These restrictions constitute the conditions for rewriting.

The deduction schema for (2) is left to the reader. By repeated use of Rep and Metatheorem 6.26A we may obtain a generalized result for any number of variables.

6.26B   Where φ' is a rewriting of φ,
$$\vdash \varphi \equiv \varphi'.$$

TABLE OF DERIVED RULES

We now collect the derived rules so far established and state without proof some additional derived rules for GPL-1. In order to do this in the simplest form, we introduce a further simplification of our notation. This notational change eliminates writing explicitly all the free variables $\alpha_n, \ldots, \alpha_1$ in φ, and is accomplished by allowing a single letter to refer to any of them. In effect, this change permits the notation for the rules in Chapter Five to apply to formulas containing polyadic predicates, as indeed we have assumed all along. Thus we rewrite 6.18* as

6.18 $\varphi(\beta)$
$\therefore\ \prod_\alpha\varphi(\alpha)$

where β does not occur free in a premise or undischarged assumption of the deduction and where $\varphi(\beta)$ is like $\varphi(\alpha)$ except for containing free occurrences of β where and only where $\varphi(\alpha)$ contains free occurrences of α.

6.18 has the form of $\prod$I in Table 5.1, but we now understand β to refer to any free variable in φ, and α to any variable bound by the universal quantifier. Thus $\varphi(\beta)$ might be

(1) $F(x,y,z) \vee G(x,y)$

or

(2) $H(w,z) \supset \prod_z[F(z,x) \mathbin{\&} G(w)]$

If we let β refer to x in (1) and w in (2) then $\prod_\alpha \varphi(\alpha)$ would be

(1′) $\prod_x [F(x,y,z) \vee G(x,y)]$

or

(2′) $\prod_w \{H(w,z) \supset \prod_z [F(z,x) \,\&\, G(w)]\}.$

However, if $\varphi(\beta)$ is (1′) and β is y, then $\prod_\alpha \varphi(\alpha)$ would be

(1″) $\prod_y \{\prod_x [F(x,y,z) \vee G(x,y)]\}.$

With this notation, 6.1 is to be understood to apply to any variables in φ which are bound as indicated by the existential and universal quantifiers, rather than to a case where there are only two variables. Thus, if $\varphi(\alpha,\beta)$ is (1) above, α being x and β being y, an instance of 6.1 is

(1‴) $\sum_x \prod_y [F(x,y,z) \vee G(x,y)] \supset \prod_y \sum_x [F(x,y,z) \vee G(x,y)].$

TABLE 6.1

We list here a number of derived rules including some previously proved. In this list, α and β are distinct variables.

6.1 $\vdash \sum_\alpha \prod_\beta \varphi(\alpha,\beta) \supset \prod_\beta \sum_\alpha \varphi(\alpha,\beta)$

6.2 $\vdash \prod_\beta \prod_\alpha \varphi(\alpha,\beta) \supset \prod_\alpha \varphi(\alpha,\alpha)$
where the α introduced for β is not bound by an internal quantifier in φ.

6.18 $\vdash \varphi(\beta) \supset \prod_\alpha \varphi(\alpha)$
(Generalized $\prod$I—limited by same restrictions as $\prod$I)

6.19 $\vdash \prod_\alpha \varphi(\alpha) \supset \varphi(\beta)$
(Generalized $\prod$E—limited by same restrictions as $\prod$E)

6.20 $\vdash \varphi(\beta) \supset \sum_\alpha \varphi(\alpha)$
(Generalized $\sum$I—limited by same restrictions as $\sum$I)

6.21 $\vdash \{\sum_\alpha \varphi(\alpha) \,\&\, [\varphi(\beta) \supset \psi]\} \supset \psi$
(Generalized $\sum$E—limited by same restrictions as $\sum$E)

6.22 $\vdash \prod_\alpha [\varphi(\alpha) \supset \psi(\alpha)] \supset [\prod_\alpha \varphi(\alpha) \supset \prod_\alpha \psi(\alpha)]$

6.23 $\vdash \prod_\alpha [\varphi(\alpha) \equiv \psi(\alpha)] \supset [\prod_\alpha \varphi(\alpha) \equiv \prod_\alpha \psi(\alpha)]$

6.24 $\vdash \prod_\alpha [\varphi(\alpha) \supset \psi(\alpha)] \supset [\sum_\alpha \varphi(\alpha) \supset \sum_\alpha \psi(\alpha)]$

6.25 $\vdash \prod_\alpha [\varphi(\alpha) \equiv \psi(\alpha)] \supset [\sum_\alpha \varphi(\alpha) \equiv \sum_\alpha \psi(\alpha)]$

6.26A (1) $\vdash \prod_\alpha \varphi(\alpha) \equiv \prod_\gamma \varphi(\gamma)$
(2) $\vdash \sum_\alpha \varphi(\alpha) \equiv \sum_\gamma \varphi(\gamma)$, where the right side of each equivalence is a result of rewriting the left side.

6.26B Where φ' is a rewriting of φ,
$\vdash \varphi \equiv \varphi'$

TABLE 6.1 *(contd.)*

6.27 $\vdash \prod_\alpha \varphi \equiv \varphi,$
where φ contains no free α.

6.28 $\vdash \prod_\alpha \prod_\beta \varphi(\alpha,\beta) \equiv \prod_\beta \prod_\alpha \varphi(\alpha,\beta)$

6.29 $\vdash \sum_\alpha \varphi \equiv \varphi,$
where φ contains no free α.

6.30 $\vdash \sum_\alpha \sum_\beta \varphi(\alpha,\beta) \equiv \sum_\beta \sum_\alpha \varphi(\alpha,\beta)$

6.31 $\vdash \sum_\alpha \varphi(\alpha,\alpha) \supset \sum_\alpha \sum_\beta \varphi(\alpha,\beta),$
where the β introduced for α is not bound by an internal quantifier in φ.

6.32 $\vdash \prod_\alpha \varphi(\alpha) \supset \sum_\alpha \varphi(\alpha)$

6.33 $\vdash \sum_\alpha \varphi(\alpha) \equiv \sim\prod_\alpha \sim \varphi(\alpha)$

6.34 $\vdash \prod_\alpha \varphi(\alpha) \equiv \sim\sum_\alpha \sim \varphi(\alpha)$

6.35 $\vdash \sim\prod_\alpha \varphi(\alpha) \equiv \sum_\alpha \sim \varphi(\alpha)$

6.36 $\vdash \sim\sum_\alpha \varphi(\alpha) \equiv \prod_\alpha \sim \varphi(\alpha)$

6.37 $\vdash [\prod_\alpha \varphi(\alpha) \,\&\, \prod_\alpha \psi(\alpha)] \equiv \prod_\alpha [\varphi(\alpha) \,\&\, \psi(\alpha)]$

6.38 $\vdash [\sum_\alpha \varphi(\alpha) \vee \sum_\alpha \psi(\alpha)] \equiv \sum_\alpha [\varphi(\alpha) \vee \psi(\alpha)]$

6.39 $\vdash \varphi \vee \prod_\alpha \psi(\alpha) \equiv \prod_\alpha [\varphi \vee \psi(\alpha)],$
where φ contains no free α.

6.40 $\vdash [\varphi \,\&\, \sum_\alpha \psi(\alpha)] \equiv \sum_\alpha [\varphi \,\&\, \psi(\alpha)],$
where φ contains no free α.

6.41 $\vdash \sum_\alpha [\varphi(\alpha) \,\&\, \psi(\alpha)] \supset [\sum_\alpha \varphi(\alpha) \,\&\, \sum_\alpha \psi(\alpha)]$

6.42 $\vdash [\prod_\alpha \varphi(\alpha) \vee \prod_\alpha \psi(\alpha)] \supset \prod_\alpha [\varphi(\alpha) \vee \psi(\alpha)]$

6.43 $\vdash \prod_\alpha [\varphi \supset \psi(\alpha)] \equiv [\varphi \supset \prod_\alpha \psi(\alpha)],$
where φ contains no free α.

6.44 $\vdash \prod_\alpha [\varphi(\alpha) \supset \psi] \equiv [\sum_\alpha \varphi(\alpha) \supset \psi],$
where ψ contains no free α.

6.45 $\vdash \sum_\alpha [\varphi \supset \psi(\alpha)] \equiv [\varphi \supset \sum_\alpha \psi(\alpha)],$
where φ contains no free α.

6.46 $\vdash \sum_\alpha [\varphi(\alpha) \supset \psi] \equiv [\prod_\alpha \varphi(\alpha) \supset \psi],$
where ψ contains no free α.

6.47 $\vdash \sum_\alpha [\varphi(\alpha) \supset \psi(\alpha)] \equiv [\prod_\alpha \varphi(\alpha) \supset \sum_\alpha \psi(\alpha)]$

6.48 $\vdash \sum_\alpha [\varphi \supset \psi(\alpha)] \supset [\varphi \supset \sum_\alpha \psi(\alpha)],$
where φ contains no free α.

6.49 $\vdash [\sum_\alpha \varphi(\alpha) \,\&\, \prod_\alpha \psi(\alpha)] \supset \sum_\alpha [\varphi(\alpha) \,\&\, \psi(\alpha)]$

6.50 $\vdash \prod_\alpha [\varphi(\alpha) \vee \psi(\alpha)] \supset [\prod_\alpha \varphi(\alpha) \vee \sum_\alpha \psi(\alpha)]$

For the most part the proofs of the theorems in Table 6.1 are left to the reader. We give here only the proofs of 6.28 and 6.30 to illustrate further conventions in analyzing deduction. Thus for 6.28 we prove one-half the biconditional as follows:

6.28 $\vdash \prod_\alpha \prod_\beta \varphi(\alpha,\beta) \equiv \prod_\beta \prod_\alpha \varphi(\alpha,\beta)$

Proof:

> 1. $\prod_\alpha \prod_\beta \varphi(\alpha,\beta)$
> 2. $\varphi(\alpha,\beta)$ 1, $\prod$E
> 3. $\prod_\beta \prod_\alpha \varphi(\alpha,\beta)$ 2, $\prod$I

4. $\prod_\alpha \prod_\beta \varphi(\alpha,\beta) \supset \prod_\beta \prod_\alpha \varphi(\alpha,\beta)$ 1–3, $\supset$I

The converse of 6.28 is proved analogously. In this deduction schema, the references to $\prod$E and $\prod$I are elliptical. We actually must use 6.18 and 6.19. Similarly, we prove the commutativity of $\sum$ in 6.30 as follows:

6.30 $\vdash \sum_\alpha \sum_\beta \varphi(\alpha,\beta) \equiv \sum_\beta \sum_\alpha \varphi(\alpha,\beta)$

Proof for the first half of the biconditional:

> 1. $\sum_\alpha \sum_\beta \varphi(\alpha,\beta)$
> 2. $\varphi(\alpha,\beta)$
> 3. $\sum_\beta \sum_\alpha \varphi(\alpha,\beta)$ 2, $\sum$I

4. $\sum_\beta \sum_\alpha \varphi(\alpha,\beta)$ 1, 2–3, $\sum$E

DUALITY

In formulating proofs for many of the schemata in Table 6.1, much effort may be saved if we first establish another derived rule of inference known as *the duality principle.* We have previously established this principle for PL in Chapter Three, Section Five. Its utility in the case of GPL-1 is much greater than in PL, because in GPL-1 we have no decision process. Fortunately, as in the case of the rule of Rep, the extension of Dual to GPL-1 is rather easily accomplished.*

For GPL-1 we define the dual X^+ of a formula X built up from the formulas $\varphi_1, \ldots, \varphi_n$ by use of $\sim$, &, $\vee$, $\prod$, and $\sum$, where $\varphi_1, \ldots, \varphi_n$ themselves may contain statement functions as well as statements, as the formula obtained by

(1) Changing φ_i to $\sim\varphi_i$ for each i and, where this results in $\sim\sim\varphi_i$, using $\vdash \varphi_i \equiv \sim\sim\varphi_i$ and Rep to get φ_i
(2) Changing & to $\vee$ and $\vee$ to &
(3) Changing $\prod$ to $\sum$ and $\sum$ to $\prod$.

---

* In the following discussion we presuppose Section Four of Chapter Three.

We may now state the derived rule of duality for GPL-1.

Dual: Let X, Y, and Z be formulas constructed of $\varphi_1, \ldots, \varphi_n$ using only $\sim$, $\mathbf{v}$, &, $\prod$, and $\sum$. Let X^+ be a formula constructed from X by changing φ_i to $\sim\varphi_i$ for each i (and where this results in $\sim\sim\varphi_i$ replacing this by φ_i), and changing & to $\mathbf{v}$, $\prod$ to $\sum$ and vice versa throughout. Under these conditions

(a) $\vdash \sim X \equiv X^+$

(b) If $\vdash Y \equiv Z$, and we change & for $\mathbf{v}$ and $\prod$ for $\sum$ and vice versa throughout Y and Z, giving Y' and Z', then

$$\vdash Y' \equiv Z'$$

(c) If $\vdash Y \supset Z$ and we change & for $\mathbf{v}$ and $\prod$ for $\sum$ and vice versa throughout Y and Z, giving Y' and Z', then

$$\vdash Z' \supset Y'.$$

Proof of (a): The proof is the same as in the case of PL, using the extension of the rules to statement functions as given in Chapter Five, Section Five, except that we must take into account the occurrence of $\prod$ and $\sum$. Because the proof is an induction, we consider the basis and the hypothesis.

> *Basis:* X is one of the formulas $\varphi_1, \ldots, \varphi_n$, say φ_i. Then $\sim X$ is $\sim\varphi_i$. But X^+ is $\sim\varphi_i$. Hence
>
> $$\vdash \sim X \equiv X^+.$$

Induction Step: We assume that the result holds when X is constructed of $\varphi_1, \ldots, \varphi_n$ and $\sim$, $\mathbf{v}$, &, $\prod$, and $\sum$, in such a way that there are n or fewer occurrences of these formulas and $\sim$. If now, X has $n + 1$ occurrences of relevant symbols, X will have the form $\sim Y$, $Y \mathbf{v} Z$, $Y \& Z$, $\prod_\alpha Y$, or $\sum_\alpha Y$. We have considered the first three cases in Chapter Three; we now consider

> *Case 4.* X is $\prod_\alpha Y$. Then X^+ is $\sum_\alpha Y^+$ By the hypothesis of the induction $\sim Y \equiv Y^+$. By 6.35, $\vdash \sim\prod_\alpha Y \equiv \sum_\alpha \sim Y$.
> Hence, by Rep,
>
> $$\vdash \sim\prod_\alpha Y \equiv \sum_\alpha Y^+$$
>
> Hence,
>
> $$\vdash \sim X \equiv X^+$$
>
> *Case 5.* X is $\sum_\alpha Y$. Then X^+ is $\prod_\alpha Y^+$. By the hypothesis of the induction, $\sim Y \equiv Y^+$. By 6.36, $\vdash \sim\sum_\alpha Y \equiv \prod_\alpha \sim Y$.
> Hence, by Rep
>
> $$\vdash \sim\sum_\alpha Y \equiv \prod_\alpha Y^+.$$
>
> Hence,
>
> $$\vdash \sim X \equiv X^+.$$

This completes the proof of (a). The proofs of (b) and (c) follow as in PL, with only one difference. In PL, in the proof of (b), we used the rule Sub to justify substitution of $\sim p$, $\sim q$, $\sim r$, ... for p, q, r, ... In GPL-1 we must substitute $\sim\varphi_1$, $\sim\varphi_2$, $\sim\varphi_3$, ..., for φ_1, φ_2, φ_3, ... ; that is, the rule Sub must be extended to statement functions to cover just this substitution. In general, substitution of statement functions involves problems in avoiding confusion of variables and other intricacies; but this particular substitution clearly does not involve such problems, since no individual variables are changed.

We may illustrate the value of the rule Dual by

1. $\prod_\alpha\prod_\beta\varphi(\alpha,\beta) \equiv \prod_\beta\prod_\alpha\varphi(\alpha,\beta)$ ZPC, (6-28)
2. $\sum_\alpha\sum_\beta\varphi(\alpha,\beta) \equiv \sum_\beta\sum_\alpha\varphi(\alpha,\beta)$ 1, Dual

Note that line 2 is 6.30.

In general, the use of Dual enables us to obtain

6.29 from 6.27
6.30 from 6.28
6.31 from 6.2
6.38 from 6.37
6.40 from 6.39
6.42 from 6.41

EXERCISE 6.3

I. Justify the following arguments by giving deductions.

1. No one but a fool will buy anything that is overpriced. Caviar is always overpriced, but some people buy it anyway. Therefore, some fools buy caviar. [F(x); C(x); O(x); B(x,y)]

2. No one but a fool will buy anything that is overpriced. Caviar is always overpriced, but some people buy it anyway. And some of those who buy caviar eat it as well. Therefore, some of those who eat caviar are fools. [F(x); C(x); O(x); B(x,y); E(x,y)]

3. If any two lines are both perpendicular to a third line, then they are parallel to each other. If any line is perpendicular to another line, then that other line is perpendicular to the first. Thus, if any two lines are not parallel, then it is not the case that there is some third line which is perpendicular to both. [L(x); P(x,y) = x is parallel to y; R(x,y) = x is perpendicular to y]

4. There are human cannibals, and cannibals all eat human beings. Each cannibal is a member of some tribe. No cannibal would eat a member of his own tribe. So there is a tribe of which some human beings are members and others are not. [H(x); C(x); E(x,y); T(x); M(x,y)]

5. Each year A.D. precedes some other year A.D. Any final year A.D. would be followed by no other year A.D. Anything follows a second thing if and only if the second precedes the first. Consequently, there is no final year A.D. [Y(x); F(x) = x is final; F(x,y) = x follows y; P(x,y); O(x,y) = x is other than y]

6. Every logician makes demonstrations. All demonstrations are proofs, and anything which is made by a person is constructed by him. There is no logician who constructs only elegant proofs, but all elegant proofs are made by some logician. Thus, if no logician constructs both elegant and inelegant proofs, then no logicians are people. [L(x); D(x); F(x) = x is a proof; P(x) = x is a person (are people); E(x) = x is elegant; M(x,y) = x makes y; C(x,y) = x constructs y]

7. Only a theory that accounts for all evidence is the hope of all scientific researchers. Some great scientific researchers have created powerful theories, but no theory yet created (by anybody) has accounted for all evidence. Thus no scientific researcher has yet created a theory for which all such researchers hope. [T(x); E(x); S(x); R(x); G(x); A(x,y); H(x,y) = x hopes for y; C(x,y) = x has created y]

8. Any wise person knows himself. Every person has a mind, and everybody who knows himself knows his own mind. Anything which is known by any person is known by the mind of that person. Therefore, if any person knows himself, then some mind, which belongs to that person, knows itself. [P(x); W(x); M(x); K(x,y); B(x,y) = x belongs to y]

9. Each year A.D. precedes some other year A.D. Any final year A.D. would be followed by no other year A.D. Only if there is a Judgment Day will everyone be judged, and there will be a Judgment Day only if there is a final year A.D. Anything follows a second thing if and only if the second thing precedes the first. Some people will, therefore, never be judged. [Y(x); F(x); P(x); P(x,y); F(x,y); J(x) = x is judged; D(x) = x is Judgment Day]

10. No person will befriend a person whom he does not respect, and anybody who does not respect himself is never respected by anybody. Therefore, any person who is befriended by someone must respect someone. [P(x); B(x,y); R(x,y)]

11. All voters are citizens, and every citizen abhors some politicians. There is a politician who is abhorred by every voter who abhors any politician at all. Any politician who is abhorred by all voters will, of course, never be elected. Thus, there is a politician who will never be elected. [V(x); C(x); P(x); E(x); A(x,y)]

12. An expert will condemn any device invented by an engineer who annoys him. Any device condemned by any expert is shunned by everyone. Anyone who shuns anything will tell somebody about whatever he shuns. Therefore, if some people are experts, then, if any engineer annoys every expert, someone will be told by somebody about any device he invents. [E(x); D(x); G(x) = x is an engineer; P(x); C(x,y); I(x,y); A(x,y); S(x,y); T(x,y,z) = x tells y about z]

13. No one will befriend a person whom he does not respect, and a person who does not respect himself is never respected by anybody. Anyone who is never befriended by anyone is never friendly to anybody. Thus, a person who respects no one will never be friendly to anyone. $[P(x);$ $B(x,y)$; $R(x,y)$; $F(x,y)]$

14. A substance is (by definition) dependent on nothing. Everything which is real is caused by something. That which causes anything is either internal or external to what it causes. Anything is caused internally if and only if it causes itself, and it is caused by something external if and only if it is dependent on something. Therefore, if a substance is real it is self-caused. $[S(x); R(x); D(x,y); C(x,y); I(x,y); E(x,y)]$

15. A car with (only) an automatic transmission can be driven by anybody who can drive any car at all. Some expensive cars with manual transmissions have been made by reputable firms. There are some people who can drive some car or other, but who can drive only those cars which have automatic transmissions. Furthermore, any transmission is automatic if and only if it is not manual. Therefore, if no one ever buys a car which he cannot drive, then there are some cars made by reputable firms which some people will never buy. $[C(x); T(x); A(x);$ $E(x); M(x); R(x); F(x); P(x); H(x,y) = x$ has y; $D(x,y); M(x,y);$ $B(x,y)]$

II. Provide the proofs for each of the theorems listed in Table 6.1, (a) without using Dual, and (b) using Dual.

III. The proof of Rep for GPL-1 is stated, in part, in the text, where the arguments are given for the negative, the universal, and the existential contexts. Provide the arguments for

1. The conjunctive context.

2. The conditional context.

3. The alternative context.

4. The biconditional context.

6.4   General Predicate Logic—Higher Order

It is natural to wonder whether the expressions Asym(R) and Irrx(R) themselves, and others like them, fall within GPL-1. After all, a statement like

$$(1) \quad \vdash \text{Asym(R)} \supset \text{Irrx(R)}$$

clearly means that if a relation has the property of asymmetry then it has the property of being irreflexive; and this involves a reference to a predicate of a predicate and not a predicate of an individual. Thus we can write (1) as

$$(1') \quad \vdash \prod_R[\text{Asym(R)} \supset \text{Irrx(R)}]$$

in which we have a universal quantifier governing a predicate, in this case R. In this way the schemata of Section Two could be rewritten with quantifiers of predicates and would thus seem to be schemata of second-order logic, or GPL-2. A first-order logic is limited to predicates of individuals, a second-order logic to predicates of predicates, a third-order logic to predicates of predicates of predicates, etc.

Actually, it is not necessary to consider the second-order character of (1) as written in (1'). In fact, our definition of Asym(R) as

$$(2) \quad \prod_\beta \prod_\alpha (\alpha R \beta \supset \sim \beta R \alpha)$$

gives us an expression in which R need not be considered as a variable, for we can introduce for R in the schema each specific dyadic relation there is. (2) is a schema in which we can introduce any specific relations for R, and so the second-order character of Asym(R) disappears.

A similar situation of a somewhat more complex sort will occupy us in Chapter Seven. There we shall introduce a conception of identity often called *Leibniz's Law*, after the great seventeenth-century philosopher and mathematician, G. W. Leibniz. One consequence of this law is the principle of the substitutivity of identity; that is,

$$(3) \quad \vdash \prod_\beta \prod_\alpha \{(\alpha = \beta) \supset \prod_\varphi [\varphi(\alpha) \equiv \varphi(\beta)]\}$$

This is a second-order statement and any logic including it would be an instance of GPL-2, at least. We may avoid this second-order logic, however, if we introduce to GPL-1 the predicate constant =, that is, if we permit expressions like $\alpha = \beta$. In order to do this, we also introduce certain rules governing the introduction and elimination of this predicate constant, as we shall see in Chapter Seven.

By contrast with this situation—where second-order predicates are not essentially present, and where we can eliminate quantifiers of predicates by introduction of specific predicates and rules—let us consider the case in which a statement is true when the predicate is quantified but false when specific predicates are introduced. An example is provided by the so-called Principle of the Identity of Indiscernables, namely

$$\vdash \prod_\beta \prod_\alpha \{\prod_\varphi [\varphi(\alpha) \equiv \varphi(\beta)] \supset \alpha = \beta\}$$

Here we cannot eliminate $\prod_\varphi$, since

$$\prod_\beta \prod_\alpha \{[F(\alpha) \equiv F(\beta)] \supset \alpha = \beta\}$$

is false, whatever F we choose. This situation is discussed further in Chapter Seven.

There are many other examples of cases of second-order predicates that are irreducible, and we shall discuss some of the characteristics of logics including such predicates in Chapter Thirteen. Higher-order logics are essentially an aspect of set theory, and are best introduced in the terms of that theory.

EXERCISE 6.4

I. Rewrite each of the theorems of Section Two as a theorem of GPL-2 (*i.e.*, with quantifiers of predicates).

SUGGESTED READINGS

1. Haskell B. Curry, *A Theory of Formal Deducibility* (South Bend, Ind.: Notre Dame Math. Lect. No. 6, 1950).

2. S. C. Kleene, *Introduction to Metamathematics* (New York: Van Nostrand Co., 1952), Ch. VII.

3. P. H. Nidditch, *Introductory Formal Logic of Mathematics* (London: University Tutorial Press, Ltd., 1957), Chs. V, VI.

4. W. V. Quine, *Mathematical Logic*, rev. ed. (Cambridge, Mass.: Harvard University Press, 1951), Ch. 5.

5. J. B. Rosser, *Logic for Mathematicians* (New York: McGraw-Hill Book Co., 1953), Ch. VI.

Chapter 7

Identity and Description

7.1 Identity

In Chapter One, there were several occasions on which steps of proofs were justified by referring to properties of the relation commonly symbolized as $=$. Consider the role of Axioms 4 and 5 in proofs of Theorems 1.1 and 1.3, for example. The use that is made of Euclid's axiom that things "equal to" the same thing are equal to one another illustrates how the properties of $=$ are appealed to in proofs in geometry and algebra.

Let us speak of $=$ as the relation of *identity*, and read $x = y$ as x is identical with y. By thus avoiding the words "equality" and "equals", we make it clear that our investigation does not involve *equations*. We shall not be interested, for example, in *solving* expressions of the form $x = y$. It would be odd to say that $x^3 + 2x^2 - 5x = 0$ expresses the *identity* of its left side with its right side. This can be said only after one or another of the roots of the equation has been substituted for x throughout.

An essential reason for developing identity theory lies in the use of different names for the same individuals, both in mathematics and in other discourse. When this occurs, it is important to be able to justify inferences based upon the identity of the values and thus to reach conclusions otherwise unattainable. For example, we say customarily that

$$\tfrac{3}{4} = \tfrac{9}{12}$$

$$\pi = 3.14159\ldots$$

$$\int x \, dx = \frac{x^2}{2} + k,$$

229

and so on, and make use of these identities in mathematical deductions. It is this use of $=$ that we now investigate.

Intuitively, when we say that $\frac{3}{4}$ and $\frac{9}{12}$ are one and the same, that is, that they are identical, there are a number of properties that are closely connected with this identity. It seems evident, for example, that everything is identical to itself. That is,

$$\prod_x(x = x).$$

Since $=$ is a relation it is thus a reflexive relation—indeed a totally reflexive relation. Again the relation of identity is symmetrical, for if x is the same as y, then surely y is the same as x. That is,

$$\prod_x\prod_y(x = y \supset y = x).$$

And, finally, it seems evident that if x is identical to y and z is identical to y, then x is identical to z. That is,

$$\prod_x\prod_y\prod_z[(x = y \;\&\; y = z) \supset x = z].$$

Thus identity is a transitive relation.

At about the same intuitive level of obviousness are two other properties of identity. The first—that identities may be substituted for identities—has been noted and used in the earliest mathematics. This property may be expressed by observing that if $x = y$ then any property that x has will also be possessed by y, and conversely. Thus we say that if $\frac{3}{4}$ is a fraction, so is $\frac{9}{12}$. Formally,

$$\prod_x\prod_y\{(x = y) \supset [F(x) \equiv F(y)]\}$$

It is this principle that enables us to substitute one name of a thing for another. Thus if $3 = \sqrt{9}$, then 3 is an integer if and only if $\sqrt{9}$ is an integer. If $e^{i\pi} = -1$, then -1 is negative if and only if $e^{i\pi}$ is negative. It seems clear also that if two things have all the same properties, they are the same. This is often referred to as *the Principle of the Identity of Indiscernibles*, and may be written

$$\prod_x\prod_y\{\prod_F[F(x) \equiv F(y)] \supset (x = y)\}$$

Note that in order to take account of the fact that for all properties, F is a property of x if and only if it is also a property of y, we must quantify over F, thus introducing a second-order formula.

These intuitions concerning the properties of identity are sound. We might introduce identity into a deduction by assuming one property or another as needed (except for the identity of indiscernibles) as a premise and avoid a formal extension of GPL-1. The use of identity in mathematics is so frequent, however, as to suggest a more formal approach. We shall follow our usual procedure and state rules for the introduction and elimination of $=$ in a deduction.* These rules will also have the merit of reducing the number of

---

* The formulation used is that of Richard Montague and Donald Kalish, "Remarks on Descriptions and Natural Deduction", *Archiv für mathematische Logik und Grundlagenforschung*, Heft 3/1-2 and 3/3-4.

basic assumptions it is necessary to make concerning $=$, for, as we shall see, the intuitive properties mentioned—except the identity of indiscernibles—are deducible by use of the rules.

We formulate our elimination rule to obtain the reflexivity of $=$ as a direct result. We state the rule schematically:

$=$E$\qquad \prod_\alpha[\alpha = \beta \supset \varphi(\alpha)]$
$\qquad \therefore\ \varphi(\beta),$

> where $\varphi(\beta)$ is like $\varphi(\alpha)$ except for containing free occurrences of β wherever $\varphi(\alpha)$ contains free occurrences of α.

Using this rule we can establish the reflexivity of $=$.

7.1 $\quad \vdash \prod_\alpha(\alpha = \alpha)$

Proof:

> 1. $(\gamma = \beta)$
> 2. $(\gamma = \beta)$ 1, Repeat

 3. $(\gamma = \beta) \supset (\gamma = \beta)$ 1-2, $\supset$I
 4. $\prod_\alpha[(\alpha = \beta) \supset (\alpha = \beta)]$ 3, $\prod$I
 5. $\beta = \beta$ 4, $=$E
 6. $\prod_\alpha(\alpha = \alpha)$ 5, $\prod$I

In this schema we take the second $\alpha = \beta$ in line 4 as $\varphi(\alpha)$.

We formulate our introduction rule to obtain the symmetry of $=$ as a direct result. We state the rule schematically:

$=$I$\qquad \varphi(\beta)$
$\qquad \therefore\ \prod_\alpha[(\alpha = \beta) \supset \varphi(\alpha)],$

> where $\varphi(\beta)$ is like $\varphi(\alpha)$ except for containing free occurrences of β wherever $\varphi(\alpha)$ contains free occurrences of α.

Using this rule we can establish the symmetry of $=$.

7.2 $\quad \vdash \prod_\alpha \prod_\beta[(\beta = \alpha) \supset (\alpha = \beta)]$

Proof:

> 1. $\beta \neq \gamma$
> 2. $\prod_\alpha[(\alpha = \beta) \supset (\alpha \neq \gamma)]$ 1, $=$I
> 3. $\delta = \beta \supset \delta \neq \gamma$ 2, $\prod$E
> 4. $\delta = \gamma \supset \delta \neq \beta$ 3, Cp
> 5. $\prod_\alpha[\alpha = \gamma \supset \alpha \neq \beta]$ 4, $\prod$I
> 6. $\gamma \neq \beta$ 5, $=$E

 7. $\beta \neq \gamma \supset \gamma \neq \beta$ 1-6, $\supset$I
 8. $\gamma = \beta \supset \beta = \gamma$ 7, Cp
 9. $\prod_\alpha \prod_\beta[(\beta = \alpha) \supset (\alpha = \beta)]$ 8, $\prod$I

In this proof schema we have used $\alpha \neq \beta$ as an abbreviation for $\sim(\alpha = \beta)$.

Continuing our program of establishing the intuitive properties of $=$, we show that the substitutivity of identities holds.

7.3 $\vdash \prod_\alpha\prod_\beta\{(\alpha = \beta) \supset [\varphi(\alpha) \equiv \varphi(\beta)]\}$

Proof:

1. $\prod_\alpha\prod_\beta[(\beta = \alpha) \supset (\alpha = \beta)]$		ZPC 7.2
2. $\delta = \gamma \supset \gamma = \delta$		1, $\prod$E
3. $\varphi(\delta)$		
4. $\prod_\alpha[(\alpha = \delta) \supset \varphi(\alpha)]$		3, $=$I
5. $\gamma = \delta \supset \varphi(\gamma)$		4, $\prod$E
6. $\varphi(\delta) \supset [\gamma = \delta \supset \varphi(\gamma)]$		3-5, $\supset$I
7. $\gamma = \delta$		
8. $\varphi(\delta)$		
9. $\gamma = \delta \supset \varphi(\gamma)$		6, 8, $\supset$E
10. $\varphi(\gamma)$		9, 7, $\supset$E
11. $\varphi(\delta) \supset \varphi(\gamma)$		8-10, $\supset$I
12. $\gamma = \delta \supset [\varphi(\delta) \supset \varphi(\gamma)]$		7-11, $\supset$I
13. $\delta = \gamma \supset [\varphi(\delta) \supset \varphi(\gamma)]$		2, 12, HS
14. $\gamma = \delta \supset [\varphi(\gamma) \supset \varphi(\delta)]$		13, $\prod$I, $\prod$E
15. $\gamma = \delta$		
16. $\varphi(\delta) \supset \varphi(\gamma)$		12, 15, $\supset$E
17. $\varphi(\gamma) \supset \varphi(\delta)$		14, 15, $\supset$E
18. $\varphi(\delta) \equiv \varphi(\gamma)$		16, 17, &I, $\equiv$I
19. $\gamma = \delta \supset [\varphi(\delta) \equiv \varphi(\gamma)]$		15-18, $\supset$I
20. $\prod_\alpha\prod_\beta\{(\alpha = \beta) \supset [\varphi(\beta) \equiv \varphi(\alpha)]\}$		19, $\prod$I

The proof schema for establishing the transitivity of $=$; *i.e.*,

7.4 $\vdash \prod_\alpha\prod_\beta\prod_\gamma[(\alpha = \beta \;\&\; \beta = \gamma) \supset \alpha = \gamma]$

is left to the reader.

One intuitive property of identity to which we referred—the identity of indiscernibles—has not been derived from the rules $=$I and $=$E. The reason is that these rules are rules of GPL-1, whereas the identity of indiscernibles can be stated only in terms of second-order logic. We may make this difference clearer if we observe that the identity of indiscernibles cannot be expressed as simply the converse of 7.3; *i.e.*,

$$\prod_\alpha\prod_\beta\{[\varphi(\alpha) \equiv \varphi(\beta)] \supset (\alpha = \beta)\}.$$

This statement is in fact false, as may be seen if we substitute for φ the predicate *is even*, and let α be some number x and β be $x + 2$. For $\alpha = \beta$ to be true it must not merely be possible to find a φ such that $\varphi(\alpha) \equiv \varphi(\beta)$; it must rather be the case that for *all* φ, $\varphi(\alpha) \equiv \varphi(\beta)$. Thus the concept of the identity of indiscernibles is stronger than the rules we have introduced. We can show this by introducing it as a ZPC of GPL-2. But care is required here, for there are dangers in working at the level of GPL-2. Indeed, complex precautions are necessary to avoid inconsistent reasoning, as we shall see in Chapter Thirteen. At the present point, we introduce reasoning in GPL-2 as a means of providing some background for later discussions as well as an illustration of the increased power of higher-order logics—power to which we shall wish to refer occasionally.

To avoid two sets of rules for $=$ introduction and elimination, we simply state the truth we need as a ZPC of GPL-2, which functions similarly to the ones in Table 2.3 for PL or, for that matter, to any of the derived biconditional rules of the preceding chapters for GPL-1. We shall refer to this ZPC as *The Principle of Leibniz* and state it schematically as

PrL $\quad \vdash \prod_\alpha \prod_\beta \{ \prod_\varphi [\varphi(\alpha) \equiv \varphi(\beta)] \equiv (\alpha = \beta) \}.$

PrL combines 7.3 and the concept of the identity of indiscernibles. In making use of PrL, we shall need to suppose that the rules for quantifier introduction and elimination can be extended to quantifiers of predicates. We now make this supposition naively and without further comment until Chapter Thirteen.

We proceed to establish the reflexivity, symmetry, and transitivity of $=$ by using PrL.

7.5 $\quad \vdash \text{Totrx}(=)$

Proof:

1. $\prod_\alpha \prod_\beta \{ \prod_\varphi [\varphi(\alpha) \equiv \varphi(\beta)] \equiv (\alpha = \beta) \}$ PrL (ZPC)
2. $\prod_\varphi [\varphi(\gamma) \equiv \varphi(\gamma)] \equiv (\gamma = \gamma)$ 1, $\prod$E
3. $\prod_\varphi [\varphi(\gamma) \equiv \varphi(\gamma)] \supset (\gamma = \gamma)$ 2, $\equiv$E, &E
4. $\prod_\delta \prod_\varphi [\varphi(\delta) \equiv \varphi(\delta)]$ ZPC (See comment below)
5. $\prod_\varphi [\varphi(\gamma) \equiv \varphi(\gamma)]$ 4, $\prod$E
6. $\gamma = \gamma$ 3, 5, $\supset$E
7. $\prod_\alpha (\alpha = \alpha)$ 6, $\prod$I
8. $\text{Totrx}(=)$ 7, Def

The comment needed on line 4 is just that as $\varphi(\gamma) \equiv \varphi(\gamma)$ is a ZPC for any γ, whence we obtain $\vdash \prod_\delta [\varphi(\delta) \equiv \varphi(\delta)]$, so is it a ZPC for any φ, whence we obtain $\vdash \prod_\delta \prod_\varphi [\varphi(\delta) \equiv \varphi(\delta)]$.

We now proceed to establish the symmetry of $=$.

7.6 $\vdash$ Sym($=$)

Proof:

1. $\prod_\alpha \prod_\beta \{\prod_\varphi [\varphi(\alpha) \equiv \varphi(\beta)] \equiv (\alpha = \beta)\}$ PrL (ZPC)
2. $\prod_\varphi [\varphi(\gamma) \equiv \varphi(\delta)] \equiv (\gamma = \delta)$ 1, $\prod$E
3. $\gamma = \delta \supset \prod_\varphi [\varphi(\gamma) \equiv \varphi(\delta)]$ 2, $\equiv$E, &E
4. $\gamma = \delta$
5. $\prod_\varphi [\varphi(\gamma) \equiv \varphi(\delta)]$ 3, 4, $\supset$E
6. $\varphi(\gamma) \equiv \varphi(\delta)$ 5, $\prod$E
7. $\varphi(\delta) \equiv \varphi(\gamma)$ 6, Comm
8. $\gamma = \delta \supset \varphi(\delta) \equiv \varphi(\gamma)$ 4-7, $\supset$I
9. $\gamma = \delta$
10. $\varphi(\delta) \equiv \varphi(\gamma)$ 8, 9, $\supset$E
11. $\prod_\varphi [\varphi(\delta) \equiv \varphi(\gamma)]$ 10, $\prod$I
12. $\gamma = \delta \supset \prod_\varphi [\varphi(\delta) \equiv \varphi(\gamma)]$ 9-11, $\supset$I
13. $\prod_\varphi [\varphi(\delta) \equiv \varphi(\gamma)] \supset \delta = \gamma$ 2, $\equiv$E, &E
14. $\gamma = \delta \supset \delta = \gamma$ 12, 13, HS
15. $\prod_\alpha \prod_\beta (\alpha = \beta \supset \beta = \alpha)$ 14, $\prod$I
16. Sym($=$)   15, Def

The schema establishing Tr($=$) is left as an exercise.

7.7 $\vdash$ Tr($=$)

EXERCISE 7.1

I. Prove Tr($=$) on the basis of the rules $=$E and $=$I, and then on the basis of PrL.

II. Use the rules, and special theorems of this chapter where applicable, to derive the conclusion of each of the following arguments from its premises. Give a derivation in GPL-1 and in GPL-2 in each case, except as indicated.

1. Adams is the cousin of Brown. But Smith is Brown's only cousin. So Adams must really be Smith.

2. Mark Twain wrote *Life on the Mississippi*, and he was really Samuel Clemens. Samuel Clemens was once a river pilot. Therefore, a one-time river pilot wrote *Life on the Mississippi*.

3. This fellow Glenmore can outrun everybody on the team. David is on the team; so, since nobody can outrun himself, David is not this fellow Glenmore.

4. $\sqrt{2} = 1.41421^{+}$. The diagonal of a square is the product of $\sqrt{2}$ with a side. Thus, the diagonal of a square is the product of 1.41421^{+} with a side.

5. Any number that is an even integer between six and ten must be eight. Any integer greater than a second and less than a third must lie between the second and the third. n is an integer less than ten and greater than six. Thus, if n is even, it is eight.

6. Only an adult could write the novels written by George Eliot. Any adult who is not a man is a woman. George Eliot was Mary Ann Evans. Mary Ann Evans was named Mary Ann, and no man was ever named Mary Ann. Therefore George Eliot was a woman.

7. The "Desert Fox" was dedicated to a discredited cause. Rommel was more dashing and more courageous than some Americans. Rommel was a German general, and "Desert Fox" was his nickname. Therefore, some general who was dedicated to a discredited cause was more courageous than some Americans.

8. Some philosopher can outthink everybody who is a professional. So, since Klagen-Hornsby is a professional philosopher, and nobody can outthink himself, there are (at least) two different philosophers.

9. Any x and y are identical if and only if any property had by either one is had by the other. Therefore, for any two nonidentical things, there will be a property which the first thing has and the second does not have, or vice-versa. (Use GPL-2.)

10. There is some property which some things possess and others do not possess. So some things are not identical with some other things, and there is something distinct from whatever thing you choose. (Use GPL-2.)

7.2 At Least and At Most

The introduction of the existential quantifier in Chapter Five fixed its meaning as "at least one". In a sense, this is an arbitrary designation of meaning, even if satisfactory. As far as English usage goes, "some" may mean exactly one rather than at least one. When we say that for every value of x there is some y such that $2x = y$, we clearly mean that there is exactly one y satisfying this functional relation for each value of x. It seems conceivable that we might also wish to say sometimes that there are at most two, or at most n, individuals having a property or standing in a relation—or that there are exactly n individuals of a certain sort. In fact, such generalization of the existential quantifier is possible through the use of $=$.

We write, then, "There is at least one individual having a property φ" as usual:

(1) $$\Sigma_{\alpha}\varphi(\alpha).$$

We write "There is at most one individual having a property φ" as

(2) $$\prod_\alpha \prod_\beta \{[\varphi(\beta) \; \& \; \varphi(\alpha)] \supset (\alpha = \beta)]\}$$

This tells us that both α and β have φ only if α and β are the same. It does not tell us that φ does in fact apply to at least one individual.

We give an informal proof that there is at most one integer y such that for every x, $x + y = x$ as an illustration of the use of this concept. Let us assume that there are two such integers. Call them y_1 and y_2. By hypothesis, then,

(1) $$x + y_1 = x$$

(2) $$x + y_2 = x$$

Now by substituting in (1), we obtain

(1') $$y_2 + y_1 = y_2,$$

and by substituting in (2), we get

(2') $$y_1 + y_2 = y_1$$

Since the left-hand sides of (1') and (2') are equal, so are the right-hand sides; *i.e.*, $y_1 = y_2$. In other words, what we have proved is

$$\prod_{y_1} \prod_{y_2} \{[\prod_x (x + y_1 = x) \; \& \; \prod_x (x + y_2 = x)] \supset y_1 = y_2\}.$$

If we reflect that $\prod_x (x + y_1 = x)$, having y_1 as its only free variable, can be treated as $F(y_1)$, and that similarly $\prod_x (x + y_2 = x)$ is $F(y_2)$, then we obtain

$$\prod_{y_1} \prod_{y_2} \{[F(y_1) \; \& \; F(y_2)] \supset (y_1 = y_2)\},$$

which has the form of schema (2).

Sometimes it is desirable to specify that a certain predicate applies to at most *two* individuals; for example, that the equation $x^2 + ax + b = 0$ has at most two distinct roots. We can spell out the assertion that there are at most two F's by writing

$$\prod_z \prod_y \prod_x \{[F(z) \; \& \; F(y) \; \& \; F(x)] \supset [(x = z) \lor (x = y) \lor (y = z)]\}.$$

The schema for the general case—there are at most n φ's—can be expressed as

(3) $$\prod_{\alpha_{n+1}\alpha_n \dots \alpha_1} \{[\varphi(\alpha_{n+1}) \; \& \; \varphi(\alpha_n) \; \& \; \dots \; \& \; \varphi(\alpha_1)] \supset$$
$$[(\alpha_1 = \alpha_2) \lor \dots \lor (\alpha_1 = \alpha_{n+1}) \lor (\alpha_2 = \alpha_3) \lor \dots$$
$$\lor (\alpha_2 = \alpha_{n+1}) \lor \dots \lor (\alpha_n = \alpha_{n+1})]\}$$

Corresponding to this we can also write "There are at least n φ's". Consider, first, "There are at least two F's".

$$\sum_y \sum_x [F(y) \; \& \; F(x) \; \& \; (x \neq y)]$$

Thus, to say that $x^4 = y$ has at least two distinct roots is to say that there is at least one y_1 that is a root and at least one y_2 that is a root such that $y_1 \neq y_2$.

The schema for the general case—there are at least n φ's—is

(4) $\sum_{\alpha_n...\alpha_1}[\varphi(\alpha_n)$ & $...$ & $\varphi(\alpha_1)$ & $(\alpha_1 \neq \alpha_2)$ & $...$
    & $(\alpha_1 \neq \alpha_n)$ & $(\alpha_2 \neq \alpha_3)$ & $...$ & $(\alpha_2 \neq \alpha_n)$ & $...$ &
    $(\alpha_{n-1} \neq \alpha_n)]$.

To say that there is at least one individual and at most one individual possessing a property is to say that there is exactly one individual possessing this property. Such statements are frequently made in talking about numbers and functions. We often have occasion to say that for each individual in one set there exists exactly one individual in a second set upon which it is mapped. Indeed, so useful is this concept that we introduce the symbol $\sum!$ for this meaning.

We may symbolize "There is exactly one even prime" as

$$\sum_x(E(x) \ \& \ P(x) \ \& \ \prod_y\{[E(y) \ \& \ P(y)] \supset x = y\})$$

or as

$$\sum!_x[E(x) \ \& \ P(x)]$$

Schematically, we have the definition

(5) $\sum!_\alpha\varphi(\alpha) \equiv_{df} \sum_\alpha\{\varphi(\alpha) \ \& \ \prod_\beta[\varphi(\beta) \supset (\alpha = \beta)]\}$

It is also possible to say that there are exactly n φ's by conjoining "There are at least n φ's" with "There are at most n φ's". That is, a conjunction of (3) and (4) provides the schema for this general statement. We may illustrate this by a schema for asserting that there are exactly two individuals of a certain kind:

(6) $\sum!_\alpha\varphi(\alpha) \equiv_{df} \sum_\beta\sum_\alpha[\varphi(\beta) \ \& \ \varphi(\alpha) \ \& \ \alpha \neq \beta] \ \&$
$$\prod_\alpha\prod_\beta\prod_\gamma\{[\varphi(\alpha) \ \& \ \varphi(\beta) \ \& \ \varphi(\gamma)] \supset \alpha = \gamma \lor \beta = \gamma\}$$

Similarly, we can introduce expressions referring to any specific number of individuals, in general $\sum_\alpha\varphi(\alpha)$.

It is also interesting to consider the relation *between* at least and at most. Suppose the statement "There is at most one element x such that $x + x = x$" is false. This means that there are at least two elements x such that $x + x = x$. For if we treat $x + x = x$ as a case of $F(x)$, then

$\vdash \sim\prod_y\prod_x[(F(y) \ \& \ F(x)) \supset x = y]$
$\equiv \sum_y\sum_x \sim \{[F(y) \ \& \ F(x)] \supset x = y\}$ QEq
$\equiv \sum_y\sum_x[F(y) \ \& \ F(x) \ \& \ x \neq y]$.   Impl and DM.

In general,

$\vdash \sim$(There are at most n F's) $\equiv$ (There are at least $n + 1$ F's).

Why this should be so can be seen by comparing the symbolizations of "There are at most n φ's" and "There are at least n φ's".

If there are at least two x's of which F(x) is false, then F(x) is true of at most all but two x's. We may similarly introduce the quantifier "at least all but n". Such quantifiers, like the ones already discussed in this section, are of interest in their own right, but are of peripheral value for the development of the central core of logical theory.

EXERCISE 7.2

I. Using suitable symbols, formalize each of the following statements (*i.e.*, express them in terms of quantification and identity).

   1. There is exactly one even prime.

   2. At most two integers x are such that $xx = x + x$.

   3. All but at most one of the windows are shut.

   4. At most all but one of the windows are shut.

   5. At least all but one of the windows are shut.

   6. Each person is entitled to at least one ticket.

   7. At least two persons are entitled to more than two tickets apiece.

   8. At least one person is entitled to two tickets.

   9. Cerberus has three heads.

   10. Eisenhower served two terms as President.

   11. Some people never do more than one thing at a time.

   12. Some people always accomplish the same thing, no matter what they attempt.

   13. If anyone is allowed by a clerk to buy more than two sale items, some customers will not get the two to which they are entitled.

   14. There is one and only one correct symbolization for this sentence, but there are at least two possible interpretations of its meaning.

   15. If at least two, and at most all but two, faculty members will each be bitten by at least one dog next year, then there are no fewer than four faculty members.

II. Prove that statement 15, in part I above, is a ZPC.

III. Write out a series of quantificational statements corresponding to the natural numbers, 1, 2, 3, ...

7.3 Descriptions

It is customary in mathematics to introduce new constants by giving a description of them. So far we have not used this technique, and it is hardly essential to a consideration of deduction in GPL-1. It is, however, a rather more important matter in higher-order logics, and so for the whole of mathematical reasoning. We discuss the issues involved here very briefly and as the barest introduction to the problem.

So far our practice in introducing new constants has been to state the rules for introducing and eliminating them, or to regard them as definitional abbreviations. In the second case, we showed how a formula in which a constant occurred could be replaced by an equivalent formula in which they did not occur. Thus, for example, we introduced constants in Chapter Six, Section Two, as follows:

$$\mathbf{Sym(R)} \equiv_{df} \prod_\beta \prod_\alpha (\alpha R \beta \supset \beta R \alpha),$$
$$\text{etc.}$$

Since $=$ has been introduced as a relational constant in the last section, it is possible to introduce new constants via identities. Thus, in arithmetic, assuming that $+$ and 1 are available, we may introduce the rest of the natural numbers via identities.

$$2 = 1 + 1$$
$$3 = 2 + 1$$
$$4 = 3 + 1$$
$$\vdots$$

On the other hand, if no primitive constant is available, there is no way to introduce one through an identity, although it could be introduced in context. That is, we could state that

$$(1) \quad (x = 1) \equiv_{df} \prod_y [x \cdot y = y]$$

Here we understand $\cdot$ as the arithmetical product. However, usual mathematical practice is to introduce constants such as 1 by describing them, rather than by an equivalence. Thus, we might say 1 is the number such that $(1 \cdot y) = y$. The crucial words here are "the number such that"; they are so crucial, indeed, that we introduce a symbol for them. Thus we symbolize this statement as

$$(2) \quad 1 = \imath x \{ \prod_y [(x \cdot y) = y] \}$$

The important point at the moment is that $\imath x$ expresses reference to the individual x such that .... $\imath x$ is called a *descriptive operator* and it binds variables as do the universal and existential quantifiers.

If we recall some of the many phrases occurring in mathematics such as "The greatest common divisor of x and y", "The least common multiple of *x* and *y*", "The greatest prime factor of *z*", we gain an impression of the importance of descriptions in designating individual constants. Indeed, the use of such descriptions aids in mathematical reasoning quite considerably. For this reason we consider the nature of such descriptions briefly. One of the pitfalls of a description is that the individual described may not exist—or that there may be more than one such individual. Thus in (2) above we have no guarantee that $\imath_x[\prod_y(x \cdot y = y)]$ refers to exactly one individual, although we probably know that there is exactly one 1 in elementary arithmetic. This situation is normal with respect to descriptions, for we may refer ostensibly to the greatest prime or the factor of 12. In the first case there is no such prime and in the second there is more than one factor of 12.

This pitfall is evident enough in ordinary English as well as mathematics as the following descriptive phrases testify: "The first woman President of the United States", and "The planet between Mercury and Jupiter". The first of these phrases might be symbolized as

$$\imath_x W(x),$$

and the second as

$$\imath_x P(x).$$

But whatever the situation in ordinary language, in mathematics it is definitely improper to use descriptions to introduce individual constants without determining that there is a unique object described. Thus, (2) would not be satisfactory as an introduction of the constant 1 until it had been established that

$$\sum_x \prod_y [(x \cdot y) = y]$$

and

$$\prod_{x_1} \prod_{x_2} (\{\prod_y [(x_1 \cdot y) = y] \,\&\, \prod_y [(x_2 \cdot y) = y]\} \supset (x_1 = x_2))$$

That is, we require that

$$\sum!_x \prod_y [x \cdot y = y].$$

If this condition were not met, contradictions of various kinds could be derived. Suppose we introduce the constant 0 by means of a description where the condition is not met.

$$(3) \quad 0 = \imath_x (x^2 = x)$$

Since $0^2 = 0$ and $1^2 = 1$, $0 = 1$. However, on other grounds we know that $0 \neq 1$; so taking this as a premise and substituting identities for identities, *i.e.*, 0 for 1, we obtain $0 \neq 0$. If we introduce 0 as

$$(4) \quad 0 = \imath_x[\prod_y(x + y = y)]$$

we should be able to avoid such difficulties, since now we can establish that

$$\sum!_x[\prod_y(x + y = y)]$$

The same considerations are further exemplified in the following "proof" that $2 = 1$.

──**1.** $a = b$
  2. $a^2 = ab$
  3. $a^2 - b^2 = ab - b^2$
  4. $(a + b)(a - b) = b(a - b)$ Factoring
  5. $a + b = b$ Divide both sides by $a - b$
  6. $2b = b$ Since $a = b$
  7. $2 = 1$ Divide by b

Of course, dividing by $a - b$ at line 5 is not permissible, since $a - b = 0$. Stated otherwise, we assume at line 5 that $0/0 = 0/0$; but this is not the case, since $0/0$ is not a unique number.

Another perspective on the difficulties involving descriptions in inference may be found by noting that, in general, it is not true that

$$(5) \quad \imath_\alpha\varphi(\alpha) = \imath_\alpha\varphi(\alpha).$$

The reason why there are cases where $\imath_\alpha\varphi(\alpha) \neq \imath_\alpha\varphi(\alpha)$ is that there may be many individuals so designated or none; thus the reflexivity of identity cannot be asserted with descriptions related as in (5). The same point holds for symmetry and transitivity. Identity is not symmetrical or transitive with respect to descriptive terms unless we know that these terms are unique.

One solution to the problems we have raised is to follow a suggestion of Bertrand Russell and eliminate all descriptions in our formulas.* This leads to notationally complex formulas and is not altogether practical, but in principle it is satisfactory, and we shall follow it here. Clearly the difficulties arise because of the ambiguity concerning the uniqueness of the individuals described. We shall replace a description where it occurs in a formula by a quantificational form that includes an assertion of the unique existence of the individual described. Thus

$$(6) \quad \psi[\imath_\alpha\varphi(\alpha)] \equiv_{\mathrm{df}} \Sigma_\alpha\{\prod_\beta[\varphi(\beta) \equiv (\alpha = \beta)] \,\&\, \psi\alpha\}.$$

Definitions such as (2) and (4) have the general form $n = \imath_\alpha\varphi(\alpha)$, which may be contextually defined by the following equivalence:

$$(7) \quad n = \imath_\alpha\varphi(\alpha) \equiv_{\mathrm{df}} \Sigma_\alpha\{\prod_\beta[\varphi(\beta) \equiv (\alpha = \beta)] \,\&\, (\alpha = n)\}.$$

Thus, (2) becomes

$$\Sigma_x(\prod_y\{\prod_z[(y \cdot z) = z] \equiv (x = y)\} \,\&\, (x = 1)).$$

Finally, we occasionally meet a descriptive identity such as $\imath_\alpha\varphi(\alpha) = \imath_\beta\varphi(\beta)$. This may be contextually defined as

$$(8) \quad [\imath_\alpha\varphi(\alpha) = \imath_\beta\psi(\beta)] \equiv_{\mathrm{df}} \Sigma_\alpha(\prod_\gamma[\varphi(\gamma) \equiv (\gamma = \alpha)] \,\&\,$$
$$\Sigma_\beta\{\prod_\delta[\psi(\delta) \equiv (\delta = \beta)] \,\&\, (\alpha = \beta)\}).$$

──────────

* Bertrand Russell, "On Denoting", *Mind*, N.S. Vol. 14, 1905.

We obtain (8) by expanding the left side of the equivalence according to the definition of $\imath_\alpha\varphi(\alpha) = n$, which gives

$$\sum_\alpha\{\prod_\gamma[\varphi(\gamma) \equiv (\alpha = \gamma)] \ \& \ [\alpha = \imath_\beta\psi(\beta)]\}.$$

This in turn can be expanded to (8).

If we expand the left side of the equivalence beginning with $n = \imath_\beta\psi(\beta)$ we find, in this case, that the result is the same.

Using these equivalences, we can eliminate all descriptions from formulas and proceed by the rules of GPL-1 plus identity to draw whatever inferences are correct. In dealing with inferences in ordinary language (as in mathematics), it is usually desirable to symbolize using the descriptive quantifier, removing this by means of the definitions given before proceeding to an analysis of the steps in the deduction. As an example we take the following story, which Cohen and Nagel attribute to Thackeray:

> An old abbé, talking among a party of intimate friends, happened to say, "A priest has strange experiences; why, ladies, my first penitent was a murderer." Upon this, the principal nobleman of the neighborhood enters the room. "Ah, abbé, here you are; do you know, ladies, I was the abbé's first penitent, and I promise you my confession astonished him!"*

The process through which the audience then reached a startling conclusion is often represented as a syllogism; but if we let n be the name of the nobleman, and use $\imath_x FP(x)$ to stand for "the abbé's first penitent" and M for "is a murderer", we obtain

1. $n = \imath_x FP(x)$		
2. $M[\imath_x FP(x)]$ $\quad /\therefore$ M(n)		
3. $\sum_x\{\prod_y[FP(y) \equiv (x = y)] \ \& \ x = n\}$	1, Def.	
4. $\sum_x\{\prod_y[FP(y) \equiv (x = y)] \ \& \ M(x)\}$	2, Def.	
5. $\prod_y[FP(y) \equiv (v = y)] \ \& \ (v = n)$		
6. $\prod_y[FP(y) \equiv (w = y)] \ \& \ M(w)$		
7. $FP(n) \equiv (v = n)$	5, &E, $\prod$E	
8. $v = n$	5, &E	
9. $FP(n)$	7, $\equiv$E, &E, 8, $\supset$E	
10. $FP(n) \equiv (w = n)$	6, &E, $\prod$E	
11. $w = n$	10, $\equiv$E, &E, 9, $\supset$E	
12. $\prod_x\prod_y\{(x = y) \supset [M(x) \equiv M(y)]\}$	7.3 (ZPC)	
13. $(w = n) \supset [M(w) \equiv M(n)]$	12, $\prod$E	
14. $M(w) \equiv M(n)$	13, 11, $\supset$E	
15. $M(w)$	6, &E	
16. $M(n)$	14, $\equiv$E, &E, 15, $\supset$E	
17. $M(n)$	4, 6-16, $\sum$E	
18. $M(n)$	3, 5-17, $\sum$E	

---

* M. Cohen and E. Nagel, *An Introduction to Logic and Scientific Method* (New York, Harcourt, Brace and Co., 1934), p. 174.

EXERCISE 7.3

I. 1. What is wrong with the statement $1/0 = \infty$?

2. Comment on the definition of a certain constant as "The sum to infinity of the series $1 + \frac{1}{2} + \frac{1}{3} + \frac{1}{4} + \ldots$".

3. Could a certain constant be defined as $\lim\limits_{n \to \infty} \dfrac{n!}{n^n}$? Explain your answer.

4. What is $\log_{10}(-3)$? If there is a difficulty here, explain it.

5. (This question presupposes a slight acquaintance with transfinite arithmetic.) Comment on the following argument:

The lowest transfinite cardinal is supposed to be $\aleph_0$, *i.e.*, the cardinal number of the integers. This claim, however, has been challenged as follows. Consider $\log_2 \aleph_0$—the power to which the number 2 would have to be raised so that the result would be $\aleph_0$. Call this number α. Thus we have $2^\alpha = \aleph_0$. Now α cannot be finite, since any finite power of 2 is finite. But α cannot be $\aleph_0$ either, since it is well known that $2^{\aleph_0} > \aleph_0$. Hence α must lie between the finite numbers and $\aleph_0$. Thus $\aleph_0$ is *not* the smallest transfinite number. Indeed, α is not either, since an extension of our argument shows that an infinite number of transfinite numbers lie between it and the finite numbers.

II. Use the rules, and definitions of this chapter where applicable, to derive the conclusion of each of the following arguments from its premises.

1. The present Shah of Iran is a romantic figure. Therefore, all present Shahs of Iran are romantic figures. [$S(x,y)$; $R(x)$; i]

2. The man who wrote the "Academic Festival Overture" wrote nothing but enduring music. Therefore, the "Academic Festival Overture" is enduring music. [$M(x)$; $W(x,y)$; $E(z)$; a]

3. The ugliest monarch was British. All British kings are dead, and all male monarchs are kings. Thus, if the ugliest British monarch was male, then the ugliest monarch is dead. [$M(x)$; $B(x)$; $D(x)$; $K(x)$; $U(x,y)$]

4. Smith is not in good health, but he and Petersen were the only entrants who finished the course. All of the entrants who were in good health finished the course, and all who finished the course fainted from exertion. If any entrant finished the course, then some entrant in good health did. So it seems that the entrant who was in good health fainted from exertion. [$H(x)$; $E(x)$; $F(x)$; $A(x)$; s; p]

5. Only the fastest member of the team can hope to qualify for the Olympics. No one on the team can run faster than the fastest member of the team, but the fastest member of the team can run faster than anyone else on the team. Nobody else on the team can run faster than

Brown. Therefore, if Brown can run faster than everyone else on the team, only he can hope to qualify for the Olympics. [M(x); H(x); F(x,y); b]

6. All rockets which fail to escape the earth, and would return to earth, must be destroyed. The escape velocity at the surface of the earth is 7 m.p.s. Any rocket fired with a velocity less than this will fail to escape and will either return to earth or burn up in the atmosphere. This Thor was fired with less than that velocity. Owing to its size, it will not burn in the atmosphere. So we must destroy it. [R(x); F(x); E(x); D(x); B(x); F(x,y); L(x,y); e; s; t]

7. The last Dutch governor of the Dutch colony on Manhattan was stern and pious. Peter Stuyvesant was the last Dutch governor of that colony, which was then named New Amsterdam. New Amsterdam is now called New York. Only administrators who are intolerable to their subjects are stern and pious governors. So the last Dutch governor of New York was intolerable to his subjects. [D(x); G(x); C(x); M(x); S(x); P(x); A(x); L(x,y); S(x,y); p; a; y]

8. Alexander had all of the properties which all great leaders have, but he had no property not had by some other great leader. The leader who was greater than all other great leaders had all the properties which have been possessed by any great leader at all. Not all great leaders have exactly the same properties. [G(x); L(x); G(x,y); a. Use GPL-2]

For the following problems, assume the following additional ZPC:

$$\vdash \prod_{\varphi} \prod_{\psi} [(\varphi = \psi) = \prod_x (\varphi_x = \psi_x)].$$

9. Nothing has all properties, and any two things have some common property. There are (at least) two distinct things. So there are at least two distinct properties.

10. All great leaders are imaginative and perspicacious. The leader who is greater than all other great leaders has all properties which any great leader at all has. Not all great leaders have exactly the same properties. Therefore, the greatest leader has some other property besides imagination and perspicacity. [G(x); L(x); I(x); P(x); G(x,y)]

SUGGESTED READINGS

1. Robert M. Exner and Myron F. Rosskopf, *Logic in Elementary Mathematics* (New York: McGraw-Hill Book Co., 1959), Ch. V, Sections 5.17–5.18.

2. Hugues Leblanc, *An Introduction to Deductive Logic* (New York: John Wiley & Sons, 1955), Ch. IV, Sections 32–36.

3. W. V. Quine, *Methods of Logic*, rev. ed. (New York: Holt, Rinehart and Winston, Inc., 1959), Sections 33–37.

4. J. B. Rosser, *Logic for Mathematicians* (New York: McGraw-Hill Book Co.,1953), Chs. VII, VIII.

5. Bertrand Russell, "On Denoting", *Mind* (Vol. 14, 1905), pp. 479–493. Reprinted in H. Feigl and W. Sellars, *Readings in Philosophical Analysis* (New York: Appleton-Century-Crofts Co., 1949), pp. 103–115.

6. Patrick Suppes, *Introduction to Logic* (Princeton, N.J.: Van Nostrand Co., 1957), Ch. V.

Part Two

Introduction to Metatheory

Chapter 8

Axiom Systems and the Axiomatic Method

8.1 Euclidian Geometry

Let us return to a consideration of the properties of axiom systems; that is, let us undertake a deeper analysis of some of the issues touched upon in Chapter One. Of course, the preceding chapters were concerned with an analysis of proof in axiom systems; but such systems have other important properties that have not yet been discussed. We can best begin this discussion by making some comments about Euclid's geometry.

We can observe Euclid's geometry with some exactness by considering the proofs of Theorems 13, 14, and 15 of that system.* These theorems are based by Euclid upon undefined terms, definitions in which the undefined terms occur, and assumptions (called "common notions" and "postulates"). In addition, these three theorems depend upon Theorem 11, which has been proved previously. Thus we may state the preliminaries necessary for proof as these:

Undefined Terms: Straight line, angle, point.

Definition 10: When a straight line set up on another straight line makes the adjacent angles equal to one another, each of the equal angles is called right, and the straight line standing on the other is called a perpendicular to it.

Common Notion I: Things equal to the same thing are equal to one another.

Common Notion II: If equals be added to equals, the wholes are equal.

---

* See T. L. Heath, *The Thirteen Books of Euclid's Elements* (New York: Dover Pub., Inc., 1956).

Common Notion III: If equals be taken from equals, the remainders are equal.

Postulate II: A terminated straight line may be produced to any length in a straight line.

Theorem 11 (previously proved): It is possible to draw a straight line at right angles to a given straight line from a given point in the latter.

Euclid referred to three of the four assumptions stated above as *common notions*, distinguishing them as self-evident general truths from what he called the *postulates* of geometrical truths, such as Postulate II. Euclid's postulates seem to have been intended as less universal than his common notions and he seems to have had in mind a distinction between assumptions peculiar to a subject and more general truths common to all deductive enquiry. Aristotle seems to anticipate the same distinction when he says that every demonstrative science must start from indemonstrable principles; otherwise, the steps of demonstration would be endless. Of these indemonstrable principles, some are (a) common to all sciences; others are (b) particular, or peculiar to a particular science.* It is customary in modern mathematics to make no distinction among kinds of axioms, but to regard them as all on a par. However, if one were to include the logical rules of inference as an explicit part of an axiom system, these rules might well be designated "common notions" and distinguished from the axioms peculiar to the subject matter studied. In fact, the first common notion cited above is a part of the logic of identity.

When we examine the proof of Theorem 13, for example, we readily note logical rules used implicitly.

8.1(E)†   (Theorem 13)

If a straight line set upon a straight line makes angles, it will make either two right angles or angles equal to two right angles.

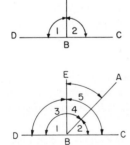

Proof:

If angle 1 is equal to angle 2, each of them is a right angle (by Definition 10).

If not, then from the point B, draw BE at right angles to CD:

This is possible by Theorem 11.

Thus angles 3 and 4 are right angles.

Now angle 4 = angle 2 + angle 5.

---

* *Ibid.*, Vol. I, pp. 117–119.

† We number these theorems 1(E)—Euclid 1, 2(E)—Euclid 2, and so on in order to separate them from the theorems essential to the development of this book as a whole.

Therefore angle 4 + angle 3 = angle 2 + angle 5 + angle 3, by Common Notion II.

Also, angle 1 = angle 3 + angle 5.

Therefore angle 1 + angle 2 = angle 3 + angle 5 + angle 2.

So, by Common Notion I, angle 1 + angle 2 = angle 3 + angle 4.

But angle 3 and angle 4 are right angles; so angle 1 and 2 are together equal to two right angles.

The first point inviting logical commentary is the form of the proof as a whole. We have shown that whether we assume that angle 1 equals angle 2 or assume that it does not, together they are equal to two right angles, because either assumption implies this and not both the assumptions can be false. Thus we have used the rule **v**E of PL. As an exercise, the reader may wish to restate this theorem in formal logical notation, incorporating this form and those to be mentioned.

Working toward the logical details of the proof now, we note that there is an implicit inference from Definition 10 by the rule $\prod$E to the conclusion about specific angles. That is, Definition 10 states a universally quantified conditional which must be referred to arbitrary instances such as angle 1 and angle 2. We then assume, as part of the use of **v**E, that angle 1 and angle 2 are equal and, by the rule $\supset$E, infer that these angles are right angles.

There is a similar implicit use of $\prod$E and $\supset$E in the application of Common Notion II and Common Notion I (as well as of Theorem 11) in the course of the proof. Finally, there is an implicit use of $\prod$I, for the theorem as stated is not restricted to the angles mentioned in the proof. Since these are arbitrary angles, the theorem is a universally quantified statement.

We next turn to a further theorem as a means of recalling the axiom system of Euclid's geometry and observing the use of logical rules of inference in it.

8.2(E)   (Theorem 14)

If, at a point in a straight line, two other straight lines on the opposite sides of it make the adjacent angles together equal to two right angles, these two straight lines are in one and the same straight lines.

Proof:

At point B in straight line AB, let the two straight lines BC and BD on the opposite sides of AB make the adjacent angles 1 and 2 together equal to two right angles.

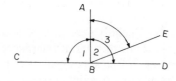

Now if BD is not in the same straight line as CB, let BE be in the same straight line as CB.

Then, by Theorem 13, angle 1 and angle 3 are together equal to two right angles.

But by hypothesis, angle 1 and angle 2 are together equal to two right angles.

Therefore, angle 1 + angle 3 = angle 1 + angle 2.

By Common Notion II, then, angle 3 = angle 2.

But this makes the less equal to the greater, which is absurd.

Therefore, BE is not in the same line with CB. Similarly no other line can be in a straight line with it except BD. Therefore, BD is in the same line with CB, since, by Postulate II, there is such a line.

The most noteworthy logical feature of this proof is the use of *reductio ad absurdum* involving the rule ∼I. The absurdity is stated here as "this makes the less equal to the greater", but could be stated in logical form as *p* & ∼*p*. The application of Theorem 13, Common Notion II, and Postulate II each involves ∏E and ⊃E as in the proof of Theorem 13, and the further logic of the use of Postulate II may be understood if we observe that this postulate asserts the existence of at least one straight line with CB.

The last theorem that we wish to consider is of more widespread geometrical importance than either Theorem 13 or Theorem 14, but it involves no new logical principles, and for this reason can be presented very briefly. The reader may state the logical principles involved at each step.

8.3(E)   (Theorem 15)

If two straight lines cut one another, the opposite angles are equal.

Proof:

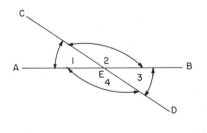

Angle 1 + angle 4 = 2 right angles [by Theorem 13].
Angle 4 + angle 3 = 2 right angles [by Theorem 13].
Therefore angle 1 + angle 4 = angle 4 + angle 3 [by Common Notion I].
Therefore, angle 1 = angle 3.
Similarly, angle 2 = angle 4.

Clearly, Euclid's geometry is a deductive system of a sort permitting analysis in terms of rules of inference. That is, Euclid proves theorems from assumptions of one sort or another by means of implicit logical rules. The similarity to modern axiom systems is marked, but there are, as we shall see, major differences as well.

EXERCISE 8.1

I. The following deductions are based upon the given axioms and PL. Cite the logical rules involved.

Ax. 1 $x \not> x$

Ax. 2 $(x > y \,\&\, y > z) \supset x > z$

Ax. 3 $(x \not> y \,\&\, y \not> x) \supset x = y$

Theorem 1. $x \neq y \supset \sim(x \not> y \,\&\, y \not> x)$

Proof:

1. $x \neq y$
2. $\sim(x \not> y \,\&\, y \not> x)$

3. $x \neq y \supset \sim(x \not> y \,\&\, y \not> x)$

Theorem 2. $x = x$

Proof:

1. $x \not> x$
2. $x \not> x$
3. $x \not> x \,\&\, x \not> x$
4. $x = x$

Theorem 3. $x > y \supset y \not> x$

Proof:

1. $x > y$
2. $y > x$
3. $x > y \,\&\, y > x$
4. $x > x$

5. $y > x \supset x > x$
6. $x \not> x$
7. $y \not> x$

8. $x > y \supset y \not> x$

Theorem 4. $(x \neq y \,\&\, x \not> y) \supset y > x.$

Proof:

1. $x \neq y \,\&\, x \not> y$
2. $x \neq y$
3. $x \not> y$
4. $\sim(x \not> y \,\&\, y \not> x)$
5. $x > y \,\vee\, y > x$
6. $y > x$

7. $(x \neq y \,\&\, x \not> y) \supset y > x$

II. Prove the indicated theorems from the following axioms, making explicit all the logical rules involved.

Ax. 1. There is at least one bla.

Ax. 2. Not all blus are contained in the same bla.

Ax. 3. At most one bla contains any two distinct blus.

Ax. 4. Every bla contains exactly three blus.

Ax. 5. Given any bla and a blu not contained in this bla, there is exactly one other bla which contains this blu and is p-related to the first bla.

Ax. 6. Given any blu and a bla not containing this blu, there is exactly one other blu contained in this bla such that no bla contains these blus.

(These postulates are essentially those given by Richardson in *Fundamentals of Mathematics.*)

Theorem 1. There is at least one blu.

Theorem 2. Any two distinct blas have at least one blu in common.

III. Do any of these proofs require information not contained in the axioms?

IV. Write the proofs of 8.1(E), 8.2(E), and 8.3(E) in formal logical notation.

8.2 The Development of Axiom Systems

In Euclidian geometry there is not any explicit reference to or statement of the logical rules of inference used in deducing the theorems of the systems. Such rules are taken for granted in this system as originally formulated. Today, however, we are much more aware of the need to state rules of inference explicitly. This awareness is in part a result of the development of the axiomatic method that began about the time of Euclid. As we observed in Chapter One, there is a marked difference between the earliest practical and intuitive geometry and that of Euclid. Still, for all the differences between the earliest geometry and the Euclidian system, there is one basic similarity. In both, the geometrical statements made are believed to be true of real space. In the case of Euclid, the statements he called postulates are presented as self-evidently true of space, and the theorems deduced were likewise thought of as true. Because of this assumption, Euclid's fifth postulate (the "parallel" postulate) has been discussed repeatedly since its statement. Euclid stated Postulate V as "If a straight line falling on two straight lines makes the interior angles on the same side less than two right angles, the two straight lines, if produced indefinitely, meet on that side on which are the angles less than the two right angles".* No doubt this statement or its reformulation as "Through a point external to a given line one and only one line parallel to the given line can be drawn" lacks something in the way of self-evidence. In fact, this lack of self-evidence in Postulate V motivated some Greeks and later thinkers to make numerous attempts to prove it from the other axioms. For centuries, mathematicians tried to establish this postulate on more fundamental grounds

---

* T. L. Heath. *op. cit.* I, 154–155.

without success, but the reason for their failure was not understood until the advent of non-Euclidian geometry in the nineteenth century. Then it was discovered through the work of Gauss, Bolyai, Riemann, and Lobachevsky that the parallel postulate was independent of the others, and thus that no proof of it from them was possible. To show that this postulate is independent, we need only give an example of a space of which all the axioms of Euclidian geometry are true except Postulate V.* This can be done in terms of the surface of a sphere. If "straight line" has the meaning of great circle arc, there are no parallel lines at all on the surface of a sphere because all great circle arcs intersect. However, the other axioms of Euclid hold true of this surface. The independence of this postulate showed that it was not a necessary part of geometry as such and suggested that it might be dropped or varied. This discovery opened the door to all sorts of non-Euclidean geometries in which the axioms were varied as desired—in particular in which the assumptions made about parallel lines received different treatment. For example, it was assumed that more than one line parallel to a second might be drawn through any point not on the second, or that no lines parallel to a second might be drawn through such a point.† The invention of non-Euclidean geometries cast new light on the status of axioms, since these geometries included examples that no one supposed to be true of "real" space. The primary task of the geometer changed from the attempt to describe "real" space in mathematical terms to that of realizing a variety of ideal spaces in the terms of axioms and proved theorems. Thus, although geometry originated in practice in, and was long concerned with a description of, "real" space, its development went beyond this orientation and, from the modern viewpoint, to say that a geometry is an account of space is not to make a mathematical assertion.

A natural consequence of this development was the conception of axioms as abstract statements whose literal reference to reality could be disregarded from the strictly mathematical viewpoint. The correctness of the deductions in an axiom system came to be seen as in no way depending upon the literal meaning of the axioms. That is, the modern axiom system is abstract. One result of this development has been a broadening of the fields in which the axiomatic method may be used. Since deductions can be carried out independently of the specific meaning of the axioms, an axiom system may be applied to any field that as a whole or in part reflects the structure of the system. Examples may be seen in the modern application of axiom systems to arithmetic, analysis, set theory, and other branches of mathematics. Recently, the axiomatic method has been successfully applied to modern mechanics, the statics of rigid bodies, the theory of special relativity, and other

---

* See this chapter, Section 5, for a more exact account of independence.

† For an excellent account of this history see E. Nagel, "The Formation of Modern Conceptions of Formal Logic in the Development of Geometry", *Osiris*, Vol. 7 (1939), pp. 142–222.

parts of physics, and with some success to parts of biology, sociology, and economics.

The modern axiom system looks, at first glance, much like Euclid's system. It begins with *undefined terms*, which are usually chosen to be suggestive of the concepts of the principal area of interpretation or application. Thus axiom systems intended to have a geometrical interpretation use such undefined terms as *point*, *between*, and *line*. In the second place, there is also a series of *definitions* in which additional terms are introduced as abbreviations for concepts involving complex relations of the undefined terms. The use of definitions is for convenience and could be avoided by the expenditure of ink, effort, and paper, just as any shorthand notation could in principle be avoided. There is, third, a list of *axioms* involving the undefined and defined terms. Although these axioms usually suggest the intended interpretation or application, such suggestion is not essential. In addition, there are assumed certain *rules of inference*, which we have called *logical rules*. Even today, practicing mathematicians are often somewhat indefinite about the rules of inference they intend to use in an axiom system, although for the most part when nothing is said about the matter one may assume that at least the rules of GPL-1 with identity are intended. Finally, there are the *theorems*, which are consequences of the axioms and derived by use of the rules of inference.

Let us use a system of axioms first published by Peano in 1899 to illustrate these points. This axiom system has its origin in the study of the natural numbers. Indeed, Peano, an Italian mathematician, conceived of his enterprise as just the axiomatization of the arithmetic of these numbers. He began by supposing that anyone has an intuitive grasp of the natural number sequence and its properties; that is, the sequence 0, 1, 2, 3, ...

It will help us to understand the spirit of Peano's enterprise if we take as undefined terms "object", O and '. These terms are involved in our intuitive grasp of the natural numbers as the objects that can be generated by beginning with zero as initial object and successively passing to its immediate successor, and to the next successor, and so on.

We can now formulate our intuition of natural numbers axiomatically by using these undefined terms.

Ax. P1. O is an object.

Ax. P2. If n is an object, then n' is an object.

Ax. P3. For any objects m and n, if $m' = n'$ then $m = n$.

Ax. P4. For any object n, $n' \neq$ O.

Ax. P5. If P is a property such that
  (i) O has the property P
  (ii) If any object n has the property P then n' has this property, then every object has the property P.

Clearly, our axioms tell us how to generate a sequence

$$O, O', O'', O''', \ldots .$$

If we let these stand for the respective numbers of the sequence

$$0, 1, 2, 3, \ldots ,$$

we have the natural numbers. It is important to note that Axiom P5 tells us that we have *all* the objects obtainable by this generating process and so, on the interpretation suggested, all the natural numbers.

Because of our discussion of rules of inference in Part One, it is evident that such logical ideas as $\supset$, $\prod$, $\neq$, and $=$ are tacitly used, and in fact we may assume that GPL-1 with identity is at least part of the underlying logic. But we say no more about this at the moment, and proceed to prove some theorems without explicit reference to logic.

8.1(P) $O' \neq O''$

1. $O' = O''$ only if $O = O'$ Ax. P3
2. $O = O'$ only if for some n, $n' = O$
3. But for all n, $n' \neq O$ Ax. P4
4. $O \neq O'$ and $O' \neq O''$

As an exercise, the reader may wish to restate the axioms used and give the proof of this theorem, using the complete notation of GPL-1 with identity.

The next theorem requires the introduction of a definition and the use of Axiom P5 in a proof. We wish to define an operation between two objects and we shall use the symbol $\circ$ for this operation.

Definition: The operation $\circ$ is defined for any objects if

(i) $n \circ O = n$
(ii)   For any m and n, $n \circ m' = (n \circ m)'$.

If we let $\circ$ stand for the usual operation $+$ in the natural number arithmetic, we have a definition of addition. We can now prove that the operation $\circ$ is associative, that is,

$$k \circ (m \circ l) = (k \circ m) \circ l.$$

To do this we use Axiom P5. A heuristic explanation suggesting the effect of this axiom may be in order for readers meeting it for the first time. Suppose that we imagine a set of dominoes arranged to stand upright on their narrow edges so that a push on one of them will knock over the next one. In this case, if we push over the first one, then all of the dominoes will fall. Here we have an analogy to the principle of mathematical induction, for if the set of dominoes has a first element and it falls, and if the falling of each domino produces the falling of its successor, then all the dominoes fall. Peano's Axiom P5 is a formulation of mathematical induction.

8.2(P)　For any k, l, m,
$$k \circ (m \circ l) = (k \circ m) \circ l$$

Proof: The use of mathematical induction in a proof involves showing first that the property in question holds when l is O. This is called the *Basis* of the induction. We then show that if we assume the property holds when l is n, it holds when l is n'. The assumption that the property holds when l is n is called the *hypothesis of the induction*, and the proof that on this assumption the property holds for n' is called the *Induction Step*. Having established the Basis and the Induction Step we use Ax. P5 to conclude that the property holds for every object.

Basis. Let $l = $ O. Then for any k, m,

$$k \circ (m \circ O) = (k \circ m) \circ O.$$

This follows since the left side of the equation equals $k \circ m$ by definition of $\circ$; and for similar reasons, the right side equals $k \circ m$.

Induction Step. We assume that the theorem holds when $l = n$. By hypothesis of the induction,

$$(k \circ m) \circ n = k \circ (m \circ n).$$

Now consider

$$(k \circ m) \circ n'$$

and

$$k \circ (m \circ n').$$

But by the definition of $\circ$, the first reduces to $[(k \circ m) \circ n]'$ and the second to $[k \circ (m \circ n)]'$. And by Ax. P2, if $(k \circ m) \circ n = k \circ (m \circ n)$, then $[(k \circ m) \circ n]'$ $= [k \circ (m \circ n)]'$. Whence, $(k \circ m) \circ n' = k \circ (m \circ n')$, and by Ax. P5 the theorem holds.

It may occur to the reader that we could also show by similar argument that $\circ$ is commutative and that the cancellation law holds for it. This is left as an exercise.

The abstractness of this axiom system is exemplified by the use of symbols like ′ and O and the word "object". These suggest that we must interpret the system in order to apply it to the natural numbers. Even more emphatic evidence of its abstractness may be seen if we note (following Bertrand Russell) that the natural numbers are only one of many applications of this system. That is, the axioms may be thought of as generating the odd positive integers, or the negative integers, to mention only two examples. Such abstractness raises certain problems that we will consider in a general way in the balance of this chapter and more rigorously in succeeding chapters.

EXERCISE 8.2

I. Pick out the undefined terms in the two axiom systems given in the exercises for Section 8.1.

II. By mathematical induction prove the following assertions.

1. $1 + 3 + 5 + 7 + \ldots + (2n - 1) = n^2$

2. $2 + 4 + 6 + 8 + \ldots + (2n) = n(n + 1)$

3. $3 + 6 + 9 + 12 + \ldots + (3n) = 3n(n + 1)/2$

4. $a + ar + ar^2 + \ldots + ar^{n-1} = a - ar^n/1 - r$

5. $x + (x + y) + (x + 2y) + \ldots + [x + (n - 1)y]$
$= n[2x + (n - 1)y]/2$

6. Given n distinct points in a plane with no three points in the same straight line, show that the number of straight lines necessary to join all pairs of the n points is $n(n - 1)/2$.

III. Restate the Axioms for Peano's system, using the notation of GPL-1.

IV. Give a full proof of 8.1(P), using logical rules.

V. Prove, using mathematical induction, that ∘ is commutative and that the cancellation law holds for it.

8.3 Boolean Algebra: An Axiom System

As another example of a modern axiom system, we consider a formulation of the so-called *algebra of classes*. This algebra was developed by Boole and Schröder as an analysis of elementary class relations.* That is, its intuitive basis is to be found in our conception of classes and the various ways in which they stand to one another in the relations of conjunction, disjunction, and inclusion.† The algebra of classes has proved to be useful as applied to problems of computation, and it has theoretical significance through its generalizations in lattice theory and its connections with PL (as we shall see).

Intuitively, we think of a class as a set of elements, a collection of things or a group of individuals. We are also aware of such truths as that for any classes a, b, c, if a is included in b and b is included in c, then a is included in c.

---

* George Boole, *The Mathematical Analysis of Logic* (New York: Philosophical Library, 1948). Originally published 1847.

E. Schröder, *Vorlesungen über die Algebra der Logik* (Leipzig, 1890–1905).

† See Chapter Twelve for a less elementary treatment.

Indeed we know that such truths can be represented by diagrams such as the following.

Diagram 8.1

From this intuitive basis we may construct an axiom system consolidating our knowledge and providing a tool for further analysis of such concepts.

As undefined terms we take a list,

$$a, b, c, \ldots , \text{ as well as V and } \Lambda,$$

and four operations

$$\cap, \cup, ^-, =.$$

In the intuitive basis of our system we may think of the entities a, b, c, etc., as referring to classes. The operations $\cup$, $\cap$, $^-$ refer to operations performed on classes. Thus we may think of $\cap$ as a conjoining operation so that $a \cap b$ means the class of things common to a and b. $a \cup b$ represents a disjunction and means the class of things belonging to a or b or both.

The symbol $=$ has the intuitive meaning of equality. Thus $a = b$ asserts the identity of the two classes a and b. $\bar{a}$ refers to the class of all things not in a. V refers to the class of all individuals, while Λ refers to the class of no individuals, the null class.

We can present our knowledge concerning class relations in the following axioms:

Ax. B1.   For every a and b,
   $$a \cup b = b \cup a$$
Ax. B2.   For every a and b,
   $$a \cap b = b \cap a$$
Ax. B3.   For every a, b, and c,
   $$a \cup (b \cap c) = (a \cup b) \cap (a \cup c)$$
Ax. B4.   For every a, b, and c,
   $$a \cap (b \cup c) = (a \cap b) \cup (a \cap c)$$
Ax. B5.   There is at least one d such that for every a,
   $$a \cap d = a$$
Ax. B6.   There is at least one e such that for every a,
   $$a \cup e = a$$
Ax. B7.   If there is exactly one d such that for every a, $a \cap d = a$, and there is exactly one such e that for every a, $a \cup e = a$, then for every f there is at least one g such that $f \cup g = d$ and $f \cap g = e$

The first four of these axioms* tell us how to combine the entities $a, b, c, \ldots$ in various ways; that is, if we use our intuitive reference, how to combine classes. Axioms 1 and 2 indicate that the algebra of classes is commutative; Axioms 3 and 4, that it is distributive. The function of axioms B5–B7 is revealed in the following theorems, which provide a transition from the variables d and e in these axioms to the constants V and Λ, and from the variable g to the term $\bar{f}$.

8.1(B) There is exactly one e such that $a \cup e = a$ (*i.e.*, $a \cup \Lambda = a$)

Proof: By Ax. B6, there is at least one such e. Now suppose that there were two such; namely, e_1 and e_2.

Then $e_2 \cup e_1 = e_2$ by Ax. B6
and $e_1 \cup e_2 = e_1$ by Ax. B6.
But $e_2 \cup e_1 = e_1 \cup e_2$ by Ax. B1.
Hence, $e_2 = e_1$; *i.e.*, there is only one such class.
From now on we shall use the symbol Λ to denote this constant.
That is, $a \cup \Lambda = a$.

The fact that this axiom system presupposes the rules of inference of Part One is clear in this proof. Indeed, the general form of the proof is that of $\sim$I. The reader may wish to state the relevant axioms and the proof in full logical form.

8.2(B) There is exactly one d such that $a \cap d = a$ (*i.e.*, $a \cap V = a$)

The proof is similar to that of 8.1(B), and the unique d is henceforth denoted by V. That is, $a \cap V = a$.

8.3(B) For every f there is at most one g such that $f \cup g = V$ and $f \cap g = \Lambda$ (*i.e.*, $a \cup \bar{a} = V$ and $a \cap \bar{a} = \Lambda$)

Proof: Assume that there are g_1 and g_2 such that

(1) $f \cup g_1 = V$
(2) $f \cup g_2 = V$
(3) $f \cap g_1 = \Lambda$
(4) $f \cap g_2 = \Lambda$.

Then $g_2 = g_2 \cap V$	8.2(B)
$= g_2 \cap (f \cup g_1)$	Assumption (1)
$= (f \cap g_2) \cup (g_1 \cap g_2)$	Ax. B4
$= \Lambda \cup (g_1 \cap g_2)$	Assumption (4)
$= (g_1 \cap f) \cup (g_1 \cap g_2)$	Assumption (3); Ax. B2
$= g_1 \cap (f \cup g_2)$	Ax. B4
$= g_1 \cap V$	Assumption (2)
$= g_1$	8.2(B)

* Essentially those of E. V. Huntington, "Sets of Independent Postulates for the Algebra of Logic", *Transactions Amer. Math. Soc.*, Vol. 5 (1904), pp. 288–309.

From 8.3(B) together with Ax. B7, it follows that with each f there is associated a unique g. Let us call this $\bar{f}$—intuitively, the *complement* of the class f. Thus we have $a \cup \bar{a} = V$ and $a \cap \bar{a} = \Lambda$.

COROLLARY: For any a and b, if $a \cap b = \Lambda$ and $a \cup b = V$ then $a = \bar{b}$.

8.4(B) $a \cup a = a$

$$
\begin{aligned}
\text{Proof: } a \cup a &= (a \cup a) \cap V && \text{8.2B} \\
&= (a \cup a) \cap (a \cup \bar{a}) && \text{8.3(B)} \\
&= a \cup (a \cap \bar{a}) && \text{Ax. B3} \\
&= a \cup \Lambda && \text{8.3(B)} \\
&= a && \text{8.1(B)}
\end{aligned}
$$

8.5(B) $a \cap a = a$

The proof is similar to that of 8.4(B).

8.6(B) $a \cap \Lambda = \Lambda$

$$
\begin{aligned}
\text{Proof: } a \cap \Lambda &= \Lambda \cap a && \text{Ax. B2} \\
&= \Lambda \cap (a \cup \Lambda) && \text{8.1(B)} \\
&= (\Lambda \cap a) \cup (\Lambda \cap \Lambda) && \text{Ax. B4} \\
&= (\Lambda \cap a) \cup \Lambda && \text{8.5(B)} \\
&= (a \cap \Lambda) \cup (a \cap \bar{a}) && \text{Ax. B2, 8.3(B)} \\
&= a \cap (\Lambda \cup \bar{a}) && \text{Ax. B4} \\
&= a \cap \bar{a} && \text{8.1(B)} \\
&= \Lambda && \text{8.3(B)}
\end{aligned}
$$

8.7(B) $a \cup V = V$

The proof of this theorem is similar to that of 8.6(B).

The following four theorems develop the Boolean Algebra enough for our present purposes and will be of use to us later. They are presented without much comment, and the reader may wish to provide justification for the steps in the proofs.

8.8(B) $a \cup (a \cap b) = a$

$$
\begin{aligned}
\text{Proof: } a \cup (a \cap b) &= (a \cap V) \cup (a \cap b) \\
&= a \cap (V \cup b) \\
&= a \cap (b \cup V) \\
&= a \cap V \\
&= a
\end{aligned}
$$

8.9(B) $a \cap (a \cup b) = a$

$$
\begin{aligned}
\text{Proof: } a \cap (a \cup b) &= (a \cap a) \cup (a \cap b) \\
&= a \cup (a \cap b) \\
&= a
\end{aligned}
$$

8.10(B) $a \cup b = \overline{\bar{a} \cap \bar{b}}$

Proof: We first establish

$$a \cup (\bar{a} \cup c) = V \text{ and}$$
$$a \cap (\bar{a} \cap c) = \Lambda.$$

Intuitively, we could say that $a \cup (\bar{a} \cup c) = (a \cup \bar{a}) \cup c) = V$. However, we have not yet established the associative law for Boolean Algebra; hence we proceed (in lieu of establishing that law) more indirectly.

$$
\begin{aligned}
a \cup (\bar{a} \cup c) &= V \cap [a \cup (\bar{a} \cup c)] \\
&= (a \cup \bar{a}) \cap [a \cup (\bar{a} \cup c)] \\
&= a \cup [\bar{a} \cap (\bar{a} \cup c)] \\
&= a \cup \bar{a} \qquad\qquad\qquad \text{By 8.9(B)} \\
&= V
\end{aligned}
$$

The proof that $a \cap (\bar{a} \cap c) = \Lambda$ is similar. We now use these results to obtain a result in the form of the corollary to 8.3(B).

$$
\begin{aligned}
(a \cup b) \cup (\bar{a} \cap \bar{b}) &= [(a \cup b) \cup \bar{a}] \cap [(a \cup b) \cup \bar{b}] \\
&= V \cap V \\
&= V
\end{aligned}
$$

$$
\begin{aligned}
(a \cup b) \cap (\bar{a} \cap \bar{b}) &= [a \cap (\bar{a} \cap \bar{b})] \cup [b \cap (\bar{a} \cap \bar{b})] \\
&= \Lambda \cup \Lambda \\
&= \Lambda
\end{aligned}
$$

This is the form of the corollary to 8.3B, hence

$$(a \cup b) = \overline{\bar{a} \cap \bar{b}}$$

8.11(B) $a \cap b = \overline{\bar{a} \cup \bar{b}}$

The proof is left to the reader.

We shall return to Boolean Algebra in the succeeding sections to illustrate some important properties of axiom systems. For the present, this system illustrates an abstract axiom system.

EXERCISE 8.3

I. Complete the proofs for 8.2(B), 8.5(B), 8.7(B), 8.11(B), and justify the steps in the proofs of 8.8(B), 8.9(B), and 8.10(B).

II. In what sense are the objects V and Λ of Boolean Algebra unique objects?

8.4 The Problem of Consistency

When we use the axiomatic method to study real space, as Euclid did, our fundamental problem is to give a true account of it. If our use of this method should lead to a contradiction (that is, if we should find ourselves able to deduce both a "theorem" and its negation), we would presume that we had made a mistake in deduction, or that we had inadvertently introduced a false axiom. In either case a definite mistake would have to be eliminated. Even when we apply the axiomatic method in its more abstract modern form to the study of non-Euclidian ideal spaces, we explain a possible contradiction as an error in deduction; or, if a check shows no such error, as involving the assumption of incompatible axioms. We do not regard the axioms of non-Euclidian geometries in general as true, so that we cannot explain the possible contradiction by saying that one of them is false. We can explain it only as an improper choice of axioms—that is, a choice involving axioms that can be shown to be incompatible.

The modern application of abstract axiomatic methods to the subjects of arithmetic, analysis, and set theory confronts us with a different and more difficult problem. Arithmetic has been known and developed for thousands of years and, at least in its elementary aspects, has a claim to acceptability that could hardly be strengthened. Analysis and set theory also comprise subjects independently of axiomatization, and, although their acceptability has been questioned, few would say that there were no achieved results in these theories. If these subjects are regarded as acceptable, it should be possible to find compatible axioms for each of them. Thus, if contradictions do occur in correct axiomatizations of these subjects, we cannot usually blame them on incompatible axioms. When we correctly axiomatize an acceptable subject matter such as arithmetic, analysis, or set theory, we must suppose that our axiomatization reflects the structure of the subject matter. Hence, if a contradiction occurs, it must have its source either in incorrect procedures used in setting up the axiom system or in the very nature of the subject matter; that is, in some error of reasoning used in it or in the methods of constructing the mathematical objects discussed. As we shall see in Chapter Thirteen, in the case of set theory there is reason for thinking that the latter is true—that intuitive set theory contains errors.

However, in the case of such an intuitively acceptable subject as arithmetic, our first inclination would be to attribute a contradiction to the incorrect procedures used in setting up the axiom system. When we set up an axiom system, we are motivated to construct it so as to obtain all the theorems needed to give a complete account of the subject matter. We usually accomplish this by increasing the number of axioms and rules of inference; and we accomplish it at the risk of inconsistency, for the continued addition of axioms and rules of inference may make it possible sooner or later to deduce a contradiction. The addition of theorems and rules of inference may lead to inconsistency. On the other hand, unless we have enough axioms and rules we shall find it impossible to get the theorems we need to represent the subject matter adequately. Failure to elaborate the system may lead to incompleteness. But the advantages of the axiomatic method are so great—first, in rigor, ease of communication, and consolidation of results, and, second, in the great power it makes available for reaching profound truths unattainable by other methods—that the twin dangers of inconsistency and incompleteness must be dealt with.

Clearly what is needed is a way of testing for consistency and completeness, so that in the case of any axiom system we may assure ourselves that it is strong enough to get the results we need and want, but not so strong as to make the deduction of contradictory theorems possible. We proceed to discuss some methods for determining whether an axiom system has these properties. We begin with the property of consistency.

In order to establish the consistency of an abstract axiom system, we might proceed to find a situation which exemplifies it; that is, a situation of which the axioms and theorems are true. Intuitively, we feel that the existence of such an exemplification assures consistency. The reasons behind our intuition run something like this: The axioms and any theorems deducible from the axioms must be true of the exemplification. Further, contradictory statements could not be true of the exemplification—that is, any two statements true of the exemplification must be consistent. Hence, the axioms and theorems of the system are consistent. There is, however, one important qualification of this reasoning: the exemplification itself must not contain a contradiction, as it might if it were another axiom system or a body of untested mathematics. Still, this method of establishing consistency is often used in mathematics, and it is worth further consideration.

We may summarize the preceding discussion in a definition.

Relative Consistency: If an axiom system has an exemplification (often called a model) it is said to be consistent relative to this model.

We now proceed to explain the meaning of the term "model" used in this definition.

In the second and third sections of this chapter we illustrated the structure of two abstract axiom systems. To obtain a test for consistency, we now need to develop an exact sense of what it means to exemplify such a system. It is usual to refer to the procedure for exemplifying the system as an *interpretation* and to the structure determined by the interpretation as a *model*.

An interpretation of an axiom system is an assignment to the undefined terms of meanings such that the axioms and theorems become true statements. This assignment presupposes that the implicit logical rules are assigned the meanings of the rules in GPL-1 with identity, or at least that the rules of inference give true conclusions from true premises.

We can illustrate the significance of an interpretation in a heuristic way by observing that the informal model of Euclidian geometry is "real" space. However, we can find also a model of the non-Euclidian geometry of Riemann in Euclidian geometry. To do this we interpret the Riemannian plane as the surface of a sphere in Euclidian three-dimensional space.

We can illustrate the significance of an interpretation more precisely by assigning meanings to the undefined terms of Peano's axiom system. To do this means to spell out in technical terms the phrase we used in Section Two "let the sequence O, O', O", ..., stand for 0, 1, 2, ...". That is, we assign the meaning *number* to the undefined term "object"; the meaning *zero* to the undefined term O; and *immediate successor* to the undefined term '. With this assignment of meanings, each of the axioms becomes a statement true of the natural numbers. Thus, we have

Ax. P1'.   Zero is a number.

Ax. P2'.   If n is a number, then the immediate successor of n is a number.

and so on, substituting for "object", for ', and for O the meanings of the interpretation.

We may also note that all theorems proved for Peano's axiom system are true of the natural numbers as restated in terms of the meanings of the interpretation. Thus 8.1(P) becomes

> **8.1(P)'**   The immediate successor of the immediate successor of zero is not equal to the immediate successor of zero.
> That is, $2 \neq 1$.

And if we interpret $\circ$ as $+$, 8.2(P) becomes

> **8.2(P)'**   For any numbers m, n, k,
> $$k + (m + n) = (k + m) + n$$

That is, addition is associative.

In pointing out that the theorems of the axiom system are true of the model, we assume that the rules of inference used preserve the truth of the axioms. Intuitively, this is fairly evident, and we shall see in the next chapter that if these rules are those of PL they do indeed preserve truth. This is the case for GPL-1 as well, as a later chapter will establish rigorously.

As a further illustration, let us interpret Boolean algebra. A number of interpretations can be given readily, but perhaps if we begin with an assignment of meanings that is *not* an interpretation, a sharpening of the concept will result. Let, then, $a, b, c, \ldots$ be assigned as meanings the natural numbers 0, 1, 2, 3, ... and let $\cup$, $\cap$ have the meanings of $+$ and $\cdot$, respectively, in ordinary algebra. If, now, we examine the axioms as written in the new terms for truth, the first two are true, but Ax. B3 is not. This is illustrated by the case where (on this interpretation) a has the value 2, b the value 3, and c the value 4; that is,

$$2 + (3 \cdot 4) = (2 + 3) \cdot (2 + 4)$$
$$14 = 30$$

In consequence, the ordinary arithmetic of the natural numbers is not a model of Boolean algebra.

The following diagram suggests an assignment of meanings that provides an interpretation of Boolean algebra:

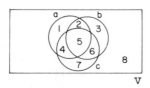

Diagram 8.2

Let a, b, and c be represented by the circles shown above. Here a consists of regions 1, 2, 4, and 5, b consists of regions 2, 3, 5, and 6, and c consists of regions 4, 5, 6, and 7. Let $a \cup b$ be the smallest region containing everything that falls either within a or within b; to wit, the area consisting of regions 1, 2, 3, 4, 5, and 6. Similarly, $a \cup c$ will consist of 1, 2, 4, 5, 6, and 7.

Let $a \cap b$ be the largest region common to a and b—in this case, the composite of regions 2 and 5. Let $\bar{a}$ be the entire region outside a; to wit, regions 3, 6, 7, and 8. Obviously, $V = a \cup \bar{a}$. Λ, or $a \cap \bar{a}$, will be the largest region common to a and $\bar{a}$. Of course, nothing is common to a and $\bar{a}$. $\Lambda \cup a$ will obviously include nothing not already included in a, and $V \cup a$ will evidently amount to the same group of regions that V already amounts to. $V \cap a$ is clearly a, since any a has its own contents *in toto* in common with V.

All the axioms may now be readily verified. According to Ax. B3, for instance, $a \cup (b \cap c) = (a \cup b) \cap (a \cup c)$. Let us express the variables in terms of the corresponding regions. Taking the left-hand side first:

a corresponds to regions 1, 2, 4, and 5.

$(b \cap c)$ corresponds to regions 5 and 6.

Hence $a \cup (b \cap c)$ corresponds to regions 1, 2, 4, 5, and 6. Let us now consider the right-hand side of the third axiom:

$(a \cup b)$ corresponds to regions 1, 2, 3, 4, 5, and 6.

$(a \cup c)$ corresponds to regions 1, 2, 4, 5, 6, and 7.

Thus $(a \cup b) \cap (a \cup c)$ will consist of all the regions common to these two lists—or 1, 2, 4, 5, and 6. But this is just what $a \cup (b \cap c)$ was shown to consist of.

The verification of the remaining axioms is left to the reader. Furthermore, the theorems of the axiom system will all hold true on this interpretation. This point is left to the reader as an exercise.

A Boolean algebra can also be interpreted in terms of electrical switches.* We assign a switch as the meaning of a, another as the meaning of b, etc. In this situation $a \cup b$ is the combination of switches a and b in parallel, and $a \cap b$ is their series combination. $\bar{a}$ is a switch that is always open when a is closed, and closed when a is open. Λ is a switch that is always open, and V is one that is always closed. The relation $=$ will have to be read "is electrically equivalent with". Thus $a \cap \Lambda = \Lambda$ because a switch in series with one that is always open is electrically equivalent with a switch that is always open. But $a \cup \Lambda = a$ because a switch that is always open will have no effect on any switch placed in parallel with it. A switch that is always closed, however, will render ineffective any switch placed in parallel with it: $a \cup V = V$. The reader will wish to show that the remaining axioms and theorems are likewise true on this assignment of meanings.

There is also a more abstract interpretation of Boolean algebra which turns out, in the end, to be more useful theoretically than either of the interpretations so far suggested. Let each of the undefined terms a, b, c, . . . have the meaning 1 or 0. V has the meaning 1 and Λ the meaning 0. We next assign meanings to the symbols $\cup$, $\cap$, $^-$ as follows. For $\cup$ we consider the possible cases,

$$0 \cup 0 = 0$$
$$0 \cup 1 = 1$$
$$1 \cup 0 = 1$$
$$1 \cup 1 = 1$$

These evaluate $a \cup b$ for all cases of a and b having the meanings 1 and 0. The results can be put in a more compact form:

$\cup$	0	1
0	0	1
1	1	1

We read this matrix as we did the matrices in Chapter Three. The matrix for $\cap$ is

$\cap$	0	1
0	0	0
1	0	1

---

* For further details, see Claude E. Shannon, "A Symbolic Analysis of Relay and Switching Circuits", *Transactions of American Institute of Electrical Engineers*, Vol. 57 (1938), pp. 713–723.

The matrix for $^-$ is

$$
\begin{array}{c|c}
- & \\
\hline
0 & 1 \\
1 & 0
\end{array}
$$

This assignment of meanings to the undefined terms $a, b, c, \ldots$ and to $\cap$, $\cup$, and $^-$ permits a restatement of the axioms in terms of these meanings. As restated they are true, provided we understand $=$ to mean having identical values. Thus, for example, Ax. B1 is

a	b	$a \cup b = b \cup a$	
1	1	1	1
0	1	1	1
1	0	1	1
0	0	0	0

This interpretation may suggest an interpretation of Boolean algebra in terms of PL. Such interpretation is left to the reader.

The fact that we have a model of an abstract axiom system tells us that this system is consistent *if* the model is consistent. When we interpret Peano's axiom system as the natural number system, we can have little doubt about its consistency, even though what we have established is *relative consistency*. Similarly, the consistency of Boolean algebra has been established relative to Diagram 8.2, to a set of switches, and to the tables of values given above. In these cases, also, we can have little doubt about consistency, for these models are finite and themselves evidently consistent.

Unfortunately, however, we cannot hope to find such acceptable models for most axiom systems, including some which are of fundamental importance in mathematics. In the case of axiomatic set theory, for example, where could we look for a model except to intuitive set theory or to one of the areas of mathematics which the axiomatic set theory reformulates? Such models are no simpler than the axiomatic set theory and so offer no real evidence for the soundness of the axiomatization. Since axiomatic set theory is so important a foundation of mathematical theories, and since there is reason for suspecting its consistency, we need some better method of establishing consistency than that of finding a model.

Clearly, relative consistency proofs are of value. It is interesting and significant to know, for example, that Euclidian geometry is consistent if algebra is consistent, as can be shown by interpreting Euclidian geometry in terms of algebra. This kind of information tells us a good deal about the interrelations of different mathematical areas. Nonetheless, we would like more. That is, we would like to establish the *absolute consistency* of an axiom system. The basic motivation in searching for absolute consistency proofs is the need to show that the axiom system in question does avoid the danger of being too complex and thus inconsistent—a danger that is possible because the system must be strong enough to provide all theorems wanted. As early as 1904,[*] David Hilbert saw the need of establishing absolute consistency, and in the 1920's he suggested and developed some methods which might be used for this purpose. These methods have come to be known as *metatheoretical* and the results obtained as *metatheory*.

The use of metatheoretical methods involves the study of the structure of an axiom system in terms of the symbols of the system as such. Metatheory, which results from such a study, contains information about the nature of axiom systems. In fact, by the use of metatheoretical methods it has been possible to establish the absolute consistency of some axiom systems, including the sets of rules of inference we studied in Part One. How this is done is the subject of the next few chapters, where the formalization of an axiom system as a principal tool will be discussed at length.

EXERCISE 8.4

I. Interpret the axiom set of Exercise 8.1 in some non-numerical way.

II. Is the following an interpretation of those axioms? Individual variables as persons, $>$ as *is an ancestor of*, and $=$ as *is unrelated to*.

III. Consider the following axioms.

Ax. 1. For every x and y there is one and only one result $x \circ y$.
Ax. 2. $x \circ y = y \circ x$
Ax. 3. $(x \circ y) \circ z = x \circ (y \circ z)$
Ax. 4. $(x \circ y = x \circ z) \supset (y = z)$
Ax. 5. $\sum_x [(x \circ x) = x]$

Does any of the following interpret these axioms?

1. Interpret x, y, z as points on the abscissa, ordinate, and height, respectively, of a Cartesian coordinate system, and $\circ$ as determining a point in a plane.

2. Let x, y, z, etc., range over the integer 1. Interpret $\circ$ as exponentiation.

3. Let x, y, z, etc., range over the integer 2. Interpret $\circ$ as exponentiation.

4. Let x, y, z, etc., range over the integers 1 and 2. Interpret $\circ$ as exponentiation.

---

[*] David Hilbert, "Über die Grundlagen der Logik und der Arithmetik", *Verhandlungen des Dritten Internationalen Mathematiker-Kongresses in Heidelberg vom 8 bis 13 August 1904* (Leipzig, 1904).

5. Interpret x, y, z, etc., as the positive integers, and $\circ$ as addition.

6. Interpret x, y, z, etc., as the positive integers, and $\circ$ as multiplication.

IV. An axiom system interpreted with the arithmetic of natural numbers is felt to be consistent. Is such consistency absolute or relative? If relative, why do we feel that the arithmetic of natural numbers is consistent?

V. Euclidian geometry was thought to be modeled by space. If this is so, can space model non-Euclidian geometries? If space cannot model Euclidian geometry as was thought, can other real models be called into question in the same manner?

VI. Interpret the following sets of axioms.

1. $\sim(x + x)$
$(x + y) \supset \sim(y + x)$
$[(x + y) \,\&\, (y + z)] \supset (x + z)$

2. $\sim(x + x)$
$(x + y) \supset \sim(y + z)$
$[(x + y) \,\&\, (y + z)] \supset \sim(x + z)$

3. $\sim(x + x)$
$(x + y) \supset (y + x)$
$[(x + y) \,\&\, (y + z)] \supset \sim(x + z)$

VII. Which of the following circuits are equivalent? Of what Boolean axioms or theorems are the equivalences models?

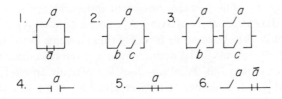

VIII. Which of the following circuits are equivalent? Of what Boolean axioms or theorems are the equivalences models?

IX. Find models for the axioms given in Exercise 8.1. What does the model prove?

X. Interpret Boolean algebra in terms of PL, as suggested in the text.

8.5 Independence and Completeness

A property of axiom systems that is as important as consistency is *completeness*. A discussion of completeness, however, is best begun with a discussion of the property of an axiom known as *independence*. Intuitively, we know that an axiom is independent if it does not repeat information given in any other axiom of the system. Thus a system having independent axioms has a certain elegance and conceptual simplicity. However, such a system may require quite complicated proofs precisely because of the independence of its axioms.

We can give to this intuitive notion of independence more precision as follows. By the *independence* of axiom A_k in the axiom set $A_1, A_2, A_3, \ldots, A_m$, we mean that A_k is not deducible from the other axioms in the set. Of course, the fact that we can not find a deduction in a given case does not mean that there is none, so that this definition does not provide an effective technique for determining independence. However, there are two tests available. First, we may note that if A_k is not independent in an axiom set, $A_1, A_2, A_3, \ldots, A_k, \ldots, A_m$, its removal as an axiom does not eliminate it as a theorem; hence, the axiom system $A_1, A_2, A_3, \ldots, \sim A_k, \ldots, A_m$—that is, the system from which A_k has been removed as an axiom and $\sim A_k$ substituted—will be inconsistent and no model will exist. Thus, if we can find a model for both the axiom system $A_1, A_2, A_3, \ldots, A_k, \ldots, A_m$, and $A_1, A_2, A_3, \ldots, \sim A_k, \ldots, A_m$, we have shown A_k to be independent.

A second (and usually easier) test follows from the observation that if A_k is independent, then, since it is not deducible from the other axioms, it may be false while they are true. If A_k were dependent, then it would be true when the other axioms were true. Hence, if we can find a model of which the axioms A_1, A_2, A_3, . . . , A_m, not including A_k, are true, and of which A_k is false, we establish its independence. This is the test most frequently used for independence.

We may illustrate this latter test by checking the axioms of Boolean algebra for independence. We can show that Ax. B1 is independent by interpreting the symbols a, b, c, . . . , as 1 or 0 and retaining the usual matrix for the complement, but interpreting $\cup$ and $\cap$ as follows:

Ax. B1

$\cup$	0	1		$\cap$	0	1
0	0	0		0	0	0
1	1	1		1	0	1

That this matrix makes Ax. B1 false is evident in the table

a	b	$a \cup b =$	$b \cup a$
1	1	1	1
0	1	0	1
1	0	1	0
0	0	0	0

However, the other axioms can be checked as true if similar tables are worked out for each of them.

The matrices for $\cup$ and $\cap$, by which the independence of the remaining axioms may be established, are listed for the axiom that is made false by that interpretation. In each case, one can show the axiom in question to be false and the other axioms to be true by constructing the appropriate tables.

Ax. B2.

$\cup$	0	1		$\cap$	0	1
0	0	1		0	0	0
1	1	1		1	1	1

Ax. B3.

$\cup$	0	1		$\cap$	0	1
0	0	1		0	0	0
1	1	0		1	0	1

Ax. B4.

$\cup$	0	1		$\cap$	0	1
0	0	1		0	1	0
1	1	1		1	0	1

Ax. B5.
(Let d be V)

$\cup$	0	1		$\cap$	0	1
0	0	1		0	1	1
1	1	1		1	1	1

Ax. B6.

(Let e be Λ)

$\cup$	0	1
0	0	0
1	0	0

$\cap$	0	1
0	0	0
1	0	1

Ax. B7.

(Let g be $\bar{f}$)

$\cup$	0	1
0	0	1
1	1	1

$\cap$	0	1
0	0	1
1	1	1

There is one point that deserves comment. In the case of Ax. B5 (and B6), Ax. B7 is satisfied trivially by the interpretation, since the conditional of Axiom 7 has a false antecedent. In the case of Ax. B1 (and B2), Ax. B7 is satisfied, since without Ax. B1 (or B2), V and Λ are not unique. That is, Ax. B7 is satisfied trivially.

Independence is not an essential property of axioms. Indeed, it is sometimes more convenient for the purposes of proof to have a certain amount of dependence among the axioms. In the historical development of axiom systems, it often happens that a theorem is difficult to prove and it is assumed as an axiom until, later, a proof is obtained. For purposes of intelligibility, moreover, dependence is sometimes a merit, since it permits a statement of an axiom set in a form closer to the intuitive basis of the system.

Ultimately, the purpose of an axiom system is to aid in the study of a subject such as arithmetic or geometry. Thus an axiom system must be consistent. It is also essential that the system be complete if we are to regard it as giving an account of a subject. Loosely speaking, an axiom system is complete when it enables us to obtain all the truths of a subject. An axiom system that provides the means of obtaining all the theorems we need exhibits the property of completeness in a clear way. Thus, a Euclidian geometry (like that discussed in Section 8.1) might have too few axioms to yield all the theorems needed to describe actual space, and so be incomplete. The abstract axiom system of Simple Order, discussed in Chapter One, permits the deduction of some of the properties of integers, but it does not permit a deduction of all the properties of the integers. Hence, if we regard this axiom system as giving an account of the integers, it will be incomplete.

There are several ways in which an abstract axiom system might fail to give a complete account of a given subject matter. First, the concepts used in the axioms might be insufficient. Thus, in the case of geometry, a given axiomatization might fail to include the concept of congruence. If this should happen, all theorems involving congruence relations would be missing. Such incompleteness of terminology is not serious, for it is readily corrected.

A second kind of incompleteness is more serious. This is the sort where the rules of inference used in the deduction of theorems from axioms are insufficient to make possible the deduction of all the truths in the interpretation. We may illustrate this situation in terms of intuitionistic logic, which lacks the rule $\sim\sim$E (See Chapter Four), and so is not strong enough to make possible the deduction of many results of classical mathematics. Similarly, the rules of inference of an axiom system might include propositional rules, but not quantificational ones. Obviously, with the aid of the latter we can deduce theorems unattainable with the aid of propositional rules alone.

A third kind of incompleteness—also serious—is the sort where there are not sufficient axioms to make possible the deduction of all truths of the subject matter. For example, if in a Euclidian geometry we leave out the axiom concerning parallel lines we shall not get the whole series of theorems we want. This kind of incompleteness might be corrected in the case of axiom systems that represent actual circumstances, such as space, by the addition of axioms that would give the needed theorems. However, this addition might not be very easy. One can imagine Euclid's predecessors, in their efforts to obtain a system adequate to space, adding and subtracting axioms and deducing results over a period of several centuries, until Euclid was able to take the decisive steps toward a presumably complete system.

In the case of an abstract axiom system, however, this remedy is not open to us, since we need not regard the axiom system as giving an account of any antecedently designated subject matter. In the case of an abstract axiom system, we must fall back upon the conception of completeness as a property of that system which supplies all theorems. Our task is to give to this idea an exact significance. Actually, this task is not too difficult. Using the concept of independence already discussed, we can define completeness:

Completeness: An axiom system with axioms $A_1, A_2, A_3, \ldots, A_m$ is said to be complete when there is no statement A_k in the terms of the system which can be added as an independent axiom without producing inconsistency.

This definition tells us that all true statements in the terms of the system are already derivable from the present set of axioms and that we obtain no new theorems by increasing the number of axioms.

Although this definition of completeness is fairly precise, it does not give us an effective test for determining the completeness of an axiom system. The fact that we might be unable to find a truth of Boolean algebra or arithmetic, for example, which is independent of the axioms given does not of itself mean that there is no such truth. It may mean only that our search has been unsuccessful. In some cases we can effectively resolve the issue. Gödel, for example, has shown by an indirect argument that certain kinds of axiom systems are never complete. Yet, on the other hand, if we can show that all interpretations of an axiom system are essentially the same—as is sometimes possible—its completeness follows.

Axiom systems for which all interpretations are essentially the same are called *categorical*. In more technical terms, a *categorical axiom system* is one in which models determined by all interpretations are isomorphic; that is, are such that there is a one-to-one correspondence between their elements, and statements true of one are true of all the others. In some cases we can establish categoricity by showing that the structures determined by any interpretation are isomorphic. When the isomorphism of structures can be shown, we do have a test for completeness, because completeness is implied by categoricity.

We shall not discuss the methods for determining isomorphism of two structures. These are a part of algebraic methods and may be studied in any introduction to modern abstract algebra.* That categoricity implies completeness, however, is easy to see. Suppose that an axiom system is categorical, but not complete. It follows from its incompleteness that there is a statement, A_k, that can be added as an independent axiom. Since A_k is independent of the other axioms, it will not be deducible from them and hence the addition of $\sim A_k$ to the original axioms will not be inconsistent. There exists, therefore, a model of the system $A_1, A_2, A_3, \ldots, A_m$ not containing A_k, of which A_k is true, and a necessarily different model of this system for which A_k is false. But, on the assumption that the system is categorical, there cannot be two such different models. Hence, if an axiom system is categorical it is complete.

EXERCISE 8.5

I. The following axioms define an equivalence relation. Are they independent?

   Ax. 1. $a = a$

   Ax. 2. $a = b \supset b = a$

   Ax. 3. $[(a = b \ \& \ b = c)] \supset a = c$

II. Show that $x \supset (y \ \& \ z)$ and $x \ \& \ (\sim y \ \mathbf{v} \sim z)$ are independent by assigning matrices to $\supset$, &, and **v**, respectively. By applying DM and Impl, state the relationship between the above two expressions.

III. Consider the axiom set of Exercise 8.1, and its various interpretations, asked for in Exercise IX, Section Four. Show that the models are isomorphic and thus the axiom set complete.

SUGGESTED READINGS

1. R. D. Carmichael, *The Logic of Discovery* (Chicago and London: Open Court Pub. Co., 1930).

2. David Hilbert, *The Foundations of Geometry* (Chicago: Open Court Pub. Co., 1902).

---

* See, for example, G. Birkhoff and S. McLane, *A Survey of Modern Algebra* (New York: The Macmillan Co., 1944).

3. R. B. Kershner and L. R. Wilcox, *The Anatomy of Mathematics* (New York: Ronald Press Co., 1950), Ch. VI.

4. E. Nagel, "The Formation of Modern Conceptions of Formal Logic in the Development of Geometry", *Osiris*, Vol. 7 (1939), pp. 142–222.

5. E. Nagel and James R. Newman, *Gödel's Proof* (New York: New York University Press, 1958), Chs. I, II, III.

6. M. Richardson, *Fundamentals of Mathematics* (New York: The Macmillan Co., 1947), Ch. II.

7. R. L. Wilder, *Introduction to the Foundations of Mathematics* (New York: John Wiley & Sons, 1952), Chs. I, II.

Chapter 9

The Metatheory of Propositional Logic

9.1 Introduction

Several times in the preceding chapters we have had occasion to refer to the area of logic presupposed by one axiom system or another. Thus, in Chapter Six we observed that certain properties of relations could be stated in terms of GPL-1. The transitivity of $<$, for example, is expressed by the quantified statement

$$\prod_x \prod_y \prod_z [(x < y \ \& \ y < z) \supset x < z]$$

Other properties of various relations, such as reflexivity and symmetry, for example, can also be stated in terms of GPL-1. In Chapter Eight we observed that Euclid's axiomatization of geometry and Peano's axiomatization of the natural numbers presupposed logical rules of inference. In particular, we suggested that these rules might be the rules of GPL-1 plus the rules for identity. These rules are more fundamental than the axioms, in the sense that they determine the form of the axioms and that alternative axioms may be stated without changes in rules. Thus, since the rules of PL are included in GPL-1, such axioms must be formulated as statements. And, since the rules peculiar to GPL-1 involve variables, the axioms must be formulated using variables, predicates, and quantifiers.

Thus, Peano's axioms, first stated in Chapter Eight, since they presuppose GPL-1 plus identity, take the explicit quantificational form

P1* $\quad O(0)$
P2* $\quad \prod_n[O(n) \supset O(n')]$
P3* $\quad \prod_m\prod_n[(m' = n') \supset (m = n)]$
P4* $\quad \prod_n[n' \neq 0]$
P5* $\quad \{F(0) \,\&\, \prod_n[F(n) \supset F(n')]\} \supset \prod_n F(n)$

Clearly, there are a large number of different axiom systems based upon the rules of GPL-1 plus identity. That is, one may vary the axioms stated while retaining the same rules of inference. Complete variation is not possible, of course. Different axiom systems have properties in common because they do use the same rules of inference. This fact makes possible the study of such properties by investigating the rules themselves. We may ask whether any system that depends on certain rules has the important properties of consistency and completeness. That is, we may ask whether the rules as such introduce inconsistency and whether the rules as such are strong enough to get all the desired conclusions.

We may answer questions concerning the consistency and completeness of any specific set of axioms (including rules of inference) by interpreting the axiom system by means of the methods of Chapter Eight. However, if we wish to solve these problems for the rules of inference as such, this method is not sufficient. There are two possibilities open to us. First, we might replace the rules by an axiom system which we could then interpret and so show to be complete and consistent. For example, we might state PL in terms of the following three axiom schemas and one rule:

> **P. Ax. 1** $\quad p \supset (q \supset p)$
> **P. Ax. 2** $\quad [s \supset (p \supset q)] \supset [(s \supset p) \supset (s \supset q)]$
> **P. Ax. 3** $\quad (\sim p \supset \sim q) \supset (q \supset p)$

(Here "P. Ax." stands for "propositional axiom schema".) The rule needed in order to derive theorems from these axiom schemata is $\supset$ E.* With this axiom system on hand we can find an interpretation in the matrices used in Chapter Eight to interpret Boolean algebra. Such an interpretation is, in effect, a partial interpretation of any specific axiom system using the rules of PL.

Secondly, and more directly, we might study the nature of the deductions defined by the rules of PL in an effort to show that these rules warrant all the results desired and that none of the axiom systems determined by them is

---

* This axiomatization is to be found in Alonzo Church, *Introduction to Mathematical Logic* (Princeton, N.J.: Princeton University Press, 1956), p. 149. It seems to originate with Łukasiewicz.

inconsistent, unless, of course, the axioms themselves are inconsistent. In this study, which we carry out in the present chapter, we use the metatheoretical method suggested by David Hilbert.* In using this method to establish the consistency of an axiom system, we do not search for a model, but show that the axioms and rules of inference do not permit the deduction of contradictory theorems. We thus establish *absolute* consistency, which we now define:

Absolute Consistency: An axiom system is absolutely consistent if contradictory theorems are not implied by the axioms and rules of inference.

EXERCISE 9.1

I. Use the rules of PL to derive the axiom schemata P. Ax. 1, P. Ax. 2, and P. Ax. 3.

II. Find an interpretation of these axiom schemata in matrices.

III. Suppose it has been proved that P. Ax. 1, P. Ax. 2, and P. Ax. 3 are consistent. What, if anything, follows with respect to the consistency of the rules of PL?

IV. Suppose it has been proved that P. Ax. 1, P. Ax. 2, and P. Ax. 3 are complete. What, if anything, follows with respect to the completeness of the rules of PL?

9.2 Consistency

When we say that a particular axiom system is absolutely consistent, we mean that we cannot derive contradictory theorems from the axioms. However, we are now to consider the consistency not of a specific axiom system, but of a set of rules, namely, the set of rules for PL as given in Chapter Two. When we say that a system of rules—for example, PL—is consistent, we mean that given any set of axioms in acceptable form, no contradictions can result unless the axioms are themselves contradictory.

Consistency of The rules of PL are consistent if and only if no zero-premise
PL Rules conclusions have the form $p \mathbin{\&} \sim p$.

ZPC's, it will be remembered, are reached in a deduction only through the discharge of all assumptions. Thus, if there are contradictions in the

---

* Of course this method can be applied to an axiomatization of the rules of PL, MPL, GPL-1, etc. Indeed it was applied to such axiomatizations first. However, such an application, if in some ways easier, is not quite as direct or as revealing of the method and the significance of its results as that followed here.

premises, these will not be carried over as contradictions into conclusions that are ZPC's.

We may illustrate this point if we consider first a deduction in which assumptions are contradictory.

$$
\begin{array}{lll}
\text{1. A} & & \\
\text{2. } \sim\!\text{A} & & \\
\text{3. A \& } \sim\!\text{A} & \quad 1, 2, \&\text{I} \\
\text{4. A} & \quad 2, \sim\!\text{I}, \sim\sim\!\text{E} \\
\text{5. A} \supset \text{A} & \quad 1\text{-}4, \supset\text{I}
\end{array}
$$

Here the ZPC resulting from the discharge of the premises is not a contradiction—indeed, it is evidently quite acceptable. Second, however, let us consider a deduction in which we arrive at a line with respect to which there are no undischarged assumptions but which has the form $p \ \& \sim\!p$.

$$
\begin{array}{lll}
\text{1.} & & \\
\vdots & & \\
\vdots & & \\
\text{k.} & \text{A \& } \sim\!\text{A} & \quad k - n, k - m, \&\text{I} \\
\text{k} + \text{1.} & \text{B} & \quad k, \sim\!\text{E}
\end{array}
$$

In this case we obtain any statement, B, as an unqualified line of a deduction—obviously an unacceptable situation. This situation does not arise, however, when it is discharged assumptions that are contradictory. Thus consider the deduction

$$
\begin{array}{lll}
\text{1. A} & & \\
\text{2. } \sim\!\text{A} & & \\
\text{3. A \& } \sim\!\text{A} & \quad 1, 2, \&\text{I} \\
\text{4. B} & \quad 3, \sim\!\text{E} \\
\text{5. } \sim\!\text{A} \supset \text{B} & \quad 2\text{-}4, \supset\text{I} \\
\text{6. A} \supset (\sim\!\text{A} \supset \text{B}) & \quad 1\text{-}5, \supset\text{I} \\
\text{7. (A \& } \sim\!\text{A}) \supset \text{B} & \quad 6, \text{Imp}
\end{array}
$$

Again, the last line is a ZPC and quite acceptable in its own right, as a double check by truth tables confirms. But if these examples suggest that the rules of PL are consistent, they by no means prove it.

We now turn our attention to a demonstration of the consistency of the rules of PL. We shall establish this consistency by showing that the deductions of PL never result in a formula of the form $p \ \& \sim\!p$ as a ZPC. This will establish the consistency of the rules of PL not in terms of a specific set of axioms or relative to any model, but absolutely. But how are we to study the deductions of PL? Evidently we cannot study them in the sense of writing all of them down, for there is an infinity of them. Equally evidently we cannot study them by using these rules in our reasoning about them, for this would be circular.

We may resolve this latter difficulty by using the methods of intuitive arithmetic to reason about the deductions of PL. Arithmetic is one of the soundest of the mathematical disciplines, so that an arithmetical argument showing the consistency of the rules of PL leaves little to be desired. Indeed, such an argument would constitute one step toward placing the powerful axiomatic method upon the firm base of arithmetic. That is, if we were able to establish the consistency and completeness of all axiom systems used in mathematics by the use of arithmetical reasoning, we should have accomplished a great deal. As it happens, we now know that we can do this for the rules of PL, MPL, and GPL-1 with identity, but that we cannot do this in general. Kurt Gödel has shown that demonstrations of consistency for some rules cannot be based upon arithmetical reasoning alone.* In this book we are interested primarily in what *can* be done along these lines, although we shall consider some general difficulties in Chapter Thirteen.

The problem of the absolute consistency of PL is a problem of determining whether there could be a deduction in PL ending in a ZPC having the form p & $\sim p$. Since a deduction in PL is a definite sort of thing, a readily recognizable procedure, this is something like asking whether we can achieve a certain result through the use of a given machine. We may wonder, for example, whether a timeclock can print "February 31", or whether it is possible to put a car equipped with automatic transmission in reverse if it is already moving forward. The answer to any such question is to be found by inspecting the design of the machine. For a more relevant example, consider a simple machine consisting of a pivoted arm on one end of which is a rubber stamp that prints the symbol A and on the other end of which is a rubber stamp that prints $\sim$A.

Suppose we ask whether this machine can print both A and $\sim$A at the same time. If we analyze the design of the machine, we see that while A is being printed, the $\sim$A stamp cannot make contact with the paper, and vice versa.

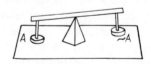

Diagram 9.1

If we represent "contact" by the symbol 1, and "noncontact" by 0, we can say that whenever A is 1, $\sim$A is 0, and whenever $\sim$A is 1, A is 0, so that A and $\sim$A cannot simultaneously be 1.

Without being too precise about details, we may conceive of PL as a

---

* Kurt Gödel, "Über formal unentscheidbare Sätze der Principia Mathematica und verwandter Systeme I", *Monats. für Math. u. Phys.*, Vol. 38 (1931), pp. 173–198.

machine that goes through the motions of inference, successively printing each line. We may think of the rules of PL as modes of operation of the machine. Thus, the rule of &I expresses the mode of operation in which, formulas of the form p and q having already occurred as lines, the machine prints a formula of the form p & q. The rule of vI describes how the machine disjoins an arbitrary q with any antecedent line. The rule of $\supset$E summarizes those operations of the machine in which, formulas of the form $p \supset q$ and p being given as lines, q is printed as a line, and so on. The mode of operation expressed by $\supset$I is somewhat different from these, for in this operation the machine adds to a sequence of lines it has already printed by printing the first member of the sequence, followed by the symbol $\supset$, followed by the last member of the sequence. This mode of operation is similar to that connected with the other rules that discharge assumptions, that is, vE and $\sim$I. The machine, as it happens, prints in different colors, as follows:

  (1) All lines resulting from the operation of discharging *all* assumptions (and premises) are in *red*.

  (2) All lines resulting from operations on lines printed completely in red are in *red*.

  (3) Other lines (including premises and assumptions) are printed in *black*.

Thus, if A had appeared in red, then A v B, resulting from vI, would be printed in red, but if A had originally appeared in black, then A v B would be black unless B itself had appeared in red.

Finally, we must note one difference between the machine and our previous practices in using PL. This difference is that previously when we got a result we wanted, we stopped inferring. The machine we are envisaging, however, stops only when each premise as well as each assumption entered into it has been discharged; that is, when (as in (1) above) for each initial black line a red line has been printed. Also, once having stopped, it can be reset to print a sequence of arbitrary length of all red lines.

The question of consistency, in these terms, is whether the machine could ever print as a red line a formula of the form p & $\sim p$. This question can be answered by analyzing the operations of the machine. The point of this example is to suggest that the analysis involved in answering the question depends in no way upon the assumption that the operations of the machine are rules of logic, or even that the symbols printed by the machine are logical symbols. We can ask whether the machine can print both a formula of the form p and one of the form $\sim p$ without having in mind any interpretation of the symbol $\sim$, since it is only the phenomenon of printing that interests us, not the meaning of what the machine prints. Our concern is not with the logical relation between p and $\sim p$; it is only with the question whether the machine could print as a last line both a certain cluster of symbols and the same cluster with the symbol $\sim$ to the left.

EXERCISE 9.2

I. Does the machine in Figure 9.1 assert the law of contradiction? (*I.e.*, can it print both *p* and ~*p* at the same time?) Why?

II. Does the machine in Figure 9.1 assert the law of excluded middle? Why?

III. Design a machine that asserts the law of excluded middle but not the law of contradiction.

IV. Design a machine that asserts both the law of contradiction and the law of excluded middle.

9.3   Formal Systems

When we study a set of rules like those of PL in order to determine whether it is consistent or possesses certain other properties, we begin by formalizing it. In Chapter Two, Section Five, in discussing statements, we took a step toward formalization. Later, in Chapter Five, Section Four, in discussing formulas, we used some of the techniques of formalization. There, as here, the goal of formalization is to state criteria by which we can recognize formulas, deductions, and conclusions without reference to their meaning. Our intention in formalizing a system is to make an object or set of objects of it, so that it can be studied much as if it were a machine.

Formalization is a continuation of a trend in the history of axiom systems. If we think of the step from axiom systems that represent real situations to uninterpreted axiom systems, we may think of a second step from these to formal systems. Thus, if we start with an uninterpreted axiom system—such as an example in Chapter Eight—we see that it still makes use of logical phrases such as "if . . . then", "and", etc., which occur as meaningful parts of sentences in the axioms and theorems. For complete formalization these phrases must be replaced by uninterpreted symbols and mechanical rules for their manipulation; that is, we must convert this portion of an uninterpreted axiom system into an uninterpreted set of symbols.

Actually, the task of formalizing PL is not great. In fact, we have only to abstract totally the meanings from the symbols used, reducing PL to a set of symbols, a stack of formulas, a number of transformations, sequences of lines, and finished sequences. Let us consider each of these five categories in turn.

SYMBOLS

When we think of PL we regard A, B, etc., as variables having sentences as substituents, taking A to have as a substituent "The Alps are mountains" and so on. Similarly, ⊃, **v**, ∼, ≡, and & we think of as meaning "if . . . then . . . ", "either . . . or . . . ", "not", and so on, while we take (ˎ) as having the significance of parentheses. For the balance of this chapter we shall ignore these meanings and regard

$$A, B, C, . . .$$
$$\&, \supset, v, \sim, \equiv, (,)$$

simply as entities without any significance whatsoever.

If we take these together in certain orders, that is, arrange them in strings, the result will usually be strange; *e.g.*:

$$(1) \quad (\,)\,) \, A \, \&$$

However, it will sometimes be significant; *e.g.*:

$$(2) \quad (A \supset B)$$

FORMULAS

The difference between (1) and (2) above raises the question as to whether we can distinguish between acceptable and unacceptable strings in PL without taking their meaning into account. If we know the meanings it is obvious whether an expression is a statement belonging to the system or not. We can easily identify D ⊃ A, for example, as a line to which the propositional rules would apply, while we do not hesitate to dismiss D ⊃ & or ⊃ D A as nonsense. But when we formalize PL, we demand a criterion for what constitutes a statement that will in no way depend upon our ability to grasp the meaning of the expression. In contemporary phraseology this is often expressed by saying what we demand is a *syntactical* criterion, not a semantical one.*

We call the strings that are acceptable in PL *well-formed formulas*, abbreviated as wffs. We can distinguish wffs from other strings without reference to their meanings by use of the following definition, quite similar to that given in Chapter Two, Section Five.

Wffs: (1) A, B, C, . . . are propositional wffs.
　　　(2) If p is a propositional wff, then $\sim p$ is a propositional wff. If p and
　　　　　q are propositional wffs, then $(p \, \& \, q)$, $(p \supset q)$, $(p \, v \, q)$, and $(p \equiv q)$
　　　　　are propositional wffs.
　　　(3) Nothing else is a propositional wff.

Here parentheses must be used around most occurrences of statements. This is a stricter requirement than our past practice suggests, but it permits us to decide without appeal to meaning whether a given expression constitutes a wff. Thus [(A & B) **v** C] is a propositional wff because (A & B) and C are

---

* Semantics is the study of meaning relations. Syntax, on the other hand, is the study of the structure of language.

both propositional wffs, and (A & B) is a propositional wff because A and B are both propositional wffs. But neither (A & B ∨ C) nor (A & B) ∨ C would count as a propositional wff. Note that brackets and braces are simply iterated parentheses, and are introduced for stylistic reasons only.

The definition of wffs takes the form of a *recursive definition*. In this it is similar to the definition of ∘ given in reference to Peano's Axiom System in Chapter Eight. In general, a property such as that of being a propositional statement is *recursively* defined by a specification of (1) the simplest individuals having the property and (2) the conditions under which if anything has the property, something else having the property may be constructed, together with (3) the assertion that nothing else has the property. The reader can see that our definition contains just these clauses.

TRANSFORMATIONS

In addition to being able to recognize a wff when we see one, we must be able to specify in a purely formal way what is involved when we write one line below others in a deduction. An effective way of doing this is to refer to the patterns established by the rules for PL. But, for the purposes of the proof of consistency, we shall modify these patterns slightly. The modification does not raise any question about the generality of our proof because the rules as originally stated can be shown to be equivalent to the modified rules. The modification has the effect of reducing to one the number of discharge rules. We retain ⊃I in its original form, but treat ∨E and ∼I as rules in which no assumptions are made and no discharge occurs. The table shown on p. 288 records the modified set.

We may demonstrate that the rules of Table 9.1 are equivalent to those of Table 2.1. To do this we first note that given any deduction of q from p we have by ⊃I, $p ⊃ q$. But further, given $p ⊃ q$ we obtain q from p in a deduction by ⊃E. Thus, the rules ⊃I and ⊃E establish the equivalence of a deduction and the logical connective ⊃. In consequence, we may replace a deduction by the ⊃ connective, and conversely, wherever we wish. From this fact we may write ∨E as ∨E′ by replacing the deductions of r from p and r from q by $p ⊃ r$ and $q ⊃ r$, and conversely. Thus,

$$p ∨ q \text{ is equivalent to } p ∨ q$$

$$
\begin{array}{ll}
\left[\begin{array}{l} p \\ \vdots \\ r \end{array}\right. & \qquad p ⊃ r \\[2em]
\left[\begin{array}{l} q \\ \vdots \\ r \end{array}\right. & \qquad q ⊃ r \\[1em]
\therefore r & \qquad \therefore r
\end{array}
$$

TABLE 9.1: THE MODIFIED PL RULES

	INTRODUCTION	ELIMINATION
&	p &I q $\therefore (p \,\&\, q)$	$(p \,\&\, q)$ $(p \,\&\, q)$ &E or $\therefore p$ $\therefore q$
⊃	⊃I $\begin{array}{c} \lceil p \\ \vdots \\ q \end{array}$ $\therefore (p \supset q)$	$(p \supset q)$ ⊃E p $\therefore q$
∨	p q ∨I or $\therefore (p \lor q)$ $\therefore (p \lor q)$	$(p \lor q)$ $(p \supset r)$ ∨E′ $(q \supset r)$ $\therefore r$
≡	$(p \supset q) \,\&\, (q \supset p)$ ≡I $\therefore p \equiv q$	$p \equiv q$ ≡E $\therefore (p \supset q) \,\&\, (q \supset p)$
∼	$[p \supset (q \,\&\, \sim q)]$ ∼I′ $\therefore \sim p$	$(p \,\&\, \sim p)$ ∼E $\therefore q$
∼∼	p ∼∼I $\therefore \sim\sim p$	$\sim\sim p$ ∼∼E $\therefore p$

Similarly, we may write either

$$\begin{array}{c} \lceil p \\ \vdots \\ q \,\&\, \sim q \end{array} \qquad \text{or} \qquad p \supset (q \,\&\, \sim q)$$
$$\therefore \sim p \qquad\qquad\qquad \therefore \sim p$$

This establishes the equivalence of ∼I and ∼I′. Since Table 9.1 differs from Table 2.1 only in respect to rules ∼I′ and ∨E′, we have established the equivalence of the two sets of rules.

The patterns of the rules in Table 9.1 enable us to recognize a deduction, when we see one, in purely formal terms. To make this explicit we define a transformation.

Transformation: A wff is transformed from another wff or wffs if it is a line related to other lines in one of the patterns of the rules of Table 9.1.

SEQUENCES

In addition to recognizing a transformation when we see one (without reference to meaning), we must also be able to designate deductions and distinguish them from unsound chains of inferences—again without attention to meaningful reasoning. To do this we need to rewrite the conditions of a deduction specified in A–D, Chapter Two, Section Ten, so as to eliminate dependence on meaning.

Let us now define a *sequence* as any series of lines, each of which is one of the following:

(A′) A wff with a straight line to the left (*i.e.*, a premise).

(B′) A wff with a straight line to the left which is extended to become a discharge line (*i.e.*, an assumption that is later discharged).

(C′) A line transformed from previous lines which are outside the scopes of B′ lines already discharged.

(D′) The last line of any sequence in which there are no lines as in A′ (*i.e.*, a zero-premise conclusion).*

FINISHED SEQUENCES

We now have a formalization of PL expressed in terms of symbols, wffs, transformations, and sequences. In order to show that PL is absolutely consistent, however, we need as a further formal category that of a *finished sequence* (*i.e.*, finished deduction). A *finished sequence* may be defined as one in which there are no lines of type A′, that is, one in which the last line is of type D′ (*i.e.*, a zero-premise conclusion). As we ordinarily interpret PL, a finished deduction is one in which there are no premises; *i.e.*, one having a ZPC as its conclusion. The reason for introducing the formal category of finished sequences is that our definition of the consistency of the rules of PL specifies that no ZPC's have the form p & $\sim p$. If lines other than ZPC's have this form, that is beside the point.

EXERCISE 9.3

I. Which part of the recursive definition for well-formed formulas does each of the following either conform to or violate?

1. (Z)   **3.** (A) & (B)

2. ($\sim$A)   **4.** (P ⊃ Q)

---

* A D′ line may be replaced in any sequence by the sequence that results in it.

5. [(A) & (B)]   8. [P ⊃ (Q)]

6. B   9. (P) ≡ (Q)

7. (A & B)   10. ~(D)

II. Name the kinds of lines which occur in the following deductions.

1.—p
  $(p \vee q)$

2. ⌐p
  | $(p \vee q)$

  $[p \supset (p \vee q)]$

3. — ~$(p \vee q)$
  ⌐p
  | $(p \vee q)$
  | ~$(p \vee q)$
  | $[(p \vee q) \, \& \, {\sim}(p \vee q)]$

  $\{p \supset [(p \vee q) \, \& \, {\sim}(p \vee q)]\}$

4. —p
  ⌐q
  | $(p \, \& \, q)$

  $[q \supset (p \, \& \, q)]$

5. —p
  ⌐q
  | p

  $(q \supset p)$

6. ⌐ ~$(p \vee {\sim}p)$
  | ⌐p
  | | $(p \vee {\sim}p)$
  | | $[(p \vee {\sim}p) \, \& \, {\sim}(p \vee {\sim}p)]$
  |
  | $p \supset [(p \vee {\sim}p) \, \& \, {\sim}(p \vee {\sim}p)]$
  | ~p
  | $(p \vee {\sim}p)$
  | $[(p \vee {\sim}p) \, \& \, {\sim}(p \vee {\sim}p)]$

  ${\sim}(p \vee {\sim}p) \supset [(p \vee {\sim}p) \, \& \, {\sim}(p \vee {\sim}p)]$
  ${\sim}{\sim}(p \vee {\sim}p)$
  $p \vee {\sim}p$

7.———— $[(p \ \& \ q) \supset (m \supset n)]$
———— $(\sim n \ \& \ m)$

        p
        q
        $(p \ \& \ q)$
        $(m \supset n)$
        m
        n
        $\sim n$
        $(n \ \& \ \sim n)$

        $[q \supset (n \ \& \ \sim n)]$
        $\sim q$

        $p \supset \sim q$

8.———— $[(p \ \& \ q) \supset (m \supset n)]$
———— $(\sim n \ \& \ m)$
        $(m \ \& \ \sim n)$
        $\sim(\sim m \lor \sim\sim n)$
        $\sim(\sim m \lor n)$
        $\sim(m \supset n)$
        $\sim(p \ \& \ q)$
        $(\sim p \lor \sim q)$
        $(p \supset \sim q)$

9. $(p \ \& \ \sim q)$
        $(p \supset q)$
        p
        q
        $\sim q$
        $(q \ \& \ \sim q)$

        $[(p \supset q) \supset (q \ \& \ \sim q)]$
        $\sim(p \supset q)$

        $[(p \ \& \ \sim q) \supset \sim(p \supset q)]$

10. ————p
        $(p \lor \sim p)$

        p
        p

        $(p \supset p)$

        $\sim p$
        p

        $(\sim p \supset p)$
        p

III. Which of the following sequences are finished? Why?

1. $-p$
   $(p \vee q)$

2. $\ulcorner -p$
   $\quad (p \vee q)$

   $[p \supset (p \vee q)]$

3. $(p \vee \sim p)$
   $-(p \supset q)$
   $-(\sim p \supset q)$
   $\ulcorner p$
   $\quad q$

   $(p \supset q)$
   $\sim p$
   q

   $(\sim p \supset q)$
   q
   $[q \,\&\, (p \vee \sim p)]$
   $[(q \,\&\, p) \vee (q \,\&\, \sim p)]$

4. $\ulcorner p$
   $\quad \ulcorner \sim p$
   $\quad\quad (p \,\&\, \sim p)$
   $\quad\quad q$

   $\quad (\sim p \supset q)$

   $[p \supset (\sim p \supset q)]$

5. $\ulcorner p$
   $\quad \ulcorner \sim p$
   $\quad\quad (p \,\&\, \sim p)$
   $\quad\quad q$

   $\quad (\sim p \supset q)$

   $[p \supset (\sim p \supset q)]$
   $[(p \,\&\, \sim p) \supset q]$

9.4 A Proof of the Consistency of PL

We are interested in establishing consistency by metatheoretical methods. Therefore, we redefine consistency in terms of the formal system.

Consistency of PL Transformations: The transformations of PL are consistent if and only if no D′ lines have the form p & $\sim p$.

It will be sufficient, then, to prove

Metatheorem 9.1:   No wff of the form p & $\sim p$ is the last line of any finished sequence.

The proposition we are to prove is stated as a metatheorem because it is a truth about the formal system and not a truth in PL. We arrive at this metatheorem by reasoning about the characteristics and properties of the formal system. In outline, our proof of the metatheorem is this: there is a property, I, which is possessed by every last line of a finished sequence but is not possessed by a wff of the form p & $\sim p$. Therefore, no wff of the form p & $\sim p$ can be the last line of any finished sequence.

We begin by defining the property I, possessed by last lines of finished sequences, in the terms of another property, 1. 1 is possessed by a compound wff built up of wffs as follows:

(1) $(p$ & $q)$ has 1 if and only if p has 1 and q has 1.
(2) $(p \supset q)$ lacks 1 if and only if p has 1 and q lacks 1.
(3) $(p \vee q)$ lacks 1 if and only if p lacks 1 and q lacks 1.
(4) $(p \equiv q)$ lacks 1 if and only if p has 1 while q lacks 1; or p lacks 1 while q has 1.
(5) $\sim p$ lacks 1 if and only if p has 1.

These conditions can be represented readily as matrices. Using 0 for "lacks 1" we have

&	1	0		⊃	1	0		∨	1	0		≡	1	0		∼	
1	1	0		1	1	0		1	1	1		1	1	0		1	0
0	0	0		0	1	1		0	1	0		0	0	1		0	1

Since these matrices are clearly similar to the ones used in connection with truth tables in Chapter Three, the use of 1 and 0 in place of **t** and **f** is intended to emphasize the metatheoretical nature of the reasoning we are conducting.

Definition of I: A wff has the property I when it is identically 1—*i.e.*, when it *always* has 1, as calculated by the matrices.

Example: A ∨ $\sim$A and $\sim$(A & $\sim$A) have the property I as evaluation by matrices will show.

We begin the proof of Metatheorem 9.1 by establishing three lemmas concerning the property I and lines in sequence.

Lemma a: The uses of ⊃I in any finished sequence in which the B′ lines possess 1 simultaneously transmit this property to the last line of the finished sequence.

Lemma b: The last line of any finished sequence including B′ lines possesses I; and any line of any finished sequence lacking B′ lines possesses I.

Example: A finished sequence including B′ lines is illustrated by

    1. A ⊃ B
    2. ∼A ⊃ D
    3. A v ∼A   D′ line
    4. B v D   1, 2, 3, vE′

    5. (∼A ⊃ D) ⊃ (B v D)   2-4, ⊃I

    6. (A ⊃ B) ⊃ [(∼A ⊃ D) ⊃ (B v D)]   1-5, ⊃I

A finished sequence lacking B′ lines is

    1. A v ∼A
    2. ∼(∼A & A)   1, DM
    3. ∼(∼A & A) v C   2, vI

Lemma c: No wff of the form p & $\sim p$ possesses I.

Proof of Lemma a: First, we show that all transformations except ⊃I— that is, all nondischarging transformations—transmit 1 (and so I) from a line (or lines) to the resulting line in a sequence. For purposes of clarity we consider two groups of transformations. (a) *The transformations* vI, ∼∼I, ∼∼E, &E, ≡I, *and* ≡E. In these cases the possession of 1 by a line transformed is transmitted to the resulting line regardless of other lines (if any) used. For example,

    vI: When vI is used as a line possessing 1, say p, the 1 it possesses is transmitted to the resulting line in every case, since the resulting line is p v q.

We establish the result in this case and the others by a kind of arithmetical calculation using the matrices above.

    We consider now the second group of nondischarging transformations. (b) *The transformations* &I, ⊃E, vE′, ∼I′, *and* ∼E. In these cases the possession of 1 by one line transformed is transmitted to the resulting line *unless* another line involved in the transformation has 0 at the same time.

For example,

    &I: When &I is used on a line possessing 1, say p, the 1 it possesses can fail to be transmitted to the next line only if q has 0 while p has 1.

    $\supset$E: When $\supset$E is used on a line possessing 1, if this is $p \supset q$, the 1 it possesses can fail to be transmitted to the resulting line only if the line p has 0 while $p \supset q$ has 1. If the line possessing 1 is p, the 1 it possesses can fail to be transmitted to the resulting line only if $p \supset q$ has 0 while p has 1.

Similar analyses for $\mathbf{v}$E′, $\sim$I′, and $\sim$E are readily stated. We conclude that in these cases when the lines transformed possess 1 simultaneously this property is transmitted to the resulting line.

    Secondly, we show that the uses of $\supset$I in any finished sequence *in which the B′ lines have 1 simultaneously*, transmit this property to the last line. Consider a sequence involving an arbitrary number of uses of $\supset$I, say m. The proof is by induction on the number of uses of $\supset$I.

Basis: The innermost use of $\supset$I results in a line to which 1 is transmitted, for, if not, the line before discharge of the innermost B′ line must possess 0 while the B′ line has 1; and this is impossible. For the line before discharge can be reached only in the following ways.

    (i) The line before discharge is a result of the use of nondischarging transformations on the innermost B′ line—but such transformations transmit the 1 possessed by this B′ line.

    (ii) The line before discharge is any B′ line repeated into the sequence. But since all B′ lines have 1 simultaneously it cannot have 0 while the innermost B′ line has 1. Or the line before discharge is a line possessing I, in which case it clearly possesses 1 when the innermost B′ line possesses 1.

    (iii) The line before discharge may be the result, in part, of the use of any B′ line or a line possessing I between the innermost B′ line and the line before its discharge. If any B′ line is used, since it possesses 1, the resulting line either will (a) have 1 when the innermost B′ line has 1 or (b) if not, fail to have 1 only because some other line used has 0 at the same time. But, case (a) occurs with the use of the transformations $\mathbf{v}$I, $\sim\sim$I, $\sim\sim$E, &E, $\equiv$I, and $\equiv$E. Case (b) occurs with the use of the transformations &I, $\supset$E, $\mathbf{v}$E′, $\sim$I′, and $\sim$E. As discussed above, 1 could fail to be transmitted from the B′ line or line possessing I only if another line in the sequence (and used in the transformation) should have 0 while the innermost B′ line and the repeated B′ line or line possessing I had 1. But clearly there are no such lines admissible in the sequence.

    (iv) The line before discharge may result as a combination of (i) and (iii). But any such combination transmits 1 from the innermost B′ line to the line before its discharge.

Thus we see that it is impossible for the line before discharge of the innermost B′ line to possess 0 while that B′ line has 1. In consequence, the line discharging the innermost B′ line has the 1 possessed by that line transmitted to it.

Induction Step: We assume as hypothesis of the induction that the kth use of $\supset$ I results in a line to which the 1 possessed by the B′ line (simultaneously with other B′ lines) it discharges is transmitted. We prove that, on this hypothesis, the $(k + 1)$st use of $\supset$ I results in a line to which the 1 possessed by the B′ line it discharges is transmitted. For if the property 1 were not so transmitted then the line before the $(k + 1)$st use of $\supset$ I must possess 0 while the B′ line that this use discharges possesses 1 simultaneously with all B′ lines. But this is impossible for much the same reasons as in the basis. The line before discharge by the $(k + 1)$st use of $\supset$ I can be reached in only four ways.

(i) The line before discharge is a result of the use of nondischarging transformations on the line discharging the previous B′ line, which by the hypothesis of the induction possesses 1 when that B′ line possesses 1 simultaneously with all B′ lines. All such nondischarging transformations transmit 1.

(ii) The line before discharge is any as yet undischarged B′ line repeated into the sequence. But then since all B′ lines possess 1 simultaneously the line before discharge by the $(k + 1)$st use of $\supset$ I will possess 1 while the B′ line it discharges possesses 1. Or the line before discharge is a line possessing I, in which case a similar argument holds.

(iii) The line before discharge may be the result, in part, of the use of any as yet undischarged B′ line or a line possessing I between the line resulting from the kth use of $\supset$ I and the line before the $(k + 1)$st use of $\supset$ I. In this case since the B′ lines possess 1 simultaneously (as will lines possessing I),. if the nondischarging transformations in group (a) are used the resulting line will possess 1 as transmitted. If the nondischarging transformations in group (b) are used, the resulting line lacks 1 only if some other line used has 0 when the B′ lines possess 1. By hypothesis of the induction and the arguments in (i) and (ii) such lines cannot occur in the sequence.

(iv) The line before discharge may result from a combination of (i) and (iii). But any such combination transmits the 1 possessed by the line discharging the kth B′ line to the line before discharge of the $(k + 1)$st B′ line in the case where all B′ lines possess 1 simultaneously.

Thus we see that it is impossible for the line before discharge of the $(k + 1)$st B′ line to possess 0 when that line has 1 simultaneously with the other B′ lines.

This completes the induction and establishes that the uses of $\supset$ I in any and so every sequence in which the B' lines possess 1 simultaneously transmit this property to the last line of the finished sequence. That is, the last line of a finished sequence cannot possess 0 while the B' lines of the sequence possess 1 simultaneously.

Proof of Lemma b: The proof involves two cases, sequences including B' lines and sequences without B' lines. We discuss the former first.

We show that if the last line of any finished sequence including B' lines fails to possess I the B' lines in the sequence must possess 1 simultaneously while the line before discharge of the last B' line possesses 0. We then go on to show this to be impossible as a consequence of Lemma a. We consider a sequence involving an arbitrary number of uses of $\supset$ I, say n, to finish it but with a last line which fails to possess I, that is, possesses 0. The proof is by induction on the number of uses of $\supset$ I in the given sequence, counting from the last use back to the first (innermost) use.

Basis: Consider the last use of $\supset$ I (to finish the sequence). If the last line of the sequence is to have 0, then the last B' line to be discharged must have 1 while the line before its discharge has 0.

Induction Step: If the last k uses of $\supset$ I discharge B' lines which possess 1 simultaneously, while the last line of the sequence fails to have I, then we prove (on this hypothesis) that the use of $\supset$ I next inside it discharges a B' line [the $(k + 1)$st] which has 1 simultaneously with those discharged by the last k uses of $\supset$ I, while the line before its discharge has 0. The proof consists in showing that if the $(k + 1)$st B' line did not have 1 simultaneously with the B' lines discharged by the last k uses of $\supset$ I, while the line before its discharge had 0, no subsequent line in the sequence could have 0—contradicting the condition that the last line of the sequence fails to have I. We state this argument in detail. The situation we consider is shown in Figure 9.1.

If the $(k + 1)$st B' line does not have 1 simultaneously with the first k B' lines while the line before its discharge has 0, then the line in which it is discharged could not have 0 while the first k B' lines have 1. But in this case no subsequent line could have 0 while the first k B' lines have 1, since all subsequent lines are arrived at only in the following ways.

(i) By the use of nondischarging transformations beginning with the line discharging the $(k + 1)$st B' line. But these transformations transmit 1, as we proved in Lemma a.

(ii) By use of any of the first k B' lines or of a line possessing I introduced into the sequence. On the hypothesis of the induction these B' lines possess 1 simultaneously, and any line possessing I will of necessity also possess 1 simultaneously with them. Thus, as discussed in detail in Lemma a, the result of the use of such lines will be a line to which 1 is transmitted in case they are used with **vI**, $\sim\sim$I, $\sim\sim$E, &E, $\equiv$I, or $\equiv$E. In case these lines are used with &I, $\supset$E, **vE**′, $\sim$I′, and $\sim$E the resulting line fails to have 1 transmitted to it only if the other line used has 0 when the B′ lines have 1. But clearly no such line can be introduced into the sequence, as the present arguments show.

(iii) By the uses of $\supset$I on the first k B′ lines, which by the hypothesis of the induction possess 1 simultaneously, and on lines before their discharge which, by the arguments in (i) and (ii), must possess 1 when the B′ lines possess 1.

Thus unless the line resulting from the discharge of the $(k + 1)$st B′ line has 0 when the first k B′ lines have 1—so that the $(k + 1)$st B′ line also has 1 —the last line of the sequence cannot fail to have I.

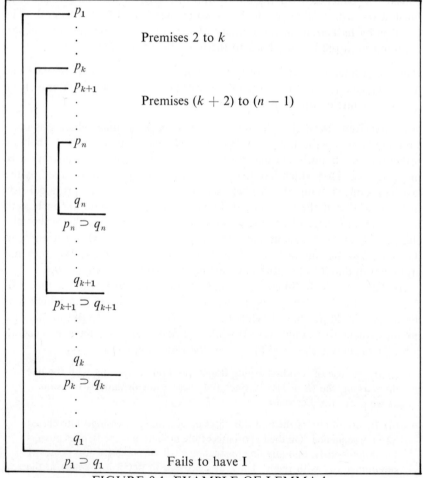

FIGURE 9.1. EXAMPLE OF LEMMA b.

However, we have shown in Lemma a that any sequence in which all B′ lines possess 1 simultaneously has a last line to which this 1 is transmitted. This contradicts the result just above and requires that we deny the condition under which we arrived at it. Thus the last line of any finished sequence including B′ lines *cannot* fail to have I.

Secondly, we consider the case of sequences without B′ lines. These cases are quite simple, for the first line of any such sequence (not being a B′ line) must be a line possessing I. In consequence, any subsequent lines are reached by the use of nondischarging transformations that transmit 1 in every instance, and which therefore also possess I. This argument is, stated formally, an induction on the number of uses of nondischarging transformations in the sequence. The formal statement is left to the reader.

Since any finished sequence either includes B′ lines or not we have now established that the last line of any finished sequence possesses I.

Proof of Lemma c. By calculation by means of the matrices, a line of the form p & $\sim p$ does not possess I. But, since all last lines of finished sequences possess I, a line of the form p & $\sim p$ cannot be such a last line.

Hence, the rules of PL are absolutely consistent; that is, we have established Metatheorem 9.1. In establishing this metatheorem we have not referred to a model, but only to the nature of the deductions possible with the rules of PL; hence, the consistency we have established is absolute. Further, we have used only the intuitive reasoning of arithmetic in our demonstration: first, in the "multiplication" tables of the matrices; and second, in the inductions of the demonstration. Since both of these types of reasoning are integral to arithmetic, any axiom system that requires no more logic than the rules of PL is at least as sound as arithmetic.

EXERCISE 9.4

I. Compare Lemma a with the assertion that if the premises of an argument are true then the conclusion must also be true. What does the word "simultaneously" mean as used in Lemma a? Does it mean that the premises are consistent?

II. What row of a truth table could be said to be designated by Lemma a? Can you illustrate this in a concrete case?

III. Show that Lemma a holds in the case of an unfinished sequence. (Hint: regard the undischarged premises as conjoined to imply the last line.)

IV. Compare the first part of Lemma b with the assertion that an argument is invalid only if the conclusion is false while the premises are true. Give an example of such an argument.

  V. Explain in terms of a truth table why in the case of a sequence having an invalid conclusion, the premises must be true while the conclusion is false.

  VI. Show that as stated in the first part of Lemma a the lines resulting from the use of $\mathbf{v}$I, $\sim\sim$I, $\sim\sim$E, &E, $\equiv$I, and $\equiv$E have 1, if the line on which they are used has 1.

  VII. Show that as stated in the first part of Lemma a the lines resulting from the use of &I, $\supset$E, $\mathbf{v}$E′, $\sim$I′ and $\sim$E on a line possessing 1 can fail to possess 1 only if the other lines involved fail to have 1 at the same time. Show that this means that these transformations transmit 1.

  VIII. Explain why in the induction in the proof of Lemma a we count uses of $\supset$I from the innermost use outward while in the induction in the proof of Lemma b we count uses of $\supset$I from the last use inward.

  IX. Why is it that if we prove Lemma a holds for a sequence having n uses of $\supset$I we can say that the Lemma holds for all sequences?

  X. In Lemma a, Basis, (iii) it is said that lines having 0 are not admissible in the sequence. Does this mean that no lines having 0 are admissible? Or does it mean that no lines having 0 when the B′ lines possess 1 are admissible? Explain carefully the difference between these restrictions.

  XI. Give an example of a sequence illustrating (i), (ii), (iii), and (iv) of the basis of Lemma a. Show in each case that 1 is transmitted under the condition of the proof.

  XII. Give an example of a sequence illustrating (i), (ii), (iii), and (iv) of the induction step of Lemma a. Show in each case how the hypothesis of the induction is used.

  XIII. On the diagram in Lemma b show that if $p_1 \supset q_1$ has 0, q_k has 0, q_{k+1} has 0, and q_n has 0. Show also that $p_1 \ldots p_n$ have 1 simultaneously on this condition. Present a rough intuitive argument.

  XIV. Formulate the formal induction (for sequences without B′ lines) in the second part of the argument in Lemma b.

  XV. Prove the consistency of the following rules alone.

XVI. Use the following definitions to derive the rules of $\sim\sim$I, &I, &E, vI, and vE from the rules given in Exercise XV.

Definitions: $(p \ \& \ q) \ \equiv_{df} \ \sim(p \supset \sim q)$

$\qquad\qquad (p \ v \ q) \ \equiv_{df} \ \sim(\sim p \ \& \ \sim q)$ **df.** $\sim p \supset q$

Example: &I

$\qquad (p \ \& \ q) \qquad\qquad$ Df.

XVII. Do exercises XV and XVI establish the consistency of the rules of PL? State your argument explicitly.

9.5 The Completeness of the Propositional Rules

In Chapter Eight we observed that a particular axiom system was complete when we could not add any independent axioms to it without producing inconsistency. This definition formulates the concept of completeness with respect to consistency, that is, it states that a system is complete when the axioms provide all possible theorems short of inconsistency. We might formulate the conception of completeness of the rules of PL in much the same way. That is, we might define the completeness of the rules by saying that the admission as rules of any schemata not derivable from the rules of PL would result in inconsistency.

This is a strong formulation of completeness and it includes a somewhat weaker concept. In the case of a particular axiom system, the weaker concept may be stated by saying that the axiom system is complete if and only if all statements formulable in its terms and, upon interpretation, true of a given model are also deducible. In the case of the rules of PL, the weaker concept states that all statements formulable in their terms and true of a model are also deducible. In establishing the completeness of the rules of PL, we shall begin by proving the weaker version. This has the advantage of permitting us to carry our methods over to the rules of GPL-1, where the stronger version does not hold.

Completeness of PL Rules: The rules of PL are complete if and only if every formula true of a model is deducible.

As in the case of consistency, we are interested in establishing completeness by metatheoretical methods. Therefore, we redefine completeness in terms of a property of the last lines of finished sequences, that is, the property I. The purpose of this redefinition is to enable us to study completeness by metatheoretical methods using only the intuitive reasoning of arithmetic.

Completeness of   The transformations of PL are complete if and only if
PL Transformations: every wff possessing I is the last line of a finished
                               sequence, that is, a D′ line.

We have established the fact that any D′ line possesses I. Hence, to show completeness, we demonstrate

Metatheorem 9.2:   If a wff, say L, of PL possesses I then it is the last line of a
                             finished sequence, that is, a D′ line.

Our proof of this metatheorem consists in showing that if a wff L possesses I it can be reached as the last line of a finished sequence that begins with premises each of which is the disjunction of one of the atomic parts of L and the same part preceded by $\sim$. Thus, for example, if L is $\sim$(A & $\sim$A), we have

$$(1) \quad (A \lor \sim A) \quad \therefore \quad \sim(A \& \sim A)$$

Here A $\lor$ $\sim$A is the specified disjunction of symbols occurring in L.

    Using this example, we now illustrate a method for obtaining the finished sequence. We evaluate L, that is, $\sim$(A & $\sim$A), by matrices and obtain

A	$\sim$(A & $\sim$A)
1	1
0	1

Since $\sim$(A & $\sim$A) has 1 whether or not A has 1, we ought to be able to prove that

$$(2) \quad \begin{array}{l} A \quad /\therefore \ \sim(A \& \sim A) \\ \sim A \quad /\therefore \ \sim(A \& \sim A) \end{array}$$

    The actual sequence proving this is

$$(3)$$

1. A		
2. A $\lor$ $\sim$A	1, $\lor$I	
3. $\sim$(A & $\sim$A)	2, DM, CM	
4. $\sim$A		
5. $\sim$A $\lor$ A	4, $\lor$I	
6. $\sim$(A & $\sim$A)	5, DM	
7. A $\lor$ $\sim$A	ZPC	
8. $\sim$(A & $\sim$A)	7, 1–3, 4–6, $\lor$E	

Note that, as in lines 3 and 6, we make use of rules derived in Chapter Two. We regard the patterns of these rules as acceptable transformations.

Since line 7 is a D' line, so is line 8. The method used here depends upon L occurring as the last line of a sequence as in (2). We now establish this in the general case as a lemma.

Lemma a: Let L be a wff of PL containing the m different atomic wffs p_1, $p_2, \ldots, p_m$. On the basis of each of the rows in the evaluation of L by means of the matrices, form the m-tuple of wffs which for each $i \leq m$ contains p_i in case p_i was assigned 1 in the row in question; but which contains $\sim p_i$ in case p_i was assigned 0. Then, if L possesses 1 for that row in the evaluation, it is the last line of a sequence in which these wffs are premises; or if L possesses 0 for that row, then $\sim$L is the last line.

Example: Let L be A $\supset$ B. Then it evaluates by matrices as

A	B	A $\supset$ B
1	1	1
0	1	1
1	0	0
0	0	1

The corresponding 2-tuples of symbols and the last lines of the sequences are

$$\text{A,} \quad \text{B} \quad /\therefore \text{ A} \supset \text{B}$$
$$\sim\text{A,} \quad \text{B} \quad /\therefore \text{ A} \supset \text{B}$$
$$\text{A,} \sim\text{B} \quad /\therefore \sim(\text{A} \supset \text{B})$$
$$\sim\text{A,} \sim\text{B} \quad /\therefore \text{ A} \supset \text{B}$$

Proof of Lemma a: This is demonstrated by induction on the number of occurrences of logical connectives $\mathbf{v}$, &, $\sim$, $\supset$, and $\equiv$ in L. We show that when there are no logical connectives the lemma holds and that if it holds for $(n - 1)$ or fewer logical connectives, it holds for n connectives.

Basis: L has no logical connectives, so L is a single symbol, say A. A has the value 1 or 0.

   Case 1. A has the value 1. Then A $/\therefore$ L since L is A.

   Case 2. A has the value 0. Then $\sim$A $/\therefore$ $\sim$L since L is A.

Induction Step: The lemma holds for $(n - 1)$ and fewer connectives. L has n connectives. Hence, L can be analyzed into q and r having $(n - 1)$ or fewer connectives in five ways; namely, $\sim q$, $q \mathbf{v} r$, $q \& r$, $q \supset r$, and $q \equiv r$. We consider each of these in turn.

Case 1: L is $\sim q$. We have to show that

(i) q $/\therefore \sim(\sim q)$

(ii) $\sim q$ $/\therefore \sim q$

In (i), since q possesses 1, L possesses 0; in (ii), since q possesses 0, L (*i.e.*, $\sim q$) possesses 1. We estadlish the subcases (i) and (ii):

(i) For by hypothesis the lemma holds for q, and hence by $\sim\sim$I for $\sim$L.

(ii) For by hypothesis the lemma holds for q, and hence for L.

Case 2: L is $q \vee r$. We have to show that

(i) $q,$ r $/\therefore q \vee r$

(ii) $\sim q,$ r $/\therefore q \vee r$

(iii) $q, \sim r$ $/\therefore q \vee r$

(iv) $\sim q, \sim r$ $/\therefore \sim(q \vee r)$

These four possibilities represent the matrix for $\vee$. The proofs of (i), (ii), and (iii) follow from hypothesis and $\vee$I. The proof of the last case is

(iv) By the hypothesis of the induction, &I and DM. Thus:
$$\sim q, \sim r \quad /\therefore \sim q \mathbin{\&} \sim r \quad /\therefore \sim(q \vee r)$$

Case 3: L is $q \mathbin{\&} r$. We have to show

(i) $q,$ r $/\therefore q \mathbin{\&} r$

(ii) $\sim q,$ r $/\therefore \sim(q \mathbin{\&} r)$

(iii) $q, \sim r$ $/\therefore \sim(q \mathbin{\&} r)$

(iv) $\sim q, \sim r$ $/\therefore \sim(q \mathbin{\&} r)$

These four possibilities represent the matrix for &. The proofs are

(i)   By hypothesis and &I

(ii)   By hypothesis, $\vee$I, and DM. Thus
$$\sim q, r \quad /\therefore \sim q \vee \sim r \quad /\therefore \sim(q \mathbin{\&} r)$$

(iii) By hypothesis, $\vee$I, and DM as in (ii)

(iv) By hypothesis, $\vee$I, and DM as in (ii)

Case 4: L is $q \supset r$. We have to show

(i) $q,$ r $/\therefore q \supset r$

(ii) $\sim q,$ r $/\therefore q \supset r$

(iii) $q, \sim r$ $/\therefore \sim(q \supset r)$

(iv) $\sim q, \sim r$ $/\therefore q \supset r$

The four possibilities represent the matrix for $\supset$. The proofs are

(i)   By hypothesis, **vI**, and Impl. Thus

     $q, r \quad /\therefore \sim q \vee r \quad /\therefore q \supset r$

(ii)   By hypothesis, **vI**, and Impl as in (i)

(iii)   By hypothesis, **&I**, DM, and Impl. Thus

     $q, \sim r \quad /\therefore q \mathbin{\&} \sim r \quad /\therefore \sim(\sim q \vee r) \quad /\therefore \sim(q \supset r)$

(iv)   By the hypothesis, **vI**, and Impl. Thus

     $\sim q, \sim r \quad \therefore \sim q \vee r \quad \therefore q \supset r$

The proof of the fifth case, in which L is $q \equiv r$, is left to the reader. This completes the proof of Lemma a. We now proceed to show in the general case that

Lemma b: Let L be a wff of PL which possesses I and contains the different atomic wffs $p_1, p_2, \ldots, p_m$. Then $p_1 \vee \sim p_1, p_2 \vee \sim p_2, \ldots,$ $p_m \vee \sim p_m \quad /\therefore$ L.

Proof of Lemma b: Since L possesses I, L is the last line of a sequence having as premises an m-tuple of wffs containing p_1 or $\sim p_1$, p_2 or $\sim p_2$, ..., p_m or $\sim p_m$, depending on whether in each row in the evaluation by matrices the wff possesses 1 or 0. We thus obtain a series of sequences by Lemma a:

$$
\begin{array}{llll}
p_1, & p_2, & p_3, & \cdots \quad /\therefore \text{ L} \\
\sim p_1, & p_2, & p_3, & \cdots \quad /\therefore \text{ L} \\
p_1, & \sim p_2, & p_3, & \cdots \quad /\therefore \text{ L} \\
\sim p_1, & \sim p_2, & p_3, & \cdots \quad /\therefore \text{ L} \\
p_1, & p_2, & \sim p_3, & \cdots \quad /\therefore \text{ L} \\
\sim p_1, & p_2, & \sim p_3, & \cdots \quad /\therefore \text{ L} \\
p_1, & \sim p_2, & \sim p_3, & \cdots \quad /\therefore \text{ L} \\
\sim p_1, & \sim p_2, & \sim p_3, & \cdots \quad /\therefore \text{ L} \\
\vdots
\end{array}
$$

If we begin with the last wff before $/\therefore$ on the right, say p_m, we may use **vE** successively to give

$$(p_m \vee \sim p_m), \ldots, (p_3 \vee \sim p_3), (p_2 \vee \sim p_2), (p_1 \vee \sim p_1) \quad /\therefore \text{ L}$$

Example: Let L contain A and B

$$
\begin{array}{lll}
A, & B & /\therefore \text{ L} \\
\sim A, & B & /\therefore \text{ L} \\
A, & \sim B & /\therefore \text{ L} \\
\sim A, & \sim B & /\therefore \text{ L}
\end{array}
$$

One use of **vE** gives

$$
\begin{array}{lll}
A, & (B \vee \sim B) & /\therefore \text{ L} \\
\sim A, & (B \vee \sim B) & /\therefore \text{ L}
\end{array}
$$

A second use of vE gives

$$(A \vee \sim A), \quad (B \vee \sim B) \quad /\therefore \ L$$

With the aid of Lemma b we may now complete the proof of Metatheorem 9.2. A wff of PL which possesses I is the last line of a sequence having as premises the different wffs in it as in Lemma b:

$$p_m \vee \sim p_m, \ \cdots, \ p_3 \vee \sim p_3, \ p_2 \vee \sim p_2, \ p_1 \vee \sim p_1, \quad /\therefore \ L$$

We see that L is the last line of a finished sequence, since each of the premises $p_m \vee \sim p_m$, $p_3 \vee \sim p_3$, etc., is a D′ line, and hence L is also a D′ line. This establishes the completeness of the rules of PL in the weaker sense.

We may now return to the stronger conception of completeness explained in Chapter Eight and mentioned at the beginning of this section, namely, that an axiom system is complete when the admission of any unprovable formulas as rules of inference results in inconsistency. The meaning that this conception has for the formal system is that the admission of any D′ lines not possessing I results in inconsistency.

To establish this, we demonstrate

Metatheorem 9.3:   If we modify the rules of PL to include a schema whose instances do not possess I, then a wff of the form $p \ \& \ \sim p$ can be obtained as a D′ line.

Proof of this metatheorem is direct. In it we use the rule of Sub discussed in Chapter Two. Let us assume that the schema whose instances do not possess I is L. Thus, the evaluation by matrices of any instance of L will have at least one row that evaluates to 0.

Example: Let an instance of L be A ⊃ B. The evaluation by matrices is

A	B	A ⊃ B
1	1	1
0	1	1
1	0	0
0	0	1

If we substitute C $\vee \sim$C for the atomic wffs in L possessing 1, and C $\& \sim$C for those possessing 0 in the row evaluating to 0, the result will be a wff whose instances evaluate to 0 in every line.

Example: Where L is A ⊃ B we substitute C $\vee \sim$C for A and C $\& \sim$C for B to obtain

C	(C $\vee \sim$C) ⊃ (C $\& \sim$C)
1	0
0	0

From Metatheorem 9.2 we know that any wff that possesses I is a D' line. Hence, if t and u have the same evaluation, $t \equiv u$ will possess I and so will be the last line of a finished sequence schema by Metatheorem 9.2.

Example: Let t be $(C \lor \sim C) \supset (C \& \sim C)$ and u be $E \& \sim E$; then

$$[(C \lor \sim C) \supset (C \& \sim C)] \equiv (E \& \sim E).$$

Clearly the left side possesses 0 in all rows and so does the right side. Hence, this wff possesses I and so is the last line of a finished sequence. Thus, the use of L as a rule gives by substitution an instance of L, say L', which possesses 0 in all rows, and we have

$$L' \equiv (E \& \sim E)$$

which possesses I and so is a D' line; hence, by $\equiv$E and $\supset$E we obtain $E \& \sim E$ as a D' line.

The deduction schema is

1. L		Assumed to be admitted as a D' line in a schema
2. L'		1, Sub
3. L' $\equiv (p \& \sim p)$		Possesses I, so by Metatheorem 9.2 is a D' line
4. L' $\supset (p \& \sim p)$		3, $\equiv$E, & E
5. $p \& \sim p$		2, 3, $\supset$E

This establishes Metatheorem 9.3 and shows that the axiom systems defined by the rules of PL are complete in the stronger sense of admitting no further D' lines without resulting in inconsistency.

EXERCISE 9.5

I. Illustrate the general method for obtaining a finished sequence by using the formula $p \supset p$.

II. Present deductions which illustrate the basis of Lemma a.

III. Prove Lemma a for the case in which L is $q \equiv r$.

9.6 Decidability

In order for a system to be *decidable* there must exist a property that belongs just to wffs provable in the system. A *decision procedure* is the process of ascertaining whether a given wff has this property or not and thus whether it is provable or not. Usually it is stipulated also that a decision procedure must be *effective*; *i.e.*, that it must be possible to find out by a mechanical procedure in a finite number of steps whether a statement has the property in question or not.

There are a few cases of this sort in mathematics. Thus we can always decide whether a polynomial with integral coefficients is the factor of another such polynomial, since division can be carried out by a preassigned definite method. Again Euclid's algorithm enables us to find the integral solutions of equations with integral coefficients, such as $ax + by = c$.

PL is also decidable. Indeed, the decidability of the system of propositional rules follows immediately from our proofs of the consistency and completeness of these rules. For, in the course of these proofs, we have shown that a wff has a property I if and only if it is the last line of a finished sequence. Since the matrices provide an effective method for determining whether any given wff has I, we have a decision procedure in the effective sense.

Not every system is decidable. It has been demonstrated, for example, that GPL-1 is not.* There are, however, decision procedures for MPL, some of which will be outlined in the following chapter. In addition, decision procedures for several specialized classes of statements in GPL-1 are known.

SUPPLEMENTARY EXERCISES

I. What defects in the method of proving consistency from models can you cite?

II. What would it be like if both A and $\sim$A could be truthfully asserted of a situation at the same moment?

III. Compare and contrast the advantages and disadvantages of interpreted and uninterpreted systems.

IV. Why should a logic be consistent?

V. Can a system without a model be consistent?

VI. Show that the system, due to Łukasiewicz, which consists of the two operators $\supset$ and $\sim$, the rules of $\supset$E and Sub and the following axioms, is consistent.

   1. A $\supset$ (B $\supset$ A)

   2. [(A $\supset$ B) $\supset$ C] $\supset$ [(C $\supset$ A) $\supset$ (D $\supset$ A)]

   3. ($\sim$A $\supset$ $\sim$B) $\supset$ (B $\supset$ A)

---

* See A. Church, "A Note on the Entscheidungsproblem", *Journal of Symbolic Logic*, Vol. I (1936), pp. 40–41.

VII. In Chapter Three, you were acquainted with stroke operation |. Nicod has shown that from the single axiom

$$[A|(B|C)]|([D|(D|D)]|\{(E|B)|[(A|E)|(A|E)]\})$$

and the single rule of inference

from A|(B|C) and A, infer C,

PL can be developed. Discuss the relationship between this rule of inference and $\supset$ E.

VIII. Hilbert and Ackermann have given a formulation of PL which consists of three operators, **v**, $\sim$, and $\supset$, the rule of $\supset$ E, Substitution, and the following four axioms:

1. $(A \mathbf{v} A) \supset A$

2. $A \supset (A \mathbf{v} B)$

3. $(A \mathbf{v} B) \supset (B \mathbf{v} A)$

4. $(A \supset B) \supset [(C \mathbf{v} A) \supset (C \mathbf{v} B)]$

Show that this system is consistent.

IX. Why should a logic be complete?

X. In what ways might a system be incomplete?

SUGGESTED READINGS

1. A. Church, *Introduction to Mathematical Logic* (Princeton, N.J.: Princeton Univ. Press, 1956), Chs. I and II.

2. David Hilbert and W. Ackermann, *Principles of Mathematical Logic* (New York: Chelsea Pub. Co., 1950), Ch. I.

3. S. C. Kleene, *Introduction to Metamathematics* (Amsterdam: North Holland Pub. Co., 1952), Chs. IV and VI.

4. A. Tarski, *Introduction to Logic*, rev. ed. (New York: Oxford Univ. Press, 1946), Chs. II and VI.

Chapter 10

The Metatheory of Monadic
Predicate Logic

10.1 The Formal System of MPL

In this chapter we continue our discussion of metatheory begun in Chapter
Nine, and extend our results to include MPL. In particular, we show that
the rules of MPL are both consistent and complete, and that the system is
decidable. Our methods of analysis will remain metatheoretical; that is, we
shall demonstrate these properties by reasoning about the formal system.
Our first task is to extend our conception of a formal system to include the
essential aspects of MPL.

SYMBOLS

The symbols of MPL are

$$A, B, C, \ldots$$
$$F, G, H, \ldots$$
$$\&, \supset, \mathbf{v}, \sim, \equiv, (,)$$
$$\underset{x}{\Sigma, \Pi}$$

As in Chapter Nine, we dissociate these symbols from whatever meaning we
might be tempted to ascribe to them. In particular we dissociate from their
previous meanings the symbols not included in the formal system of PL; that

is, we dissociate F, G, etc., from their previous meanings as predicates, $\sum$ and $\prod$ from their previous meanings as quantifiers, and x from its previous meaning as a variable.

FORMULAS

As before, we call the strings that are acceptable in MPL *well-formed formulas*, abbreviated wffs. We distinguish wffs from other strings by the following criteria:

(1) A, B, C, ... are wffs.
　　F(x), G(x), H(x), ... are wffs.
(2) If α is an individual variable and $\varphi(\alpha)$ is a wff then $\prod_\alpha[\varphi(\alpha)]$ and $\sum_\alpha[\varphi(\alpha)]$ are wffs.
(3) If φ and ψ are wffs then so are $(\varphi \supset \psi)$, $(\varphi \,\&\, \psi)$, $(\varphi \vee \psi)$, and $(\varphi \equiv \psi)$. If φ is a wff so is $\sim\varphi$.
(4) Nothing else is a wff.

TRANSFORMATIONS

In addition to recognizing the patterns of the rules of PL as transformations, we recognize the patterns of the rules $\prod$E, $\prod$I, and $\sum$I. In order to simplify our consistency proof somewhat, however, we shall reformulate $\sum$E as a rule involving no discharge.

$\sum$E′

$$\sum_\alpha\varphi(\alpha)$$
$$\varphi(\beta) \supset \psi$$
$$\therefore \psi$$

(with the same restrictions as for $\sum$E)

We are entitled to do this for the same reasons that justified the introduction of vE′ and $\sim$I′ in Chapter Nine. That is, $\sum$E is equivalent to $\sum$E′ because $\supset$I and $\supset$E establish the equivalence of a deduction and $\supset$.

SEQUENCES

As in Chapter Nine, we are able to designate deductions and distinguish them from unsound chains of inferences without attention to meaningful reasoning. To do this, we rewrite the conditions of deductions A–D as in Chapter Nine but include the wffs and transformations of MPL. We admit in a sequence the following lines only:

(A*) A wff with a straight line to the left.
(B*) Any wff with a straight line to the left which is extended to become a discharge line.

(C*) A line transformed from previous lines not in the scopes of B* lines already discharged according to the patterns of the rules of PL (Table 9.1) and $\prod E$, $\prod I$, $\sum E'$, $\sum I$.

(D*) The last line of some other sequence in which there are no lines as in A*.

FINISHED SEQUENCES

A finished sequence is one in which there are no lines of type A*.

We have taken pains to extend this conception of a formal system in some detail because, although it is quite similar to the conception defined in connection with PL, it is an essential element in metatheory. In fact, it constitutes the subject matter of metatheory, since it is about the formal system that we reason. Now the reasoning used in metatheoretical analysis must be beyond reproach; there must be no reasoning more acceptable than it. Thus the reasoning used to establish the consistency of PL was restricted to that used in arithmetic—to a kind of multiplication and to mathematical induction. This is a sound approach, for it bases our study of axiom systems upon the simplest kind of metatheoretical reasoning. As we shall see, the consistency of MPL can be established by the same kind of reasoning. However, the fact that every D* line in MPL possesses I—a fact that in the case of MPL is not implied by the consistency of the system—requires stronger metatheoretical methods. The discovery of the exact point at which stronger methods become essential reveals something about the nature of metatheory.

10.2   Validity

In Chapter Nine we evaluated the wffs of PL by assigning 1 or 0 to each atomic statement and by using matrices to evaluate the molecular wffs. If a wff evaluated to 1 for every assignment of 1 or 0 to its elements it was said to possess I. We use the same approach to the wffs of MPL.

Clearly the propositional wffs within any wff of MPL can be assigned 1 or 0 as in PL. There is also no change needed in the methods used to evaluate compounds including the familiar connectives $\supset$, $\mathbf{v}$, $\&$, $\sim$, $\equiv$. However, monadic predicate wffs contain statement functions and quantifiers as well as propositional wffs. To assign 1 and 0 to a quantified predicate with individual variables it is necessary to take into account the fact that a wff containing individual variables is *true* of many things, or of one thing, or of nothing, and *false* of the remainder. This introduces complications in evaluating a formula as 1 or 0. Thus if we consider

$$(1) \quad A \mathbf{v} \left[\sum_x F(x) \right]$$

we can say that A possesses either 1 or 0. Further, if we know that there are just two values of the individual variable x, say a and b, we could evaluate (1) by matrices as follows:

(1′)	A	F(a)	F(b)	A v [F(a) v F(b)]
	1	1	1	1
	1	1	0	1
	1	0	1	1
	1	0	0	1
	0	1	1	1
	0	1	0	1
	0	0	1	1
	0	0	0	0

There are two points to be noted here. The first is the reminder that existentially quantified wffs are, in effect, disjunctions. Similarly, universally quantified wffs are, in effect, conjunctions. The second point is that assignment of values to the wffs in monadic predicate logic involves a consideration of the number of ways in which the individual variables must be substituted for. This is so crucial to the problem of evaluating such formulas that we consider it in detail.

As a further example of a wff of monadic predicate logic, let us take

$$(2)\quad \textstyle\sum_x F(x) \supset \prod_x F(x)$$

Clearly this is not provable, since we have no rules for going from $\sum$ to $\prod$. However, if we consider a domain of one individual, a, then for all predicates (2) is identically 1:

(2′)	F(a)	F(a) ⊃ F(a)
	1	1
	0	1

But in a domain of two individuals, a and b, (2) is not identically 1:

(2″)	F(a)	F(b)	[F(a) v F(b)]	⊃	[F(a) & F(b)]
	1	1	1	1	1
	1	0	1	0	0
	0	1	1	0	0
	0	0	0	1	0

It is clear that (2) would not be identically 1 in any domain larger than one containing a single individual.

If we consider the contradictory of (2), that is, $\sum_x F(x)\ \&\ \sim\!\prod_x F(x)$, or, by QEq,

$$(3)\quad \textstyle\sum_x F(x)\ \&\ \sum_x \sim\! F(x)$$

we see that in a domain that has only one member, (3) is identically 0 whatever the predicate F may be, for it is impossible for F both to apply and not to apply to an individual. Thus, if x ranges over even prime numbers, any F for which $\sum_x F(x)$ is true (for example, *is a factor of 10*) will be a predicate for which $\sum_x \sim F(x)$ is false; while any F for which $\sum_x \sim F(x)$ is true (for example, *is a factor of 15*) will be a predicate for which $\sum_x F(x)$ is false. But whether (3) is identically 0 depends upon the number of individuals in the domain considered, for we can see that in a domain of two individuals (3) is not identically 0.

(3′)	F(a)	F(b)	[F(a) v F(b)] & [∼F(a) v ∼F(b)]		
	1	1	1	0	0
	1	0	1	1	1
	0	1	1	1	1
	0	0	0	0	1

There are many quantificational wffs, of which $\sum_x F(x) \supset \prod_x F(x)$ is an example, that are identically 1 in domains of some cardinal number of individuals and not in other domains. Thus, in order to evaluate quantificational formulas, we must take into account the cardinal number of the domain over which the individual ranges. This point can be diagrammatically presented if we use a rectangle to represent the domain. Then (2′) can be expressed as follows.

DOMAIN OF ONE INDIVIDUAL, a

Here we represent the case where F(a) is 1 by a solid circle and the case where F(a) is 0 by a dotted circle. Either circle stands for any specific predicate. For a domain of two individuals (2) is

DOMAIN OF TWO INDIVIDUALS, a AND b

Here the four circles represent the four alternatives expressed in (2″) above; that is, the case where F(a) and F(b) are 1, F(a) is 1 but F(b) is 0, F(b) is 1 but F(a) is 0, and F(a) and F(b) are 0. Domains having a larger number of individuals require more elaborate diagrams.

Thus the evaluation of quantificational wffs differs from the similar evaluation of propositional wffs since it involves consideration of the size of the domain. It is necessary to take account of this situation by calling a wff *k-valid* when it is identically 1 in a domain of *k* individuals and calling a wff *universally valid* only if it is identically 1 in domains of all numbers of individuals. Thus a universally valid quantificational wff will be one that evaluates to 1 for all assignments (without restriction) to its elementary constituents. A universally valid quantificational formula is the analogue of a tautologous propositional wff. We shall use the word "valid" as a synonym for "universally valid" in contexts where confusion is not likely to arise.

k-VALIDITY

The decisive difference among domains, for our purposes, is difference in cardinal numbers. If a wff possesses 1 in a certain domain of one individual, then it possesses 1 in any other domain of one individual. Thus, $\sum_x F(x) \supset \prod_x F(x)$ possesses 1 whether *x* ranges over even primes, present Presidents of the U.S., or planets whose orbit lies wholly between that of Venus and that of Mars. Again, if a statement possesses 0 in a certain domain of two individuals, it possesses 0 in any other domain of two individuals. Thus, $\sum_x F(x) \supset \prod_x F(x)$ possesses 0 whether *x* ranges over primes less than 4, opposing football teams, or known satellites of the planet Mars. Similar remarks apply to wffs that possess 0 in a domain of one individual, or possess 1 in a domain of two individuals. In general, the only difference among domains that is relevant to the validity of wffs in these domains is difference of number. Thus, to determine whether a quantificational wff is valid in any particular domain, we need evaluate it only in one domain of that numerical size.

It is always possible to assign 1 and 0 to any monadic predicate wff for a domain of a given numerical size, say *k*, and to evaluate it by matrices to check its *k*-validity. We have done this in some cases above, but let us give one more example. Is

$$\prod_x[B \supset F(x)] \lor (\sim C \& B)$$

2-valid? To determine this, we evaluate to obtain

B	∼C	F(a)	F(b)	{B ⊃ [F(a) & F(b)]} ∨ (∼C & B)			
1	0	0	0	0	0	0	0

As we see, at least one row of the table contains 0 in the final-evaluation column; hence, the wff is not 2-valid.

Similar procedures may be applied in the case of other domains and in the case of other formulas. The procedure may be tedious, but it can always be finished. Let us summarize some of these results schematically.

$\prod_\alpha \varphi(\alpha)$ *possesses* 1 *in a domain of k elements* if and only if $\varphi(\alpha)$ possesses 1 for every value of α in the domain; that is, the conjunction of these values is 1.

$\sum_\alpha \varphi(\alpha)$ *possesses* I *in a domain of k elements* if and only if $\varphi(\alpha)$ possesses 1 for some value in the domain; that is, the disjunction of these values is 1.

A wff of MPL possesses I *in a domain of k elements* if and only if it evaluates identically to 1 on calculation by matrices as in PL using the two preceding definitions.

UNIVERSAL VALIDITY

With one exception, if a wff is universally valid it evaluates to 1 in domains of all sizes. The exception is an empty domain. Let us take as an example the wff $\prod_x F(x) \supset \sum_x F(x)$. This can be proved as a D* line.

1. $\prod_x F(x)$
2. $F(x)$ 1, $\prod$E
3. $\sum_x F(x)$ 2, $\sum$I

4. $\prod_x F(x) \supset \sum_x F(x)$ 1–3, $\supset$I

It is valid in a domain of one, such as the domain of even primes, as is easily checked. But what of the case in which the range of x is a domain having *no* members? It may be tempting to say that where there are no members there is no domain either. But it is clearly possible to speak of domains having no members. Female Presidents of the United States constitute one such domain. Another consists of all even primes greater than two. The existence of such domains is implied by the very fact that we can say that they have no members. A domain having no members is said to be *null*. The question, then, is whether $\prod_x F(x) \supset \sum_x F(x)$ is valid in a null domain. We first note that every existentially quantified formula possesses 0 in a null domain since there can be no individual of which its predicates hold true. Thus, for every predicate F, $\sum_x F(x)$ and $\sum_x \sim F(x)$ alike possess 0. But by QEq, $\vdash \prod_x F(x) \equiv \sim[\sum_x \sim F(x)]$; and $\vdash \prod_x \sim F(x) \equiv \sim[\sum_x F(x)]$. So if $\sum_x \sim F(x)$ and $\sum_x F(x)$ both possess 0, then $\prod_x F(x)$ and $\prod_x \sim F(x)$ both possess 1, whatever F may be. In other words, in a null domain every universally quantified statement possesses 1. If we now turn to the schema $\prod_x F(x) \supset \sum_x F(x)$ we see that on the analysis just given, the antecedent has 1 while the consequent possesses 0; hence, the wff is not valid in a null domain.

A universally valid quantificational wff, then, need not possess 1 in a null domain, although it must possess 1 in domains of every other numerical size. (We say that a valid quantificational wff possesses 1 in every non-null domain.) The reader may wonder why it is that we are so lenient toward an exception when the domain has no members, but will admit no other exceptions. Might there not be a perfectly good sense of "valid" in which a quantificational wff tautologous in every domain having more than one member but yet lacking 1 in a one-membered domain could be valid? The answer is that there would never be any use for this sense of "valid", since if a quantificational wff lacks 1 in a domain of one individual it lacks 1 in every other domain as well, with the possible exception of the null domain. In general, a wff lacking 1 in a domain of k individuals lacks 1 in every domain having more than k members. The *only* exception to this is the case in which $k = 0$.

Let us consider the meaning of "*every* non-null domain". How many domains containing members are there? There must be at least as many different domains as there are positive integers; that is, there are domains having each of 1, 2, . . . , k, . . . individuals as members. These are finite domains. Then there is a domain having as many members as all the integers just referred to. This latter domain of all the integers is called denumerably infinite because we can enumerate its members. If we designate a domain having one individual as $\{1\}$, two individuals $\{1,2\}$, etc., we can say that we have the domains

$$\{1\}, \{1,2\}, \ldots , \{1,2, \ldots\}$$

Here $\{1,2, \ldots\}$ is the domain we call denumerably infinite. But there are still other domains, as for example that of the individual points on a line in Euclidian space, which have more elements. In fact, there is a whole series of these domains that are called nondenumerable because we cannot enumerate their members. We owe the discovery of these nondenumerable domains to the German mathematician Cantor. If a valid quantificational wff is tautologous in all domains, it must possess I in nondenumerably infinite domains as well as the denumerably infinite domain and finite domains. We would not want to call a wff universally valid if it were valid in finite domains and the denumerably infinite domains only, but not valid in a nondenumerable domain. Of course, if quantificational wffs never had to refer to members of nondenumerably infinite domains, we might regard the question of validity in these domains as merely academic. In point of fact, however, in studies such as analysis, we have to assume the validity of quantificational wffs in which the variables range over nondenumerably infinite domains. One could not even express the concept of *continuity*, on which analysis depends, without making use of wffs of that kind.

There is, then, a problem of determining validity in nondenumerably infinite domains; it would be a mistake to suppose that the meaning of validity is simply possession of I in all finite domains and in the denumerably infinite domain. We see that we must define the possession of I in terms of all domains. To do this, we need to define the possession of I schematically for wffs of the form $\prod_{\alpha}\varphi(\alpha)$ and $\sum_{\alpha}\varphi(\alpha)$.

$\prod_{\alpha}\varphi(\alpha)$ possesses I if and only if $\varphi(\alpha)$ has the value 1 for every value of α in every non-null domain—finite, denumerably infinite, and nondenumerably infinite.

$\sum_{\alpha}\varphi(\alpha)$ possesses I if and only if $\varphi(\alpha)$ possesses 1 for some value of α in every non-null domain—finite, denumerably infinite, and nondenumerably infinite.

A wff of MPL possesses I (is universally valid) if and only if it "evaluates"*
identically to 1 on calculation by matrices as for PL and the two preceding
definitions, that is, for every assignment of 1 or 0 to its elementary constituents in every non-null domain.

It is important to note that a wff of MPL will have a "table" of values that
is infinite for infinite domains. Such an infinite table cannot be effectively
calculated; and this fact introduces certain difficulties into a discussion of the
metatheory of MPL. Something of what is involved here may be seen by
trying to write down the evaluation table for $\prod_x F(x)$ in a denumerably infinite
domain.

Example:

$$F(1) \ \& \ F(2) \ \& \ \ldots \ \& \ F(k) \ \& \ldots$$

1	1	...	1	...
0	1	...	1	...
1	0	...	1	...
0	0	...	1	...
.	.	...	.	...
.	.	...	.	...
.	.	...	.	...

EXERCISE 10.2

I. Evaluate the following formulas in the indicated domains.

1. $\sum_x[F(x) \vee G(x)] \equiv [\sum_x F(x) \vee \sum_x G(x)]$
(0-domain, 3-domain)

2. $\prod_x[F(x) \ \& \ G(x)] \equiv [\sum_x F(x) \vee \sum_x G(x)]$
(0-domain, 2-domain)

3. $\{\sum_x[F(x) \ \& \ G(x)] \ \& \ \sum_x[G(x) \ \& \ F(x)]\} \supset \sum_x[F(x) \ \& \ H(x)]$
(0-domain, 1-domain, 2-domain)

4. $\{\sum_x[F(x) \ \& \ G(x)] \ \& \ \sum_x[G(x) \ \& \ H(x)] \ \& \ \sum_x[H(x) \ \& \ I(x)]\} \supset$
$\sum_x[F(x) \ \& \ I(x)]$ (2-domain, 3-domain)

5. $\prod_x[F(x) \ \& \ G(x)] \equiv [\prod_x F(x) \ \& \ \prod_x G(x)]$
(0-domain, 1-domain, 2-domain)

6. $\prod_x[F(x) \supset G(x)] \supset [\prod_x F(x) \supset \prod_x G(x)]$
(1-domain, 2-domain)

7. $[\prod_x F(x) \supset \prod_x G(x)] \supset \prod_x[F(x) \supset G(x)]$
(1-domain, 2-domain)

8. $\prod_x F(x) \equiv \sim \sum_x \sim F(x)$ (0-domain, 4-domain)

---

* We put "evaluates" in quotation marks here because the table will be infinite.

9. $\prod_x[F(x) \supset G(x)] \supset [\sum_x F(x) \supset \sum_x G(x)]$
(0-domain, 1-domain)

10. $[\sum_x F(x) \supset \sum_x G(x)] \supset \prod_x[F(x) \supset G(x)]$
(1-domain, 2-domain)

II. Löwenheim has proved that any quantificational statement valid in a denumerably infinite domain is valid in every domain. Show that if the formula $\prod_x F(x) \supset \sum_x F(x)$ is valid in a denumerably infinite domain, it is valid in all non-null finite domains. (Hint: assume that the formula is invalid for some non-null finite domain and show that it would be invalid in every larger domain.)

III. Given that a valid formula is one which is k-valid for all $k > 0$, define invalidity.

IV. Which of the following are true? False? Why?

   1. Some universally quantified expressions are not valid in the null domain.

   2. Expressions valid in the null domain are universally quantified.

   3. If an expression is not valid in the null domain, it is not universally quantified.

   4. Existentially quantified expressions are invalid in the null domain.

   5. If an expression is invalid in a domain of five individuals, it can be valid in a domain of more than five individuals.

   6. If an expression is invalid in the null domain, it is invalid in all domains.

   7. If an expression is invalid in the domain of fifteen individuals, it can be valid in some lesser domain.

   8. If an expression is valid in a domain of nine individuals, it can be invalid in a domain of one individual.

   9. An expression can be valid in all finite domains and not be universally valid.

   10. An expression can be valid in a denumerably infinite domain and be invalid in some finite domain. (Hint: see exercise II.)

10.3   The Consistency of the Rules of MPL

We shall now prove by a study of the formal system of MPL that a wff of the form $\psi \,\&\, \sim\psi$ cannot be the last line of a finished sequence—that is, a D* line—and, thus, that MPL is consistent.

Metatheorem 10.1:   No wff of the form $\psi \,\&\, \sim\psi$ is the last line of any finished sequence—that is, a D* line.

It happens that in the proof of this metatheorem we need consider only a domain of one individual. Thus, the problem referred to at the end of the last section—that of effectively evaluating formulas for infinite domains—does not arise here.

As for PL, we establish three lemmas, this time for deductions involving lines of type A*–D*.

Lemma a: The uses of ⊃I in any finished sequence in which the B* lines possess 1 simultaneously in a domain of one individual transmit this property to the last line of the finished sequence.

Lemma b: The last line of any finished sequence including B* lines is 1-valid, and any line of any finished sequence lacking B* lines is 1-valid.

Lemma c: No wff of the form ψ & $\sim\psi$ is 1-valid.

Proof of Lemma a: To extend the proof given in Metatheorem 9.1 to MPL, we must show first that the additional nondischarging transformations $\prod$E, $\prod$I, $\sum$E′, and $\sum$I transmit 1 from a line to its successor in a sequence. We consider these in turn.

$\prod$E: Let $\prod_\alpha\varphi(\alpha)$ possess 1 in a domain of one individual. This means that $\varphi(a)$ possesses 1. Thus $\varphi(\beta)$ possesses 1 since $\varphi(\beta)$ will be $\varphi(a)$.

$\prod$I: Let $\varphi(a)$ possess 1 in a domain of one individual. Then $\prod_\alpha\varphi(\alpha)$ possesses 1 since α ranges over only one individual.

$\sum$E′: Let $\sum_\alpha\varphi(\alpha)$ possess 1 in a domain of one individual. This means that $\varphi(a)$ possesses 1. If $\varphi(a) \supset \psi$ also possesses 1 then ψ possesses 1.

$\sum$I: Let $\varphi(a)$ possess 1 in a domain of one individual. Then $\sum_\alpha\varphi(\alpha)$ possesses 1 since α ranges over that individual.

Since these transformations (as well as the nondischarging transformations of PL considered in Metatheorem 9.1) transmit the property 1 in a domain of one individual, they also transmit the property I, that is, the property of being a tautology, in a domain of one individual.

The proof of Lemma a now follows by an exact analogue of the second half of the proof of Lemma a of Metatheorem 9.1.

Proof of Lemma b: We next show that the last line of any finished sequence involving B* lines or any line of any finished sequences lacking B* lines is tautologous in some finite domain. The proof of Lemma b is an exact analogue of that of Lemma b of Metatheorem 9.1, except that consideration must be given to $\prod$I, $\prod$E, $\sum$E′, and $\sum$I. The complete statement is left to the reader.

Proof of Lemma c: It is evident by calculation of the matrices that a wff of the form ψ & $\sim\psi$ is not 1-valid.

The proof of the metatheorem follows from the lemmas. By Lemma b every D* line is 1-valid and by Lemma c a wff of the form $\psi \mathbin{\&} \sim\psi$ is not 1-valid. Hence, no wff of the form $\psi \mathbin{\&} \sim\psi$ can be the last line of a finished sequence.

The restriction in this proof to a domain of one individual makes possible establishment of the consistency of MPL without reference to the difficult cases of infinite domains, a rather remarkable fact.*

EXERCISE 10.3

I. Why need we consider only a domain of one individual to prove Metatheorem 10.1?

II. Do the answers to problems I-V of Exercise 9.4 require any modification if understood as applying to MPL?

III. Complete the proof of Lemma a in a manner analogous to that of Lemma a of Metatheorem 9.1.

IV. Complete the proof of Lemma b in a manner analogous to Lemma b of Metatheorem 9.1.

V. Construct a proof of Lemma a for MPL where $\sum E'$ is replaced by $\sum E$. (Hint: simply extend the proof to cover those cases which arise when $\sum E$ is involved.)

10.4 The Completeness of MPL

To establish the completeness of the transformations of MPL, we must show that a wff of MPL possesses I in every non-null domain (is a valid wff) if and only if it is the last line of a finished sequence. This establishes the fact that the set of valid wffs is equivalent to the set of deducible wffs. The line of attack in establishing the completeness of PL was to prove Metatheorem 9.2, which states that every valid wff of PL is a D' wff. However, in the case of PL we knew from Metatheorem 9.1 that every D' wff is valid. We do not yet know for MPL that every D* wff is valid, since the proof of the consistency of MPL depends only upon 1-validity. All that has been demonstrated is that every D* wff is 1-valid. We begin our proof of completeness by establishing that all last lines of finished sequences in MPL—that is, D* lines—are valid in every non-null domain. This proof requires more powerful methods than those we have so far used, and thus it represents a crucial juncture in metatheory.

---

* For a generalized discussion of this kind of proof, see H. Wang, "Arithmetic Translations of Axiom Systems", *Trans. Amer. Math. Society*, Vol. 71 (1951), pp. 283–293.

Metatheorem 10.2:   Every D* line is valid (*i.e.*, possesses I in every non-null domain).

Lemma b of Metatheorem 10.1 states that every D* line is 1-valid. We use an analogous method to prove the present metatheorem, but there are significant differences in our reasoning. We state only as much of the proof as is essential to indicate the new methods used. First, as in Lemma a of Metatheorem 10.1, we show that the uses of $\supset$ I in any finished sequence in which the B* lines possess 1 simultaneously in any non-null domain transmit this property to the last line of the finished sequence.

As in Metatheorem 10.1, we show that the nondischarging transformations $\prod$E, $\prod$I, $\sum$E′, and $\sum$I transmit 1 from a line to its successor. We consider.

$\prod$E: Let $\prod_\alpha \varphi(\alpha)$ possess 1 in every non-null domain. This means that every value of $\varphi(\alpha)$ in every domain possesses 1. Thus $\varphi(\beta)$ possesses 1 since β will have one of these values.

$\prod$I: Let $\varphi(\beta)$ possess 1 for an arbitrary value in every non-null domain. Then $\prod_\alpha \varphi(\alpha)$ possesses 1.

$\sum$E : Let $\sum_\alpha \varphi(\alpha)$ possess 1 in every non-null domain. This means that for some value, say a, in any domain, $\varphi(a)$ possesses 1. Let $\varphi(\beta) \supset \psi$ possess 1 in every non-null domain. Since $\varphi(\beta)$ will take the value a, ψ must possess 1 under these conditions.

$\sum$I: Let $\varphi(\beta)$ possess 1 for some value in every non-null domain. Then $\sum_\alpha \varphi(\alpha)$ possesses 1.

The conclusion in each of these cases depends upon our judgment that a formula possesses 1 when evaluated in infinite domains. This is something we cannot determine effectively by examining evaluation tables, for these cannot be infinite. In consequence, our conclusion in each of these cases is based not upon constructive reasoning about finite tables, but upon reasoning in principle about infinite tables. This is not necessarily objectionable. Indeed, the reasoning seems quite acceptable. However, the difference in character is important and must be noted.

The statement and proof of Lemma b for this metatheorem follow the similar lemmas and proofs of Metatheorems 9.1 and 10.1, except that our reasoning must deal with infinite domains and evaluation tables. The explicit modifications of the arguments are left to the reader. This completes the proof of Metatheorem 10.2.

We may now proceed to establish that every valid wff of MPL is a D* wff. The analogous result for PL was obtained in Metatheorem 9.2. The line of proof used there depends upon the fact that wffs of PL have a finite number of statement variables. A similar proof might be given for MPL if we restricted the wffs to have reference to finite domains, but this restriction would greatly reduce the value of the proof. We must find a new line of attack.

The proof we shall give is most readily outlined and presented with the use of a new concept. We begin by defining this new concept:

Satisfiability: A wff of MPL is satisfiable if and only if it evaluates to 1 for some assignment of 1 or 0 to its values in some non-null domain.

Example: A wff of the form $[\prod_\alpha \varphi(\alpha) \supset \prod_\alpha \psi(\alpha)] \supset \prod_\alpha [\varphi(\alpha) \supset \psi(\alpha)]$ is satisfiable in a domain of two individuals. Thus

$$\{[\varphi(1) \ \& \ \varphi(2)] \supset [\psi(1) \ \& \ \psi(2)]\} \supset \{[\varphi(1) \supset \psi(1)] \ \& \ [\varphi(2) \supset \psi(2)]\}$$
$$\ \ \ 0 \ \ \ \ 0 \ 0 \ \ \ \ \ 1 \ \ \ 0 \ \ \ \ 0 \ 0 \ \ \ \ \ \ 1 \ \ \ \ 0 \ \ \ \ 1 \ 0 \ \ \ \ \ \ 1 \ 0 \ \ \ \ \ 1 \ 0$$

Example: A wff of the form $\sum_\alpha [\varphi(\alpha) \ \& \sim\varphi(\alpha)]$ is not satisfiable in any non-null domain since when values are substituted from any non-null domain we get a contradiction that evaluates to 0.

The last example suggests that validity and satisfiability are related—a statement being valid when its negation is not satisfiable.

Metatheorem 10.3: Any wff of MPL is valid if and only if its negation is not satisfiable.

Proof: A wff, Δ, is valid if and only if it possesses I in every non-null domain. This is equivalent to saying that the wff Δ evaluates to 1 for every assignment of values to its variables. This in turn is equivalent to saying that there can be no assignment of values to $\sim\Delta$ which evaluates to 1. But by definition this is equivalent to saying that $\sim\Delta$ is not satisfiable.

Inconsistency (Consistency): A wff, Δ, is inconsistent if there exists a wff of the form $\psi \ \& \sim\psi$ which can be deduced from Δ. Otherwise Δ is called consistent.

Example: $\sim(A \lor \sim A)$ is inconsistent since the following deduction exists:

$$\text{——} \ 1. \ \sim(A \lor \sim A)$$
$$\ \ \ \ \ \ 2. \ \sim A \ \& \ A \ \ \ \ \ \ \ 1, \text{DM}$$

We now outline the proof that every valid wff of MPL is a D* wff. We shall establish this result by means of the following steps:

(1) If Γ is valid, then $\sim\Gamma$ is not satisfiable.
(2) If $\sim\Gamma$ is not satisfiable, then $\sim\Gamma$ is not consistent.
(3) If $\sim\Gamma$ is not consistent, then Γ is a D* line.
(4) Thus if Γ is valid, Γ is a D* line.

Metatheorem 10.3 justified the first step in this chain. We have next to justify the second step. In order to do this, we prove the following metatheorem:

Metatheorem 10.4: If a wff, Δ, of MPL is not satisfiable then it is inconsistent.

In terms of the definitions just given, this metatheorem states that if a wff of MPL does not possess 1 upon evaluation, it is possible to deduce a wff of the form ψ & $\sim\psi$ from it. It thus relates satisfiability and consistency. Our proof consists in reducing a wff, Δ, to an equivalent normal form and establishing that either this is satisfiable or ψ & $\sim\psi$ can be reached from it.

In the following steps of the proof we restrict our discussion to wffs of MPL that do not contain statement variables of PL.* This restriction simplifies the discussion. Since it will be removed later, we are justified in stating the metatheorem in its full generality. We develop the proof in schematic form.

Beginning with a schema of MPL without statement variables, we reduce it to an equivalent normal form by the following steps:

(1) Replace all universal quantifiers with existential quantifiers by use of QEq and eliminate all quantifiers within quantified statements using appropriate derived rules of MPL.

(2) State the portions of each schema in the brackets following a $\sum$, *i.e.*, $\sum[\ ]$, as a DNF by the methods of Chapter Three applied to statement functions.

(3) Distribute $\sum$'s wherever possible.

(4) Reduce the whole schema to DNF unless it is a conjunction of quantified statements (which of course is already DNF).

The result of these procedures will be an equivalent schema in normal form.

Example: $\sum_\alpha [\varphi(\alpha) \supset \psi(\alpha)]$. This schema includes no statement variables. We reduce to normal form as follows:

$$
\begin{array}{lll}
\rule{2em}{0.4pt}\ \textbf{1.}\ \sum_\alpha[\varphi(\alpha) \supset \psi(\alpha)] & \\
\textbf{2.}\ \sum_\alpha[\sim\varphi(\alpha) \vee \psi(\alpha)] & \text{1, Impl} \\
\textbf{3.}\ \sum_\alpha \sim\varphi(\alpha) \vee \sum_\alpha \psi(\alpha) & \text{2, 5.7} \\
\textbf{4.}\ \text{Not necessary as (3) is DNF} &
\end{array}
$$

Example: $\prod_\alpha [\chi(\alpha)\ \&\ \psi(\alpha)]$.

$$
\begin{array}{lll}
\rule{2em}{0.4pt}\ \textbf{1.}\ \sim\sum_\alpha \sim[\ \chi(\alpha)\ \&\ \psi(\alpha)] & \text{QEq} \\
\textbf{2.}\ \sim\sum_\alpha[\sim\chi(\alpha) \vee \sim\psi(\alpha)] & \text{1, DM} \\
\textbf{3.}\ \sim[\sum_\alpha \sim\chi(\alpha) \vee \sum_\alpha \sim\psi(\alpha)] & \text{2, 5.7} \\
\textbf{4.}\ \sim\sum_\alpha \sim\chi(\alpha)\ \&\ \sim\sum_\alpha \sim\psi(\alpha) & \text{3, DM}
\end{array}
$$

---

* The method of this proof was developed by W. V. Quine, *Methods of Logic*, rev. ed., (New York: Holt, Rinehart, and Winston, Inc., 1959). See pp. 94–118. Quine uses the method to establish a decision procedure as discussed in Section 10.6.

Example: $\prod_\alpha(\varphi(\alpha) \supset \{\sum_\beta\psi(\beta) \ \& \ \prod_\gamma[\chi(\gamma) \supset \Gamma(\alpha)]\})$

We proceed from inner quantifications outward, using the equivalence theorems for the distribution of quantifiers. Since γ is not free in $\Gamma(\alpha)$, for example, we have

$$\prod_\alpha(\varphi(\alpha) \supset \sum_\beta \{\psi(\beta) \ \& \ [\sum_\gamma\chi(\gamma) \supset \Gamma(\alpha)]\})$$

Since β is not free in $\sum_\gamma\chi(\gamma) \supset \Gamma(\alpha)$, we can write

$$\prod_\alpha(\varphi(\alpha) \supset \{\sum_\beta\psi(\beta) \ \& \ [\sum_\gamma\chi(\gamma) \supset \Gamma(\alpha)]\})$$

Using the principles that $[p \supset (q \ \& \ r)] \equiv [(p \supset q) \ \& \ (p \supset r)]$,

and that $\prod_\alpha(\varphi \ \& \ \psi) \equiv (\prod_\alpha\varphi \ \& \ \prod_\alpha\psi)$, we obtain

$$\prod_\alpha[\varphi(\alpha) \supset \sum_\beta\psi(\beta)] \ \& \ \prod_\alpha\{\varphi(\alpha) \supset [\sum_\gamma\chi(\gamma) \supset \Gamma(\alpha)]\}$$

Since α is not free in $\sum_\beta\psi(\beta)$, the first conjunct reduces to

$$\sum_\alpha\varphi(\alpha) \supset \sum_\beta\psi(\beta)$$

Using the rules of Impl, CM, and Exp, we can reduce the second conjunct to

$$\prod_\alpha\{\sum_\gamma\chi(\gamma) \supset [\varphi(\alpha) \supset \Gamma(\alpha)]\}$$

Since α is not free in $\sum_\gamma\chi(\gamma)$, this conjunct becomes

$$\sum_\gamma\chi(\gamma) \supset \prod_\alpha[\varphi(\alpha) \supset \Gamma(\alpha)]$$

Now eliminating $\prod$ in favor of $\sum$, we have

$$\sum_\gamma\chi(\gamma) \supset \sim\!\sum \sim[\varphi(\alpha) \supset \Gamma(\alpha)]$$

Putting both conjuncts together again, and replacing β and γ by α, which we can now do without danger of confusion, we obtain

$$[\sum_\alpha\varphi(\alpha) \supset \sum_\alpha\psi(\alpha)] \ \& \ \{\sum_\alpha\chi(\alpha) \supset \sim\!\sum_\alpha \sim[\varphi(\alpha) \supset \Gamma(\alpha)]\}$$

We now state the schemata within the parentheses as DNF's.

$$[\sim\!\sum_\alpha\varphi(\alpha) \ \mathbf{v} \ \sum_\alpha\psi(\alpha)] \ \& \ \{\sim\!\sum_\alpha\chi(\alpha) \ \mathbf{v} \sim\!\sum_\alpha[\varphi(\alpha) \ \& \sim\!\Gamma(\alpha)]\}$$

Reduction of this to DNF is now possible, on the principle that

$$[(p \ \mathbf{v} \ q) \ \& \ (r \ \mathbf{v} \ s)] \equiv [(p \ \& \ r) \ \mathbf{v} \ (p \ \& \ s) \ \mathbf{v} \ (q \ \& \ r) \ \mathbf{v} \ (q \ \& \ s)].$$

The preceding examples illustrate some of the techniques used in the reduction of schemata of MPL to normal forms. As the examples suggest, the resultant normal forms will in general be either

(i) $\sum_\alpha[\varphi(\alpha) \ \& \ \psi(\alpha) \ \& \sim\!\chi(\alpha)]$ or some variation involving a conjunction of more or fewer predicates with or without negations, or

(ii) $\sim\sum_\alpha[\varphi(\alpha) \ \& \sim\psi(\alpha)]$ or some variation involving a conjunction of more or fewer predicates with or without negations, or

(iii) A conjunction of schemata of type (i), or

(iv) A conjunction of schemata of type (ii), or

(v) A conjunction of schemata of types (i) and (ii), or

(vi) A disjunction of schemata of types (i)–(v).

That the normal form will be one of these is evident from the considerations that QEq as used in step 1 can always be applied and elimination of quantifiers within parentheses achieved; that reduction of statement functions to DNF is always possible by the methods of Chapter Three and Chapter Five, Section Five; that existential quantifiers can be distributed through **v**; and that the resultant schema can be reduced to DNF, *i.e.*, a disjunction of (possibly conjoined) quantified schemata of statement functions.

We have now to show that if any of the schemata of types (i)–(vi) is not satisfiable in a finite domain, then we can deduce a contradiction from it. We consider each type in turn.

(i) We suppose that the normal form is of type (i) and examine the evaluation in a finite domain. Clearly, the values for such a schema would be satisfiable in a finite domain unless the conjunction contains a contradiction.

Example: $\sum_\alpha[\varphi(\alpha) \ \& \sim\psi(\alpha)]$
In a domain of two individuals we have

$$\varphi(1) \ \& \sim\psi(1) \ \textbf{v} \ \varphi(2) \ \& \sim\psi(2)$$

Here the first disjunct $\varphi(1) \ \& \sim\psi(1)$, for instance, possesses 1 when $\varphi(1)$ possesses 1 and $\sim\psi(1)$ possesses 1; hence, the wff is satisfiable.

Example: $\sum_\alpha[\varphi(\alpha) \ \& \sim\varphi(\alpha) \ \& \ \psi(\alpha)]$
In a finite domain the occurrence of the conjunct $\varphi(\alpha) \ \& \sim\varphi(\alpha)$ makes possession of 1 clearly impossible as we determine by the matrix for &.

If the conjunction contains a contradiction, then we can deduce $\psi \ \& \sim\psi$ as follows:

1. $\sum_\alpha[\varphi(\alpha) \ \& \sim\varphi(\alpha) \ \& \ \psi(\alpha)]$		
2. $\varphi(\alpha) \ \& \sim\varphi(\alpha) \ \& \ \psi(\alpha)$		
3. $\varphi(\alpha) \ \& \sim\varphi(\alpha)$	2, &E	
4. $\psi \ \& \sim\psi$	3, $\sim$E	
5. $\psi \ \& \sim\psi$	1, 2–4, $\sum$E*	

---

* As in·Chapter Nine, having established the consistency of the rules using $\supset$I as the sole discharge rule, we now admit the old $\sum$E, in order to simplify the discussion.

(ii) We suppose that the normal form is of type (ii). In a finite domain a conjunction of values for such a schema would always be satisfiable.

Example: $\sim\sum_\alpha[\varphi(\alpha) \,\&\, \sim\varphi(\alpha)]$
In a domain of one individual we have

$$\sim[\varphi(1) \,\&\, \sim\varphi(1)]$$

But this clearly possesses 1; indeed, it possesses I.

(iii) We suppose that the normal form is of type (iii). If we select a domain with as many individuals as there are conjuncts, the schema is satisfiable.

Example: $\sum_\alpha[\varphi(\alpha)] \,\&\, \sum_\alpha[\sim\varphi(\alpha) \,\&\, \psi(\alpha)]$
If we select a domain of one individual we get

$$\varphi(1) \,\&\, [\sim\varphi(1) \,\&\, \psi(1)]$$

which is not satisfiable since $[\varphi(1) \,\&\, \sim\varphi(1)]$ occurs in it. However, in a domain of two individuals we get

$$[\varphi(1) \,\mathbf{v}\, \varphi(2)] \,\&\, \{[\sim\varphi(1) \,\&\, \psi(1)] \,\mathbf{v}\, [\sim\varphi(2) \,\&\, \psi(2)]\}$$

Letting $\varphi(1)$ possess 1 and $\varphi(2)$ possess 0 while $\psi(1)$ possesses 1 and $\psi(2)$ possesses 1 the schema is satisfiable.

As the example illustrates, it is necessary to consider the domain to contain a sufficient number of individuals in order to avoid conflicts of predicates which might prevent satisfiability.

(iv) We suppose that the normal form is of type (iv). Each of the conjuncts is satisfiable. In a finite domain it will be possible for the conjuncts to possess 1 together unless upon deletion of quantifiers the result is a contradiction, as in $\sim\sum_\alpha \sim[\varphi(\alpha) \,\&\, \sim\psi(\alpha)] \,\&\, \sim\sum_\alpha[\varphi(\alpha) \,\&\, \sim\psi(\alpha)]$. But in this case we can deduce a schema of the form $\psi \,\&\, \sim\psi$, by use of QEq, &E, and $\sim$E.

Example: $\sim\sum_\alpha[\varphi(\alpha) \,\&\, \psi(\alpha)] \,\&\, \sim\sum_\alpha[\sim\varphi(\alpha) \,\&\, \psi(\alpha)]$
In a domain of one individual we have

$$\sim[\varphi(1) \,\&\, \psi(1)] \,\&\, \sim[\sim\varphi(1) \,\&\, \psi(1)]$$
$$00$$

which is satisfiable as indicated.

Example: $\sim\sum_\alpha[\varphi(\alpha) \,\&\, \psi(\alpha)] \,\&\, \sim\sum_\alpha \sim[\varphi(\alpha) \,\&\, \psi(\alpha)]$

This will not be satisfiable in a finite domain, because the right conjunct denies the left. We may deduce $\psi \mathbin{\&} \sim\psi$ as follows:

—1. $\sim\sum_\alpha[\varphi(\alpha) \mathbin{\&} \psi(\alpha)] \mathbin{\&} \sim\sum_\alpha \sim[\varphi(\alpha) \mathbin{\&} \psi(\alpha)]$	
2. $\sim\sum_\alpha[\varphi(\alpha) \mathbin{\&} \psi(\alpha)]$	1, &E
3. $\prod_\alpha \sim[\varphi(\alpha) \mathbin{\&} \psi(\alpha)]$	2, QEq
4. $\sim[\varphi(\beta) \mathbin{\&} \psi(\beta)]$	3, $\prod$E
5. $\sim\sum_\alpha \sim[\varphi(\alpha) \mathbin{\&} \psi(\alpha)]$	1, &E
6. $\varphi(\beta) \mathbin{\&} \psi(\beta)$	5, QEq, $\prod$E
7. $\psi \mathbin{\&} \sim\psi$	6, 4, &I, $\sim$E

(v) We suppose that the normal form is of type (v). Thus it is a conjunction of schemata of types (i) and (ii). We consider first two examples where this form is not satisfiable.

Example: $\sum_\alpha[\varphi(\alpha)] \mathbin{\&} \sim\sum_\alpha[\psi(\alpha)] \mathbin{\&} \sim\sum_\alpha[\varphi(\alpha)]$
From this schema by &E and $\sim$E we can deduce $\psi \mathbin{\&} \sim\psi$.

Example: $\sum_\alpha[\varphi(\alpha) \mathbin{\&} \psi(\alpha) \mathbin{\&} \sim\chi(\alpha)] \mathbin{\&} \sim\sum_\alpha[\varphi(\alpha)]$
From this schema we can deduce $\psi \mathbin{\&} \sim\psi$ as follows:

—1. $\sum_\alpha[\varphi(\alpha) \mathbin{\&} \psi(\alpha) \mathbin{\&} \sim\chi(\alpha)] \mathbin{\&} \sim\sum_\alpha[\varphi(\alpha)]$	
2. $\sum_\alpha[\varphi(\alpha) \mathbin{\&} \psi(\alpha) \mathbin{\&} \sim\chi(\alpha)]$	1, &E
3. $\varphi(\beta) \mathbin{\&} \psi(\beta) \mathbin{\&} \sim\chi(\beta)$	
4. $\varphi(\beta)$	3, &E
5. $\sum_\alpha\varphi(\alpha)$	4, $\sum$I
6. $\sum_\alpha\varphi(\alpha)$	2, 3–5, $\sum$E
7. $\sim\sum_\alpha\varphi(\alpha)$	1, &E
8. $\psi \mathbin{\&} \sim\psi$	6, 7, &I, $\sim$E

The difficulty in satisfying schemata of this type arises when, although the conjoined schemata of type (i) and type (ii) are satisfiable, one of those of type (i) permits the deduction of one of those of type (ii) with the negation deleted. Thus, in the first of the two examples, $\sum_\alpha\varphi(\alpha)$—the right conjunct with its negation deleted—is the left conjunct. In the second example, the right conjunct with its negation deleted is derivable from the left. When this happens it becomes impossible to satisfy all the conjuncts at once and so the whole schema. If this is not the case, then the schema of type (v) can be satisfied in a finite domain having as many individuals as there are conjuncts of type (i)—as in the case of schemata of type (iii).

(vi) We suppose the normal form is of type (vi). Then it is satisfiable if any of its disjuncts is satisfiable. If no disjuncts are satisfiable then, as we have seen in the case of each schema of types (i)–(v), it will be possible to deduce $\psi \mathbin{\&} \sim\psi$ from each, and by vE, $\psi \mathbin{\&} \sim\psi$ from the schema of type (vi).

Example: $\sum_\alpha[\varphi(\alpha) \ \& \sim\varphi(\alpha) \ \& \ \psi(\alpha)] \ \mathbf{v} \ \sum_\alpha[\varphi(\alpha) \ \& \sim\varphi(\alpha) \ \& \sim\psi(\alpha)] \ \mathbf{v}$
$\sum_\alpha[\psi(\alpha) \ \& \sim\psi(\alpha) \ \& \ \varphi(\alpha)] \ \mathbf{v} \sim\sum_\alpha[\psi(\alpha)] \ \& \ \sum_\alpha[\psi(\alpha) \ \& \ \varphi(\alpha)]$
Call this schema L.

   —— 1. L
   —— 2. $\sum_\alpha[\varphi(\alpha) \ \& \sim\varphi(\alpha) \ \& \ \psi(\alpha)]$
   —— 3. $\varphi(\alpha) \ \& \sim\varphi(\alpha) \ \& \ \psi(\alpha)$
   4. $\varphi(\alpha) \ \& \sim\varphi(\alpha)$ 3, &E
   5. $\psi \ \& \sim\psi$ 4, $\sim$E

   6. $\psi \ \& \sim\psi$ 3–5, $\sum$E

   —— 7. $\sum_\alpha[\psi(\alpha) \ \& \sim\varphi(\alpha) \ \& \sim\psi(\alpha)]$
   8.

We proceed to show that each disjunct in L implies $\psi \ \& \sim\psi$ and, hence,

$$\vdots$$

 k. $\psi \ \& \sim\psi$ 2–6, 7–*k*, etc.
                vE

   We now remove the restriction on the schemata considered in Metatheorem 10.4 to permit occurrence of statement variables. We have shown in Metatheorem 9.2 that two schemata of PL having the same evaluation table are equivalent (since $r \equiv s$ will be valid and hence provable). Consequently, if a schema of PL is not satisfiable it is equivalent to $p \ \& \sim p$ and hence inconsistent. Thus, (1) if a schema containing variables and quantifiers inessentially reduces to a nonsatisfiable schema of PL, it is inconsistent—otherwise it is satisfiable.

 Example: $\sum_\alpha\varphi(\alpha) \ \& \sim\sum_\alpha\varphi(\alpha)$. This schema might be written as $p \ \& \sim p$. Hence it is inconsistent.

Again, (2) if a schema containing statement variables as well as individual variables and quantifiers reduces to a nonsatisfiable schema of PL it is inconsistent—otherwise it is satisfiable.

 Example: $\sim[p \ \mathbf{v} \ \sum_\alpha\varphi(\alpha) \ \& \ \sum_\alpha\varphi(\alpha)]$
We evaluate this by assigning 1 and 0 to the statement variables—but *not* to the quantified schemata—and determining the value of the result as 1, 0, or a quantified schema. Thus,

$$\sim[p \ \mathbf{v} \ \textstyle\sum_\alpha\varphi(\alpha)] \ \& \ \sum_\alpha\varphi(\alpha)$$
$$0 \quad 1 \ 1 \qquad\qquad 0$$
$$\sim\textstyle\sum_\alpha\varphi(\alpha) \ 0 \ \sum_\alpha\varphi(\alpha) \qquad 0$$
$$\text{(final column)}$$

Example:

$p \supset \{q \& \sim \sum_\alpha [\varphi(\alpha) \& \psi(\alpha)]\}$

p	⊃	{q	&	∼∑_α[φ(α) & ψ(α)]}
1	λ_1	1	λ_1	
0	1	1	λ_1	
1	0	0	0	
0	1	0	0	

$\&$ $q \supset \sum_\alpha \{\varphi(\alpha) \& [\psi(\alpha) \vee \chi(\alpha)]\}$

&	[λ_1 & (λ_2 & ∼λ_3)]	1	λ_2
	0	1	λ_2
	0	0	1
	0	0	1

$\&$ $\sim$ $\{p \supset \sum_\alpha [\chi(\alpha) \& \sim\psi(\alpha)]\}$

&	(λ_2 & ∼λ_3)	∼	∼λ_3	1	λ_3
	0	λ_3	0	0	1
	∼λ_3	∼λ_3	1	λ_3	
	0	λ_3	0	0	1

(final column)

In this evaluation we let

λ_1 be $\sim\sum_\alpha [\varphi(\alpha) \& \psi(\alpha)]$

λ_2 be $\sum_\alpha \{\varphi(\alpha) \& [\psi(\alpha) \vee \chi(\alpha)]\}$

λ_3 be $\sum_\alpha [\chi(\alpha) \& \sim\psi(\alpha)]$

Note that the matrix evaluates to 0 in every row but the first, where its value is

$$\sim\sum_\alpha [\varphi(\alpha) \& \psi(\alpha)] \& \sum_\alpha \{\varphi(\alpha) \& [\psi(\alpha) \vee \chi(\alpha)]\} \& \sim\sum_\alpha [\chi(\alpha) \& \sim\psi(\alpha)]$$

This schema must now be evaluated by the methods of reducing to a normal form of types (i)–(vi) and testing for consistency.

FIGURE 10.1. Evaluation of MPL Formula

331

Note that the 0 in the final column of the last row results from evaluating $\sim\!\sum_\alpha\varphi(\alpha)$ & $\sum_\alpha\varphi(\alpha)$ as equivalent to p & $\sim\!p$ and hence 0. This schema of the example is inconsistent.

Finally, (3) if a schema containing statement letters, as well as variables and quantifiers, reduces to a quantified schema, this schema must be evaluated by the methods discussed in connection with reduction to a normal form of types (i)–(vi). See the example in Figure 10.1.

We next state the metatheorem toward which we have been building:

Metatheorem 10.5:   Every valid wff of MPL is a D* line.

We recapitulate the steps so far taken in the proof of this metatheorem. Metatheorem 10.3 establishes that if a wff Γ is valid, then $\sim\!\Gamma$ is not satisfiable. Metatheorem 10.4 establishes that if $\sim\!\Gamma$ is not satisfiable then $\sim\!\Gamma$ is not consistent. We have now only to show that if $\sim\!\Gamma$ is not consistent, then Γ is a D* line, for then by HS the result follows.

If $\sim\!\Gamma$ is not consistent we can deduce a wff of the form ψ & $\sim\!\psi$ from it (by definition); hence the following proof schema exists:

1.	$\sim\!\Gamma$	
$\vdots$		
k.	ψ & $\sim\!\psi$	1, Assumption that $\sim\!\Gamma$ is inconsistent
k + 1.	Γ	$k, \sim\!I, \sim\!\sim\!E$

Hence Γ is a D* line, and since Γ is any valid wff, the metatheorem follows.

EXERCISE 10.4

    I. Show that a discharging transformation according to $\supset\!I$ results in D* wffs by an argument similar to that of Lemma a of Metatheorem 9.1.

    II. Modify the arguments in Metatheorem 10.1 to complete the proof of Metatheorem 10.2 (*i.e.*, complete the induction of Lemma a and state and prove Lemma b).

    III. Which of the formulas of exercise 10.2, part I, are satisfiable in the indicated domains?

    IV. Reduce each of the following to normal form.

        1. $\prod_x[F(x) \supset G(x)]$

        2. $\sim\!\prod_x[F(x) \supset F(x)]$

        3. $\sim\![\sum_x F(x) \supset \sim\!\prod_x\!\sim\!F(x)]$

        4. $\sim\!\{\prod_x[F(x) \vee \sim\!F(x)] \vee \prod_x\!\sim\![G(x)$ & $\sim\!G(x)]\}$

        5. $\sim\!\{\prod_x[F(x)$ & $G(x)] \supset [\prod_x F(x)$ & $\prod_x G(x)]\}$

V. Which of the above are satisfiable?

VI. Deduce ψ & $\sim\psi$ from any that are not satisfiable.

VII. Which types of normal forms do the above illustrate?

VIII. Try to construct inconsistent formulas of types (ii) and (iv). Can you conclude anything from this?

IX. Construct formulas to illustrate cases (1), (2), and (3) on pages 330–332 for removing the restriction on the proof of Metatheorem 10.4 to quantified formulas.

X. Prove the metatheorem: Any formula of MPL that has the form of a tautologous propositional formula is valid.

XI. Prove that every consistent formula of MPL is satisfiable.

XII. Apply the method of proof of completeness for MPL to PL.

10.5 Decidability

We have now shown that every wff of MPL that is provable possesses I, and that if a wff of MPL possesses I then it is provable. The first point is made in Metatheorem 10.2, the second in Metatheorem 10.5. Clearly, for a wff of MPL, the property of possessing I—that is, validity—is equivalent to deducibility. Given a method for effectively determining whether a wff possesses I, there would be a decision procedure for MPL just as there is for PL.

The task of determining whether a wff of MPL is valid is not solvable by the matrix methods of PL alone. We can determine the validity or invalidity of a wff for a domain of one individual, of course. Indeed, the matrix methods of Section 10.2 enable us to determine the validity or invalidity of a wff for any finite domain. Yet apparently this is not sufficient, for validity of a wff in MPL is validity in infinite domains as well as finite ones.

As a further elaboration of the problem, we may note that we can establish the invalidity of a wff of MPL by finding a finite domain in which it fails to possess I. The fact that a wff of the form $\sum_\alpha \varphi(\alpha) \supset \prod_\alpha \varphi(\alpha)$ is invalid in a domain of two individuals establishes its universal invalidity. In the somewhat more complicated case of wffs of the form

$$\{\sum_\alpha[\varphi(\alpha) \ \& \ \psi(\alpha)] \ \& \ \sum_\alpha[\varphi(\alpha) \ \& \sim\psi(\alpha)]\} \supset \prod_\alpha [\psi(\alpha) \supset \varphi(\alpha)]$$

we can establish invalidity in a domain of three individuals. In a domain of one individual a wff of this form is valid, as we determine by testing

$$\{[\varphi(1) \ \& \ \psi(1)] \ \& \ [\varphi(1) \ \& \sim\psi(1)]\} \supset [\psi(1) \supset \varphi(1)]$$

In a domain of two individuals it is also valid, as we determine by testing the schema

$$(\{[\varphi(1) \ \& \ \psi(1)] \ \mathbf{v} \ [\varphi(2) \ \& \ \psi(2)]\} \ \& \ \{[\varphi(1) \ \& \sim\psi(1)] \ \mathbf{v}$$
$$[\varphi(2) \ \& \sim\psi(2)]\}) \supset \{[\psi(1) \supset \varphi(1)] \ \& \ [\psi(2) \supset \varphi(2)]\}$$

In a domain of three individuals, however, a wff of this form is invalid, as the following assignment of values shows:

$$\{[\varphi(1) \ \& \ \psi(1)] \lor [\varphi(2) \ \& \ \psi(2)] \lor [\varphi(3) \ \& \ \psi(3)]\}$$
$$\quad\quad 1 \quad\quad\quad 1 \quad\quad\quad 1$$

$$\& \ \{[\varphi(1) \ \& \sim\!\psi(1)] \lor [\varphi(2) \ \& \sim\!\psi(2)] \lor [\varphi(3) \ \& \sim\!\psi(3)]\}$$
$$\quad\quad\quad\quad\quad\quad 1 \quad\quad\quad 1 \quad\quad\quad 1 \quad 0$$

$$\supset \ \{[\psi(1) \supset \varphi(1)] \ \& \ [\psi(2) \supset \varphi(2)] \ \& \ [\psi(3) \supset \varphi(3)]\}$$
$$\quad 1 \quad\quad\quad\quad 0 \quad\quad\quad\quad 0$$

Testing a wff for invalidity in finite domains is often useful in practice, since in many cases invalidity is relatively easy to establish. However, it is evident that failure to establish invalidity in this way does not establish validity, since we cannot test all domains.

The reader has noted that in discussing the metatheory of MPL we have repeatedly dealt with finite domains only. Thus Metatheorem 10.1 establishes the consistency of MPL in the terms of an analysis referring to a domain of but one individual. Similarly, Metatheorem 10.4 establishes that if a wff of MPL is not satisfiable then it is not consistent by an analysis that in fact deals with finite domains—even though the metatheorem actually refers to properties holding in infinite domains as well. The success of these analyses suggests the possibility of an equally successful attack along finite lines upon the problem of the decidability of MPL. In fact, it is possible effectively to determine the validity of a wff of MPL in all non-null domains by an analysis restricted to finite domains. Indeed, we have only to note that since the negation of a valid wff is not satisfiable, and satisfiability can be determined by an analysis of finite domains (as in Metatheorem 10.4), we need test only the negation of the wff we consider for satisfiability: if the negation of a wff is not satisfiable, then the wff is valid. This approach does provide a decision procedure, but in the interests of further insight into the structure of MPL we shall develop a different method.

As has been observed, the clue to the problem of finding a decision process is to reduce the determination of validity to an analysis of a finite domain. In order to simplify our analysis, we restrict our discussion to wffs of MPL without statement variables, called pure wffs.* We introduce the proof by an intuitive consideration of the relation of predicates and individuals in a domain. Any pure wff of MPL contains a number of different predicates that hold or fail to hold of the several individuals in the domain.

---

* More general decision procedures are to be found in L. Löwenheim, "Über Möglichkeiten im Relativkalkül", *Math. Annalen*, Vol. 76 (1915), pp. 447–470; in H. Behmann, "Beiträge zur Algebra der Logik, insbesondere zum Entscheidungsproblem", *Math. Annalen*, Vol. 86 (1922), pp. 163–229; and in W. Ackermann, *Solvable Cases of the Decision Problem* (Amsterdam: North Holland Pub. Co., 1954), pp. 34 ff.

Example: $\prod_x[F(x) \supset G(x)]$ contains two predicates.
$\sum_x[F(x)\ \&\ H(x)]\ \lor\ \prod_x[\sim G(x)]$ contains three predicates.

For any individual in a given domain each predicate will hold or fail to hold, as the case may be. If we assign 1 or 0 in these cases, then where there are m predicates there will be 2^m possible different assignments.

Example: $\sum_x[F(x)\ \&\ G(x)]$. This schema contains two predicates. For any individual each predicate may be assigned 1 or 0—thus there are $2^2 = 4$ different assignments possible.

There will not be more than 2^m different assignments, for no matter how many individuals are considered with reference to the predicates, 2^m exhausts the possibilities. Further, no two assignments can hold of the same individual. However, each different assignment can hold of a (different) individual.

Example: $\sum_x[F(x)\ \&\ H(x)]$. Here the four possible assignments can be arranged in a matrix:

	F	H
(1)	1	1
(2)	0	1
(3)	1	0
(4)	0	0

No additional different assignments are possible. No two of the assignments (1), (2), (3), (4) can hold of the same individual without resulting in a contradiction. Thus, if we assume (1) and (2) hold of a single individual, a, then F(a) & $\sim$F(a) will be true. On the other hand, in a domain of four individuals each of the assignments could hold of one of the four individuals.

We may generalize the discussion of the example. Given a pure wff of MPL with m predicates there are 2^m different assignments only. These cannot hold of the same individual, but each may hold of one of 2^m different individuals. It is therefore sufficient to test the wff for validity in a domain of 2^m individuals, because in such a domain all possible assignments to predicates can occur. Hence, if the wff is m-valid it will be universally valid.

Example: We test the wff of the last example for validity by testing it for 4-validity.

[F(1) & H(1)] $\lor$ [F(2) & H(2)] $\lor$ [F(3) & H(3)] $\lor$ [F(4) & H(4)]

1	1	1	1	
0	1	1	1	
1	0	1	1	
0	0	1	1	etc.
1	1	0	1	
0	1	0	1	
1	0	0	1	
0	0	0	1	

The matrix requires 256 rows when completed. It is evaluated by the usual methods discussed in Chapter Three and in this chapter.

We proceed to establish these results in a formal way.

Metatheorem 10.6: If a pure wff of MPL with m predicates is valid in a domain of at least 2^m individuals, it is valid in every non-null domain.

Proof of Metatheorem 10.6: We assume that a pure wff, Δ, of MPL with m predicate variables is valid in a domain D′ which has at least 2^m individuals. Let D″ be any other domain of more or fewer individuals. We assign 1 or 0 to each of the m predicates of Δ for each of the individuals in D″. There will be at most 2^m such different assignments, for the reasons discussed above.

We group all individuals in D″ corresponding to the same such assignment thus obtaining at most 2^m classes of individuals. We form a domain D made up of one representative from each such class. Thus, D contains at most 2^m individuals, while D″ contains at least as many individuals as D. The domains D and D″ are related as follows:

(1) For each individual in D″ there is one corresponding individual in D, and for each individual in D there are one or more corresponding individuals in D″.

(2) If $\varphi(\alpha)$ is 1 (or 0) for an individual in D, then $\varphi(\alpha)$ is 1 (or 0) respectively, for the corresponding individual or individuals in D″.

Further, the domains D and D′ can be related in the same way by suitable assignments of individuals and definition of predicates, since D′ contains at least as many individuals as D.

(1) For each individual in D′ there is one corresponding individual in D, and for each individual in D there are one or more corresponding individuals in D′.

(2) If $\varphi(\alpha)$ is 1 (or 0) for an individual in D, then $\varphi(\alpha)$ is 1 (or 0) for the corresponding individuals in D′.

For all domains related in this way any pure wff of MPL possesses 1 in one such domain if and only if it possesses 1 in the other. We prove this generalization as a lemma.

Lemma a: A pure wff, Δ, of MPL possesses 1 for a set of values of its individual variables in a domain D* if and only if it possesses 1 in a domain D** containing at least as many individuals as D* under the following conditions.

(1) Each individual in D** corresponds to one individual in D* and each individual in D* corresponds to one or more individuals in D**.

(2) If $\varphi(\alpha)$ is 1 (or 0) for an individual in D*, then $\varphi(\alpha)$ is 1 (or 0) respectively for the corresponding individual or individuals in D**.

We prove this lemma by an induction on the number of occurrences of the connectives of PL and of quantifiers in Δ.

Basis: Suppose there are no connectives of PL and no quantifiers in Δ, then Δ is of the form $\varphi(\alpha)$.

If Δ possesses 1 in D* then a predicate, say φ, will possess 1 in D** because of condition (2).

On the other hand, if we assume Δ possesses 1 in D** but does not possess 1 in D*, its corresponding value in D** will not possess 1, contrary to the assumption; hence, Δ possesses 1 in D*.

Thus, the lemma holds in this case.

Induction Step: We assume that the lemma holds for $n - 1$ or fewer connectives of PL and quantifiers occurring in Δ. We show that it holds for n such occurrences, that is, in the cases where Δ is of the form $\sim\psi$, $\psi \vee \chi$, $\psi \& \chi$, $\psi \supset \chi$, $\psi \equiv \chi$, $\sum_\alpha\psi(\alpha)$, or $\prod_\alpha\psi(\alpha)$.

Case 1: Δ is $\sim\psi$:

If Δ possesses 1 in D** then by PL ψ possesses 0 in D**. Hence, by the hypothesis of the induction ψ possesses 0 in D* and so $\sim\psi$ possesses 1 in D*.

If Δ possesses 1 in D* then by PL ψ possesses 0 in D*. Hence, by the hypothesis of the induction, ψ possesses 0 in D**, and $\sim\psi$ possesses 1.

Case 2: Δ is $\psi \vee \chi$.   Similar proof.

Case 3: Δ is $\psi \supset \chi$.   Similar proof.

Case 4: Δ is $\psi \equiv \chi$.   Similar proof.

Case 5: Δ is $\sum_\alpha\psi(\alpha)$.

If Δ possesses 1 in D** then there is an individual for which $\psi(\alpha)$ possesses 1 in D**. By hypothesis $\psi(\alpha)$ possesses 1 in D*; hence there is an individual in D* making $\psi(\alpha)$ possess 1, and $\sum_\alpha\psi(\alpha)$ therefore possesses 1 in D*.

If Δ possesses 1 in D* then there is an individual for which $\psi(\alpha)$ possesses 1 in D*. By hypothesis $\psi(\alpha)$ possesses 1 in D** for some corresponding individual and so $\sum_\alpha\psi(\alpha)$ possesses 1 in D**.

Case 6. Δ is $\prod_\alpha\psi(\alpha)$. Since $\prod_\alpha\psi(\alpha)$ is equivalent to $\sim\sum_\alpha\sim\psi(\alpha)$ the proof follows the lines of Case 5.

This completes the proof of the lemma.

On the assumption that Δ is valid in D′ it will possess 1 for an arbitrary choice of values of its individual variables in this domain. For corresponding individuals it will also possess 1 in D by Lemma a. And since D is related to D″ as in the lemma, for corresponding individuals Δ will possess 1 in D″. As the choice of values was arbitrary, Δ, if valid in D′, will be valid in D″. This establishes the metatheorem, since D″ is an arbitrary domain.

Metatheorem 10.6 establishes the fact that if a wff of MPL is valid in a domain of at least 2^m individuals it is valid in every non-null domain; hence it is sufficient to test a wff for validity in a finite domain to determine validity. This establishes

Metatheorem 10.7: Any pure wff of MPL is decidable.

EXERCISE 10.5

I. Complete the proof of the induction step of Lemma a.

II. Take the formula $\{\prod_x[F(x) \supset G(x)]\} \supset [\prod_x F(x) \supset \prod_x G(x)]$.
   1. Show that it is *m*-valid.
   2. Show that in a higher domain, it will remain valid, thus illustrating Metatheorem 10.6.

III. Test the following formulas for universal validity.
   1. $\prod_x[F(x) \supset G(x)] \supset [\sum_x F(x) \supset \sum_x G(x)]$
   2. $\prod_x[F(x) \supset G(x)] \supset \{\sum_x[H(x) \supset F(x)] \supset \sum_x[H(x) \supset G(x)]\}$
   3. $\prod_x[F(x) \supset G(x)] \supset \prod_x[\sim G(x) \supset \sim F(x)]$
   4. $\prod_x[F(x) \supset G(x)] \supset \sum_x[G(x) \,\&\, F(x)]$
   5. $[\prod_x F(x) \equiv \prod_x G(x)] \supset \prod[F(x) \equiv G(x)]$

IV. What relationships has the decision procedure developed in this section to the decision procedure for PL?

10.6 Note on Decision Procedures

The decision procedure presented in the last section is effective in the technical sense, but it is not especially practical in use. To select a schema of MPL at random and test it for validity is usually sufficient to convince anyone that the procedure is long and tedious. There have been various attempts made to provide a more practical procedure, but although these attempts are interesting, they have not been more than moderately successful.

Perhaps the most practical procedure was developed by Quine.* His method is to conjoin the premises of an argument and to combine them with the conclusion, using ⊃ ; to negate the resulting schema; and to test the result

---

* *Op. cit.*

for satisfiability by the methods of Section 10.4. In many cases this can be done reasonably briefly.

   Example: Given the inference

$$\prod_x[F(x) \supset G(x)]$$
$$\sum_x[H(x) \mathrel{\&} \sim G(x)]$$
$$\therefore \sum_x[H(x) \mathrel{\&} \sim F(x)]$$

we rewrite as

$$\sim\{\prod_x[F(x) \supset G(x)] \mathrel{\&} \sum_x[H(x) \mathrel{\&} \sim G(x)] \supset \sum_x[H(x) \mathrel{\&} \sim F(x)]\}$$

We reduce this to normal form and determine whether it is satisfiable—if not, the argument is valid.

   Another procedure which is often short enough to be used originated with Behmann* and has been developed by Quine† and von Wright.‡ This procedure begins with the insight that a wff of MPL involving m predicates holds or fails to hold of an individual in a domain in at most 2^m ways, as discussed in Section 10.5. Since a wff of MPL can be reduced to a normal form involving existentially quantified wffs which are disjoined, these at most 2^m ways can be represented in a normal form. Hence, we can test directly by matrix methods. The following example suggests the technique, but reference should be made to von Wright for details.

   Example:

$$\prod_x[F(x) \supset G(x)]$$
$$\sum_x[H(x) \mathrel{\&} \sim G(x)]$$
$$\therefore \sum_x[H(x) \mathrel{\&} \sim F(x)]$$

   Given this inference to decide concerning validity we proceed:

I.   First, rewrite the premises and conclusion, obtaining

$$\sim\sum_x[F(x) \mathrel{\&} \sim G(x)]$$
$$\sum_x[H(x) \mathrel{\&} \sim G(x)]$$
$$\therefore \sum_x [H(x) \mathrel{\&} \sim F(x)]$$

For convenience, we drop the variables and ampersands, and write $\bar{F}$ instead of $\sim F$:

$$\sim\sum F\bar{G}$$
$$\sum H\bar{G}$$
$$\therefore \sum H\bar{F}$$

---

   * *Op. cit.*, see Section Five.
   † W. V. Quine, "On the Logic of Quantification", *Journal of Symbolic Logic*, Vol. 10 (1945), pp. 1–12.
   ‡ G. H. von Wright, *Logical Studies* (London: Routledge and Kegan Paul, 1957), pp. 1–43.

II. Now we conjoin $(H \vee \bar{H})$ to the statement function of the first premise, and $(F \vee \bar{F})$ to that of the second, and $(G \vee \bar{G})$ to that of the conclusion.

$$\sim\!\sum[(F\bar{G}) \,\&\, (H \vee \bar{H})]$$
$$\sum[(H\bar{G}) \,\&\, (F \vee \bar{F})]$$
$$\therefore\ \sum[(H\bar{F}) \,\&\, (G \vee \bar{G})]$$

III. The next step is to "multiply out", using Dist:

$$\sim\!\sum(F\bar{G}H \vee F\bar{G}\bar{H})$$
$$\sum(H\bar{G}F \vee H\bar{G}\bar{F})$$
$$\therefore\ \sum(H\bar{F}G \vee H\bar{F}\bar{G})$$

IV. At this point we make use of

5.9 $\ \vdash \sum_\alpha[\varphi(\alpha) \vee \psi(\alpha)] \equiv [\sum_\alpha\varphi(\alpha) \vee \sum_\alpha\psi(\alpha)]$

to obtain

$$\sim\!(\sum F\bar{G}H \vee \sum F\bar{G}\bar{H})$$
$$\sum H\bar{G}F \vee \sum H\bar{G}\bar{F}$$
$$\therefore\ \sum H\bar{F}G \vee \sum H\bar{F}\bar{G}$$

Now, for convenience, put each triad of letters in alphabetical order (this is justified, of course, by Assoc and CM), and write the deduction out horizontally:

$$\sim\!(\sum F\bar{G}H \vee \sum F\bar{G}\bar{H}) \,\&\, (\sum F\bar{G}H \vee \sum \bar{F}\bar{G}H)\ \ /\therefore\ (\sum \bar{F}GH \vee \sum \bar{F}\bar{G}H)$$

Now count each triad together with the initial $\sum$ as an atomic statement, and use the method of assigning truth-values to test the soundness of the deduction:

V. $\ \sim\!(\sum F\bar{G}H \vee \sum F\bar{G}\bar{H}) \,\&\, (\sum F\bar{G}H \vee \sum \bar{F}\bar{G}H)\ \ /\therefore\ (\sum \bar{F}GH \vee \sum \bar{F}\bar{G}H)$
    $\ \ \ 0\ \ \ \ 1 \qquad\qquad\qquad\quad 1 \qquad\quad 0 \quad\ S \quad\ \ 0 \qquad\quad 0$

Only the values essential to the decision that this deduction is sound have been assigned here, but in making this assignment we have taken into account the assignment to each predicate.

Although the method is not general, if we take advantage of Löwenheim's theorem (to be proved in Chapter Eleven) that a wff of GPL-1 (and so also of MPL) is valid if it is valid in the denumerably infinite domain, we can often determine validity by an inductive method. That is, we establish validity of a wff in a domain of one individual and show that if the wff is k-valid it will be $k + 1$ valid. Thus, the wff is valid in the denumerably infinite domain and by Löwenheim's theorem in all domains.

Example: Given the wff $\prod_x[F(x) \vee G(x)] \supset [\prod_x F(x) \vee \prod_x G(x)]$. In a domain of one individual this is readily evaluated to possess I. In a domain of k individuals we have

$$\{[F(1) \vee G(1)] \, \& \, \ldots \, \& \, [F(k) \vee G(k)]\} \supset \{[F(1) \, \& \, \ldots \, \&$$
$$F(k)] \vee [G(1) \, \& \, \ldots \, \& \, G(k)]\}$$

We let the antecedent be Γ and the consequent Δ.
We assume as hypothesis of the induction that $\Gamma \supset \Delta$. We prove that

$$(\Gamma \supset \Delta) \supset (\{\Gamma \, \& \, [F(k+1) \vee G(k+1)]\} \supset \{\Delta \, \&$$
$$[F(k+1) \vee G(k+1)]\})$$

Since this is a propositional statement, it can be evaluated by means of truth tables.

EXERCISE 10.6

I. Test the formulas 1, 2, and 5 of Exercise III, Section 10.5, by Quine's method of negation.

II. Test the formulas 3, 4, and 5 of Exercise III, Section 10.5, by the method originated by Behmann.

III. Give an instance to which the inductive "method" of decision does not apply. That is, show by a counter-example that it is not a decision method.

SUGGESTED READINGS

1. A. Church, *Introduction to Mathematical Logic* (Princeton, N.J.: Princeton Univ. Press, 1956), Chs. III, IV.

2. I. M. Copi, *Symbolic Logic* (New York: The Macmillan Co., 1954), Ch. IX.

3. S. C. Kleene, *Introduction to Metamathematics* (Amsterdam: North Holland Pub. Co., 1952), Ch. VII.

4. W. V. Quine, *Methods of Logic*, rev. ed. (New York: Holt, Rinehart and Winston, Inc., 1959), Part. II.

5. G. H. von Wright, *Logical Studies* (London: Routledge & Kegan Paul, 1957), pp. 22–43.

Chapter 11

Aspects of the Metatheory of General Predicate Logic

11.1 The Formal System of GPL-1

In this chapter we continue the discussion of metatheory begun in Chapter Nine. We extend our results to include some metatheorems of GPL-1, and demonstrate these metatheorems by reasoning about the formal system of GPL-1. Hence, we begin by extending the formal system of PL to GPL-1. Since this extension is analogous to that for MPL in Chapter Ten, it will be stated briefly.

SYMBOLS

The symbols of GPL-1 are

$$A, B, C, A_1, B_1, C_1, A_2, \ldots$$
$$F, G, H, F_1, G_1, H_1, F_2, \ldots$$
$$F^2, G^2, H^2, F_1^2, G_1^2, H_1^2, F_2^2, \ldots$$
$$\vdots$$
$$F^n, G^n, H^n, F_1^n, G_1^n, H_1^n, F_2^n, \ldots$$
$$\&, \supset, \mathbf{v}, \sim, \equiv, (\,,)$$
$$\Sigma, \Pi$$
$$x_1, x_2, x_3, \ldots$$

The symbols $F^k, G^k, H^k, \ldots$ are to be dissociated from their interpretation as k-place predicates, just as the other symbols are to be dissociated from the meanings they ordinarily have in GPL-1.

FORMULAS

We call the strings of symbols that are acceptable in GPL-1 *well-formed formulas*. These wffs satisfy the following criteria:

(1) A, B, C, A_1, B_1, C_1, ... are wffs. $F^k(x_1 \ldots x_k)$, $G^k(x_1 \ldots x_k)$, $H^k(x_1 \ldots x_k)$, ... are wffs.
(2) If α is an individual variable and $\varphi(\alpha)$ is a wff, then $\prod_\alpha[\varphi(\alpha)]$ and $\sum_\alpha[\varphi(\alpha)]$ are wffs.
(3) If φ and ψ are wffs, then so are $(\varphi \supset \psi)$, $(\varphi \ \& \ \psi)$, $(\varphi \lor \psi)$, and $(\varphi \equiv \psi)$. If φ is a wff, so is $\sim\varphi$.
(4) Nothing else is a wff.

TRANSFORMATIONS

We recognize the patterns of the rules of PL as stated in Chapter Nine, and those of $\prod$E, $\prod$I, $\sum$E', and $\sum$I, as transformations.

SEQUENCES

We designate deductions and distinguish them from unsound chains of inferences by rewriting the conditions of deductions A–D as in Chapters Nine and Ten, and by extending the conditions to include the wffs and transformations of GPL-1. This is left to the reader. We designate the lines admitted in a sequence of GPL-1 as A+, B+, C+, and D+.

FINISHED SEQUENCES

A finished sequence is one in which there are no A+ lines.
We now proceed to study the formal system of GPL-1 and to establish some of its properties, that is, to prove some metatheorems of GPL-1.

EXERCISE 11.1

I. Rewrite the conditions of deduction for GPL-1, that is, state A+–D+.

11.2 *k*-Validity and Consistency

Although the labor involved is often greater than in the case of MPL, it is possible to evaluate a wff of GPL-1 in any finite domain and so determine its *k*-validity. The method of evaluation in these cases is the same as that given in Chapter Ten, Section Two. We consider, for example, the dyadic wff $\prod_x\prod_y R(x,y) \supset \sum_x\sum_y R(x,y)$. In a domain of two individuals, $R(x,y)$ can have 4 (*i.e.*, 2^2) values depending on the individuals of the domain (*i.e.*, $R(1,1)$,

R(2,2), R(1,2), R(2,1)). Each of these in turn has the values 1 and 0 as a possibility; thus, 16 truth-value assignments are required to evaluate this formula, as follows:

[R(1,1) & R(2,2) & R(1,2) & R(2,1)] ⊃ [R(1,1) v R(2,2) v R(1,2) v R(2,1)]

1	1	1	1	1	1	1	1	1
1	1	1	0	1	1	1	1	0
1	1	0	1	1	1	1	0	1
1	1	0	0	1	1	1	0	0
1	0	1	1	1	1	0	1	1
1	0	1	0	1	1	0	1	0
1	0	0	1	1	1	0	0	1
1	0	0	0	1	1	0	0	0
0	1	1	1	1	0	1	1	1
0	1	1	0	1	0	1	1	0
0	1	0	1	1	0	1	0	1
0	1	0	0	1	0	1	0	0
0	0	1	1	1	0	0	1	1
0	0	1	0	1	0	0	1	0
0	0	0	1	1	0	0	0	1
0	0	0	0	1	0	0	0	0

Notice that as with MPL, we take $\prod$ to refer to a conjunction and $\sum$ to refer to a disjunction. Thus $\prod_x \prod_y R(x,y)$ becomes

$$\prod_x [R(x,1) \ \& \ R(x,2)]$$

and then

$$R(1,1) \ \& \ R(2,1) \ \& \ R(1,2) \ \& \ R(2,2)$$

We assign values to ⊃, &, v, ≡, and ∼ in the same way as in PL and MPL.

The technique illustrated can be extended to any wff and to any finite domain. Any wff of GPL-1 may contain statement variables, predicate variables, and individual variables. The statement variables possess 1 or 0, as they do in PL. A predicate with n individual variables represents a statement function with n variables. In consequence, it possesses 1 or 0 for each of the possible values. There are, in a domain of k individuals, k^n such instances and so 2^{k^n} assignments of 1 or 0.

In the example above, the dyadic predicate in R(x,y) requires 2^{2^2} assignments of 1 or 0 in a domain of two individuals. The triadic predicate in R(x,y,z) requires 2^{3^3} assignments of 1 or 0 in a domain of three individuals.

We assign 1 or 0 to the logical connectives of PL on the basis of the matrices given in Chapter Nine. We assign 1 to $\prod_x F(x)$ if $F(x)$ has the assignment 1 for every value of x in the domain and otherwise we assign 0. We assign 1 to $\sum_x F(x)$ if $F(x)$ has the assignment 1 for some value of x in the domain and otherwise we assign 0.

Using these procedures we may evaluate any wff of GPL-1 in a finite domain and determine its k-validity.

k-Validity: A wff of GPL-1 is said to be k-valid when it evaluates to 1 identically upon the assignment of 1 and 0 to its atomic elements, as described above in a domain of k individuals.

We shall now prove that a wff of the form $\psi \ \& \sim\psi$ cannot be the last line of a finished sequence, that is, a D⁺ line, so that GPL-1 is consistent. The proof is analogous to that given for the consistency of MPL in Chapter Ten. It depends upon the fact that a wff of the form of $\psi \ \& \sim\psi$ cannot possess 1 in any domain, whereas every D⁺ line possesses 1 in a domain of one individual.

Metatheorem 11.1: $\psi \ \& \sim\psi$ cannot be a D⁺ line.

We establish this metatheorem as for PL and MPL with the aid of three lemmas. We follow the proofs of Metatheorems 9.1 and 10.1 and assume analogous definitions.

Lemma a: The uses of $\supset$ I in any finished sequence in which the B⁺ lines possess 1 simultaneously transmit this property to the last line of the finished sequence.

Lemma b: The last line of any finished sequence including B⁺ lines is 1-valid; and any line of any finished sequence lacking B⁺ lines is 1-valid.

Lemma c: A wff of the form $\psi \ \& \sim\psi$ is not 1-valid.

The proofs of these lemmas, and of the metatheorem, are similar to that for Metatheorem 10.1, so that they are left to the reader to formulate explicitly. We observe only that the proof deals with wffs containing n individual variables. Thus, in Lemma a, when we show that $\prod$E transmits 1, we reason as follows:

$\prod$E: Let a wff of the form $\prod_{\alpha_n}\prod_{\alpha_{n-1}} \cdots \prod_{\alpha_1} \varphi(\alpha_n, \alpha_{n-1}, \ldots, \alpha_1)$ possess 1 in a domain of one individual. This means that $\varphi(1, 1, \ldots, 1)$ possesses 1. Thus, $\varphi(\beta)$ possesses 1 since $\varphi(\beta)$ is $\varphi(1, 1, \ldots, 1)$.

EXERCISE 11.2

I. Evaluate the following wffs in the indicated domains.

1. $\prod_x\sum_y\{[A \supset F(x,y)] \vee [\sim F(x,y) \ \& \ A]\}$ 1-domain, 3-domain

2. $\prod_x\prod_y\{[A \supset F(x,y)] \vee [\sim F(x,y) \ \& \ A]\}$ 0-domain, 3-domain

3. $\prod_x\prod_y[H(x,y)] \equiv \prod_y\prod_x[H(x,y)]$ 1-domain, 2-domain

II. Write a wff illustrating the case 2^{k^n} where $n = 0$.

III. State the proof of Metatheorem 11.1 in full. Explain carefully why it is necessary to consider only the 1-domain.

11.3 Infinite Domains and the Metatheory of GPL-1

The metatheory of GPL-1 is somewhat more complicated than any so far discussed. However, we may establish without especial difficulty

Metatheorem 11.2: Every D^+ line of GPL-1 is universally valid.

Indeed, the proof of this metatheorem is so similar to that of Metatheorem 10.2 that its explicit formulation is left to the reader. We observe only that universal validity is validity in every non-null domain and that the reasoning used, as in Metatheorem 10.2, involves the application of the law of excluded middle to infinite domains. This reasoning is thus stronger than that used to prove the consistency of PL.

In the case of PL, the admission of any schema not universally valid as a rule results in inconsistency, as was proved in Metatheorem 9.3. In the case of GPL-1, however, we can see from Metatheorem 11.1 that as long as the invalid schema we add as a rule is 1-valid, the system remains consistent. Thus, for example, if we take $\sum_\alpha \varphi(\alpha) \supset \prod_\beta \varphi(\beta)$ (which is clearly 1-valid) as a rule, we shall not be able to deduce any line of the form $\psi \mathbin{\&} \sim\!\psi$. The existence of wffs of GPL-1 which, although not universally valid, are yet 1-valid permits the acceptance of these schemata as ZPC's without destroying the consistency of the system. Of course, the same is true for MPL as well. To accept a schema as a ZPC is to add it to the system in the form, for example, of

$$\vdash \sum_\alpha \varphi(\alpha) \supset \prod_\beta \varphi(\beta)$$

Metatheorem 9.3 places a restriction on the nature of the ZPC's that can be added to PL. There is greater flexibility with respect to the rules of GPL-1, where we may certainly introduce as a rule any schema that is 1-valid. Thus, we may introduce $\vdash \prod_\alpha \prod_\beta [\varphi(\alpha,\beta) \supset \varphi(\beta,\alpha)]$ as a ZPC. To do so means that we restrict the interpretation of GPL-1 plus this rule to the domain of one individual, since this schema is 1-valid only. We might add the schema

$$\vdash \sum_\alpha \sum_\beta \{\varphi(\alpha) \mathbin{\&} \varphi(\beta) \mathbin{\&} \prod_\gamma [\varphi(\gamma) \supset (\gamma = \alpha \mathbin{\vee} \gamma = \beta)]\}$$

to GPL-1, thus restricting the interpretation to domains of at most two individuals. If we add as a schema to GPL-1 a schema that is k-valid for $k \leq n$, we restrict the interpretation to domains of n or fewer individuals. In all such systems the definition of universal validity is changed to mean validity in all non-null domains of n or fewer individuals.

The proofs of Metatheorems 11.1 and 11.2 might suggest that there is really little difference between MPL and GPL-1. It would be a mistake to assume this. A very significant difference occurs in the fact that for MPL a wff that is k-valid for every finite k is valid in the denumerably infinite domain (and all nondenumerably infinite domains as well), whereas a formula of GPL-1 is not necessarily valid under the same conditions. The proof of this property of MPL was given in Metatheorem 10.6, where it was shown that a wff of MPL with k predicates, which is valid in a domain of at least 2^k individuals, is universally valid.

In GPL-1, however, this is not the case. An example of a wff that, while valid in all finite domains, is invalid—that is, possesses 0 for some assignment of values—in an infinite domain is the schema

$$\Gamma: \sim\{\textstyle\prod_\alpha\sum_\beta\varphi(\alpha,\beta) \mathbin{\&} \prod_\alpha\sim\varphi(\alpha,\alpha) \mathbin{\&} \prod_\alpha\prod_\beta\prod_\gamma[\varphi(\alpha,\beta) \mathbin{\&} \varphi(\beta,\gamma) \supset \varphi(\alpha,\gamma)]\}.$$

If we interpret the relation φ as $<$ in the usual arithmetical sense of "less than", an interpretation of the schema Γ becomes clear. It is, in fact, a negation of a conjunction of axioms, describing the order relation $<$ in a domain of natural numbers. The conjuncts state, first, that there is no greatest number; second, that no number is less than itself; and third, that the relation $<$ is transitive.*

A wff of the form of Γ is valid in any finite domain because of the first conjunct, $\prod_\alpha\sum_\beta\varphi(\alpha,\beta)$, which states that there is no greatest number. This is false in any finite domain; hence the negation of its conjunction with any other statements is valid in any finite domain. On the other hand, since $\prod_\alpha\sum_\beta\varphi(\alpha,\beta)$ is satisfiable in the denumerably infinite domain of the natural numbers, as are the other two conjuncts as well, the negation of Γ will not be valid in this domain. Thus, although Γ is valid in all finite domains, it is invalid in the denumerably infinite domain.

In consequence, a wff of the form of $\sim\Gamma$ is valid in infinite domains only. If $\sim\Gamma$ is added as a ZPC to GPL-1 it restricts the interpretation of GPL-1 to infinite domains and requires redefinition of validity to mean validity in all infinite domains. This is often quite useful, since it permits the study of infinite domains as such.

When an *axiom schema of infinity*, as such a ZPC is called, is added to GPL-1 for the purposes of obtaining a system dealing with truths about infinite domains, certain complications are introduced into the metatheory as well. First, the consistency proof given in Metatheorem 11.1 cannot be used in the case of such systems. Clearly the theorems of these systems are not 1-valid and the proof fails. It might be supposed that some other technique of proof would be open to us. However, if we insist that the methods of a consistency proof should be limited to those of intuitive arithmetic, no

---

* The second and third of these conjuncts appear in the form of Ax. 1 and Ax. 2 of the system of simple order given in Chapter One, Section Two.

proof is available. Gödel has shown that the reasoning used in a consistency proof of this sort must be more complex than that of intuitive arithmetic. Our concern in this book is not with these problems, but only with the metatheory of GPL-1 as such. We turn in the next sections to a proof of the completeness of GPL-1.

EXERCISE 11.3

I. State the proof of Metatheorem 11.2 in full. Explain carefully where and to what extent stronger reasoning is required than is needed for the analogous metatheorems about PL.

II. Discuss the interpretation of GPL-1 plus each of the following schemata taken as ZPC's.

1. $\prod_\alpha \sum_\beta \prod_\gamma \{ [\varphi(\gamma,\alpha) \supset \varphi(\gamma,\beta)] \ \& \ [\sim\varphi(\alpha,\alpha) \ \& \ \varphi(\alpha,\beta)] \}$

2. $\prod_\alpha \sum_\beta (\varphi(\alpha,\beta) \ \& \ \prod_\alpha \prod_\beta \{ \varphi(\alpha,\beta) \supset \prod_\gamma [\varphi(\alpha,\gamma) \supset (\beta = \gamma)] \}$
  $\& \ \prod_\alpha \prod_\beta \{ \varphi(\beta,\alpha) \supset \prod_\gamma [\varphi(\gamma,\alpha) \supset (\beta = \gamma)] \} \ \& \ \sum_\alpha \prod_\beta \sim\varphi(\beta,\alpha))$

3. $\prod_\alpha \sum_\beta (\varphi(\alpha,\beta) \ \& \ \prod_\alpha \prod_\beta \{ \varphi(\beta,\alpha) \supset \prod_\gamma [\varphi(\gamma,\alpha) \supset (\beta = \gamma)] \}$
  $\& \ \sum_\alpha \prod_\beta \sim\varphi(\beta,\alpha))$

III. **1.** Select a valid wff of GPL-1. Express it in terms of a 2-domain. Show that the result is deducible in PL; that is, construct a deduction.

2. Show that the expression of a valid wff of GPL-1 in a k-domain gives a result that is deducible in PL.

11.4   Completeness of GPL-1: Preliminary Concepts

We wish to establish the fact that every valid schema is a D^+ line; that is, that every valid schema is deducible. Since we have already established the fact that every D^+ line is valid, this fact will prove that GPL-1 is complete; that validity and deducibility are equivalent. The situation is somewhat complex and we prepare the ground for the proof by introducing in this section some essential facts. These could be introduced as lemmas for the metatheorems of Section 11.5, but they are interesting in their own right and are perhaps more simply treated independently.

ENUMERATION OF WFFS

Whenever we have used an inductive proof, we have ordered the wffs of the system under discussion in some way. Frequently this way has been by counting the number of logical connectives in the formula. It is interesting to note that all the wffs of GPL-1 as such can be enumerated. One method of enumerating them is as follows.

First, we enumerate the symbols of GPL-1:

$$(\quad \lor \quad \& \quad) \quad \sim \quad \equiv \quad \supset \quad \Pi \quad \Sigma$$
$$1 \quad 2 \quad 3 \quad 4 \quad 5 \quad 6 \quad 7 \quad 8 \quad 9$$

These are all the symbols we need for the expression of a wff. After these symbols we list the individual variables

$$(1) \quad x_1, x_2, x_3, \ldots$$

the statement symbols

$$(2) \quad A, B, C, A_1, B_1, C_1, A_2, \ldots$$

the monadic predicate symbols

$$(3) \quad F, G, H, F_1, G_1, H_1, F_2, \ldots$$

the dyadic predicate symbols

$$(4) \quad F^2, G^2, H^2, F_1^2, G_1^2, H_1^2, F_2^2, \ldots$$

the triadic predicate symbols

$$(5) \quad F^3, G^3, H^3, F_1^3, G_1^3, H_1^3, F_2^3, \ldots$$

and so on to m-adic predicate variables.

We do not count these directly. In fact we approach their enumeration quite obliquely. We begin by enumerating ordered pairs,* $\langle i\,j \rangle$ where i, j take integral values as follows: $\langle k\,l \rangle$ precedes $\langle m\,n \rangle$ if $(k + l) < (m + n)$; where $(k + l) = (m + n)$, $\langle k\,l \rangle$ precedes $\langle m\,n \rangle$ if $k < m$; where $k = m$, $\langle k\,l \rangle$ precedes $\langle m\,n \rangle$ if $l < n$.

This enumerative procedure is also illustrated by the following diagram.

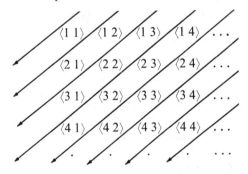

Here the ordered pairs, $\langle i\,j \rangle$, are enumerated along each arrow. When the head of any given arrow is reached, the following pair is to be found at the

---

* The concept of an ordered pair is taken as an undefined term in this chapter. The concept is defined in Chapter Twelve, Section Six.

tail of the next. Any designated pair can, of course, be reached through a suitable extension of the diagram.

Thus we enumerate ordered pairs as follows:

$$\text{(I)}\quad \langle 1\ 1\rangle,\ \langle 1\ 2\rangle,\ \langle 2\ 1\rangle,\ \langle 1\ 3\rangle,\ \langle 2\ 2\rangle,\ \langle 3\ 1\rangle,\ \langle 1\ 4\rangle, \ldots$$

We are able to enumerate ordered pairs, triads, tetrads, and so on, to ordered m-ads by the same methods as used for ordered pairs. Thus, we enumerate ordered triads,

$$\langle 1\ 1\ 1\rangle,\ \langle 1\ 1\ 2\rangle,\ \langle 1\ 2\ 1\rangle,\ \langle 2\ 1\ 1\rangle, \ldots,$$

the ordered tetrads,

$$\langle 1\ 1\ 1\ 1\rangle,\ \langle 1\ 1\ 1\ 2\rangle,\ \langle 1\ 1\ 2\ 1\rangle,\ \langle 1\ 2\ 1\ 1\rangle, \ldots,$$

etc. The rules for ordering are generalizations of those given for ordered pairs. Thus, if we consider two m-tuples, $\langle i_1 \ldots i_m\rangle$ and $\langle j_1 \ldots j_m\rangle$, then $\langle i_1 \ldots i_m\rangle < \langle j_1 \ldots j_m\rangle$ if $i_1 + i_2 + \ldots + i_m < j_1 + j_2 + \ldots + j_m$. If the sums are equal and $i_1 = j_1, i_2 = j_2, \ldots, i_k = j_k, i_{k+1} < j_{k+1}$ then $\langle i_1 \ldots i_m\rangle < \langle j_1 \ldots j_m\rangle$.

We let (II) stand for an enumeration of triads, tetrads, etc.

$$\text{(II)}\quad \langle 1\ 1\ 1\rangle,\ \langle 1\ 1\ 2\rangle,\ \langle 1\ 2\ 1\rangle, \ldots$$
$$\langle 1\ 1\ 1\ 1\rangle,\ \langle 1\ 1\ 1\ 2\rangle,\ \langle 1\ 1\ 2\ 1\rangle, \ldots$$
$$\langle 1\ 1\ 1\ 1\ 1\rangle, \ldots$$
$$\vdots$$

Each of the ordered pairs in (I) that begins with a 1, as the first, the second, the fourth, the seventh, etc., refers to an individual variable. In fact, we specify that $\langle 1, m\rangle$ refers to the mth individual variable in (1) on p. 350. Each of the ordered pairs in (I) that begins with a 2, as the third and the fifth, refers to a statement symbol. In fact, we specify that $\langle 2, m\rangle$ refers to the mth statement symbol in (2) on p. 350. Each of the ordered pairs in (I) that begins with a 3, as the sixth, refers to a monadic predicate symbol, and so on.

Example: $\langle 1\ 4\rangle$ refers to x_4; $\langle 3\ 1\rangle$ refers to F; $\langle 4\ 3\rangle$ refers to H².

We now count the symbols in (1), (2), (3), ... as follows. We assign to each symbol the number obtained by adding 9 to the number of the position of the ordered pair in (I).

Example: x_4 has the number $9 + 7 = 16$, since $\langle 1\ 4\rangle$ is the seventh ordered pair; F has the number $9 + 6 = 15$, since $\langle 3\ 1\rangle$ is the sixth ordered pair.

The number 9 enters because there are an initial nine symbols. We are able to enumerate all symbols of GPL-1 by this method and can refer to them by number.

Referring now to the ordered m-tuples of (II), we count the symbol combinations of GPL-1 (which include wffs, of course) as follows. The kth symbol combination in GPL-1 is found by picking the kth ordered pair in (I). Suppose the kth ordered pair is $\langle l\ m \rangle$. Then we turn to the ordered m-tuples and pick the lth one. Suppose the lth m-tuple is $\langle l_1\ l_2\ l_3 \ldots l_m \rangle$ where each l_1 is a positive number. We select the l_{1st} symbol in our ordered symbols, and follow it by the l_{2nd}, then the l_{3rd}, and so on. The result of arranging these symbols will be a symbol combination. All such symbol combinations include the wffs of GPL-1, and so a list of them is an enumeration of these wffs, if we delete the symbols that are not wffs.

> *Example:*   Let us determine the third symbol combination. We select the third ordered pair in (I). This is $\langle 2\ 1 \rangle$. We now turn to the ordered 1-tuples and pick the second one, that is, $\langle 2 \rangle$. We thus pick the second symbol, which is **v**. Thus, **v** is the third symbol combination, which we see is not a wff.
>
> Similarly, to get the seventh symbol combination we select $\langle 1\ 4 \rangle$ from (I). We now turn to the ordered quadruples and pick the first one, that is, $\langle 1\ 1\ 1\ 1 \rangle$. We thus pick the first symbol, which is (, and follow it by this symbol three times. Thus, ((((is the seventh symbol combination. And so on.

MAXIMAL CONSISTENT CLASSES

The proof of completeness that we shall give in Section 11.5, like that given in Metatheorem 10.4 for MPL, depends upon demonstrating that if a wff is consistent then it is satisfiable. Because we cannot reduce the wffs of GPL-1 to certain normal forms, each of which can be examined for satisfiability and consistency, we shall wish to consider all consistent wffs. And in order to do this, we will need to be concerned with the *maximal consistent class* of wffs of GPL-1. We now show how to construct such a class.

In Chapter Ten we defined the inconsistency of a wff to mean that a wff of the form $\psi\ \&\ \sim\psi$ could be deduced from it. We shall now extend this definition to a class of wffs. In addition, we shall define a maximal consistent class.

Inconsistency of a Class of wffs (Consistency):   A class of wffs is said to be inconsistent if there is a finite number of them, say $\varphi_1 \ldots \varphi_k$ such that a deduction can be found with $\psi\ \&\ \sim\psi$ as a line in it. Otherwise the class is consistent.

Maximal Consistent Class of wffs: A maximal consistent class of wffs contains an initially selected consistent class of wffs, and each and every other wff of the formal system that is consistent with the wffs in the maximal consistent class is a member of it.

We now show how to construct a maximal consistent class out of the wffs of GPL-1. First we enumerate the wffs, using the methods just described. Thus, we can refer to the first wff of GPL-1, the second wff, and so on, since for every wff there is a corresponding positive integer. Next we select an arbitrary consistent class of wffs of GPL-1. We call this class, Λ. Taking the class $\Lambda = \Gamma^0$ we add to it the first wff of GPL-1, if this is consistent with the wffs in Λ, to form the consistent class $\Gamma^1 = \{\Lambda, \text{wff}_1\}$. If the first wff of GPL-1 is not consistent with Λ, $\Gamma^1 = \Gamma^0$. To Γ^1 we add the second wff of GPL-1, if this is consistent with the wffs in Γ^1, to form the consistent class $\Gamma^2 = \{\Gamma^1, \text{wff}_2\}$. If the second wff of GPL-1 is not consistent with Γ^1, $\Gamma^2 = \Gamma^1$. In general, to Γ^{n-1} we add the nth wff of GPL-1, if this is consistent with the wffs in Γ^{n-1}, to form the consistent class Γ^n. If the nth wff of GPL-1 is not consistent with Γ^{n-1}, $\Gamma^n = \Gamma^{n-1}$.

Metatheorem 11.3:   The classes Γ^0, Γ^1, . . . are consistent.

Proof: By mathematical induction. *Basis:* Γ^0 is consistent since $\Gamma^0 = \Lambda$ and Λ was chosen as consistent. *Induction step:* Assume Γ^{n-1} is consistent; then Γ^n is consistent because of the method of construction.

Now let Γ be the union of the classes Γ^0, Γ^1, ... This means that a wff of GPL-1 is a member of Γ if and only if it is a member of some Γ^n.

Metatheorem 11.4: Γ is a maximal consistent class of GPL-1.

Proof: We first show that Γ is consistent. Assume that Γ is inconsistent; then there are wffs of GPL-1, say $\varphi_1 \ldots \varphi_k$, such that $\psi \,\&\, \sim\!\psi$ is deducible from them. But φ_1 is the lth wff of GPL-1, φ_2 the nth, and so on. Let m be the greatest of these integers; then by the manner of construction, Γ^m is inconsistent, contradicting the assumption that Γ is the union of consistent classes.

We now show that Γ is maximal. Select an arbitrary wff, say wff_n, of GPL-1 that is consistent with Γ. Wff_n is consistent with Γ^{n-1} since it is consistent with Γ. Hence, wff_n is included in Γ^n and so in Γ. Since wff_n is arbitrary, all consistent wffs are included in Γ.

SIMULTANEOUS SATISFIABILITY

In Chapter Ten we defined the satisfiability of a wff to mean that it possessed 1 for some assignment of values to its elementary constituents. We need to extend the concept of satisfiability so that it will apply to a class of wffs—for the purposes of the next section. This is readily done.

Simultaneous Satisfiability in a Domain: A class of wffs is simultaneously satisfied if for some assignment of values in the domain each wff of the class possesses 1.

APPLIED LOGICS

In Chapter Seven, Section One, we referred to the development of the theory of identity made possible by the addition of the relational constant $=$ to GPL-1. This addition of $=$ serves to introduce a specific binary relation having the properties of reflexivity, symmetry, and transitivity. Other such constants might also be introduced to serve particular purposes. Whenever predicate constants, individual constants, or statement constants are added to GPL-1, we say that the system is *applied*. Similarly, if we added statement constants to PL, we would say that the resulting system was applied.

Applied GPL-1:   The system GPL-1 is said to be an applied system when statement constants, individual constants, or predicate constants have been added to it.

The case of an applied system that will interest us in the next section is one in which an infinity of individual constants is added to GPL-1.

Example: In GPL-1 we have the individual variables x_1, x_2, x_3, ... We get an applied logic by adding u_1, u_2, u_3, . . . , where these are an infinity of individuals. This addition permits us to form such wffs as $F(u_1)$, $G(u_1u_2)$, etc. These wffs possess 1 or 0, depending upon whether the predicate holds of the individual or individuals in question.

EXERCISE 11.4

  I. Show how to enumerate the following sets by using ordered pairs.
     1. The rational numbers
     2. The even integers
     3. The wffs of PL
     4. The wffs of MPL

 II. Enumerate the following without using ordered pairs.
     1. The rational numbers
     2. The integers (positive and negative)

III. Select an initial class of consistent wffs of PL and show how to form a maximal consistent class. Do the same for GPL-1.

IV. 1. Which wffs of PL are simultaneously satisfiable by a truth table?
     2. Which wffs of MPL are simultaneously satisfiable in a domain of one individual?

 V. An applied logic need not be based upon GPL-1. Consider the applied logic constructed of the rules of GPL-1, but containing only two predicate constants, $+(x,y,z)$ and $\cdot (x,y,z)$. This system is to contain no statements, that is, none of A, B, C, . . . , nor does it contain any predicates or individual constants. Determine for this system, if the individual variables take the natural numbers 0, 1, 2 . . . as values, the conditions under which a wff is satisfied.

11.5   Completeness of GPL-1: Proof

The proof of completeness we shall give here we owe to Henkin.* The core of this proof is the demonstration that if a class of wffs is consistent then it is satisfiable in an enumerably infinite domain. We shall show how this leads to completeness at the end of this section. We begin by establishing the core.

Metatheorem 11.4:   If a class of wffs of GPL-1 is consistent, then it is simultaneously satisfiable in an enumerably infinite domain.

We establish this fact by selecting an initial arbitrary class of wffs of GPL-1 without free variables and constructing from this a maximal consistent class of wffs in such a way as to show that the maximal consistent class (and so the initial class) is satisfiable. Since we begin with an arbitrary class, we may conclude that any consistent class of wffs is satisfiable.

In Section 11.4 we showed how to construct a maximal consistent class by adding wffs to an initially selected class. This technique will serve us again. However, we must ensure now that the maximal consistent class we construct is always satisfiable by including in it exactly those wffs which give this result. What wffs are these? In particular, these wffs are the result of substituting an enumerable infinity of individual constants for the variables in wffs of the form $\sum_\alpha \psi(\alpha)$, as we shall show.

Proof of Metatheorem: I. *Construction of a maximal consistent class,* Γ_ω, *which contains the result of substituting individual constants for variables in the wffs of the form* $\sum_\alpha \psi(\alpha)$.

We select an arbitrary class of consistent wffs without free variables, Λ, from GPL-1. From Λ we construct a maximal consistent class of the wffs of GPL-1, Γ, using the methods of Section 11.4. We call Γ, $\Gamma_0{}^0$.

We add to the symbols of GPL-1 an enumerable infinity of individual constants, which we designate as

$$u_{00}, \ u_{10}, \ u_{20}, \ \ldots$$

The resulting applied system we call GPL-1_1. Using the methods of Section 11.4, we enumerate these wffs.

If the first wff of GPL-1_1 is of the form $\sum_\alpha \psi(\alpha)$ and is a member of $\Gamma_0{}^0$, we add the wff $\psi(u_{00})$ to $\Gamma_0{}^0$ to form the class $\Gamma_0{}^1$; otherwise $\Gamma_0{}^1$ is $\Gamma_0{}^0$. Similarly, if the $m + 1^{st}$ wff of GPL-1_1 is of the form $\sum_\alpha \psi(\alpha)$ and is a member of $\Gamma_0{}^0$, we add the wff $\psi(u_{m0})$ to $\Gamma_0{}^m$ to form the class Γ_0^{m+1}; otherwise Γ_0^{m+1} is $\Gamma_0{}^m$.

---

* Leon Henkin, "The Completeness of the First-Order Functional Calculus", *Journal of Symbolic Logic*, Vol. 14 (1949), pp. 159–166.

The union of the classes $\Gamma_0{}^0$, $\Gamma_0{}^1$, $\Gamma_0{}^2$, ... is called $\Gamma_1{}^0$, and is a maximal consistent class of the wffs of GPL-1. We first show by induction that $\Gamma_1{}^0$ is consistent.

Basis: $\Gamma_0{}^0$ is consistent by the method of its construction.

Induction Step: Assume that $\Gamma_0{}^m$ is consistent. If Γ_0^{m+1} were inconsistent then the following deduction would exist, since Γ_0^{m+1} must then contain $\psi(u_{m0})$.

$$
\begin{array}{ll}
\text{1.} & \Gamma_0{}^m \\
\text{2.} & \psi(u_{m0}) \\
\;\;\vdots & \\
k. & \varphi \;\&\; \sim\!\varphi \\
\end{array}
$$

$$
\begin{array}{lll}
(k+1). & \sim\!\psi(u_{m0}) & 2-k,\;\sim\!\text{I} \\
(k+2). & \prod_\alpha \sim\!\psi(\alpha) & k+1,\;\prod\text{I (Note: } u_{m0} \text{ does not} \\
 & & \text{occur free in any premise)} \\
(k+3). & \sim\!\sum_\alpha \psi(\alpha) & k+2,\;\text{QEq} \\
\end{array}
$$

Here line (1) represents a sequence of assumptions selected from the class $\Gamma_0{}^m$. None of these assumptions has free variables; hence the use of $\prod$I in line $(k+2)$ is justified. Line $(k+3)$ shows that $\sim\!\sum_\alpha \psi(\alpha)$ is consistent with $\Gamma_0{}^m$, since it is deducible from this class. However, $\sum_\alpha \psi(\alpha)$ is a member of $\Gamma_0{}^m$, which contradicts the assumption that $\Gamma_0{}^m$ is consistent for every m, and so $\Gamma_1{}^0$ is consistent.

Further $\Gamma_1{}^0$ is a maximal consistent class of the wffs of GPL-1, since it contains $\Gamma_0{}^0$.

The introduction of the individual constants u_{i0} ($i = 1, 2, \ldots, n$) as additional symbols increases the number of wffs in GPL-1_1 so that there are some that are not in GPL-1. For example, the wff $\prod_y \prod_x F(x,y)$ occurs in GPL-1. It also occurs in GPL-1_1, but so do $\sum_x F(x,u_{00})$, $\sum_x F(x,u_{10})$, and so on. Thus, we do not have a maximal consistent class of GPL-1_1, nor have we included all wffs obtained by substituting individual constants in wffs of the form $\sum_\alpha \psi(\alpha)$. For example, $\sum_x F(x,u_{00})$ does not occur in $\Gamma_1{}^0$, nor does $F(u_{10},u_{00})$. We proceed to rectify this. First, we form the maximal consistent class of GPL-1_1, then we add to the symbols of GPL-1_1 (to form GPL-1_2) an enumerable infinity of individual constants designated as

$$u_{01},\; u_{11},\; u_{21},\; \ldots\; .$$

As for $\Gamma_0{}^1$, $\Gamma_0{}^2$, $\Gamma_0{}^3$, ..., we construct the classes $\Gamma_1{}^1$, $\Gamma_1{}^2$, $\Gamma_1{}^3$, ... The union of these classes is called $\Gamma_2{}^0$ and is a maximal consistent class of the wffs of GPL-1_1 by the same reasoning as given for $\Gamma_1{}^0$.

Of course, the introduction of the individual constants u_{i1} ($i = 1, 2, \ldots, n$) increases the number of wffs in GPL-1_2 so that there are some not in GPL-1_1.

Hence, $\Gamma_2{}^0$ is not a maximal consistent class of GPL-1$_2$, nor does it contain the results of substituting individual constants in all wffs of the form $\sum_\alpha \psi(\alpha)$. For the purpose of our proof we rectify this recurrent situation in general.

We add to the symbols of GPL-1$_n$ (to form GPL-1$_{(n+1)}$) an enumerable infinity of individual constants designated as

$$u_{0n}, u_{1n}, u_{2n}, \ldots$$

As for $\Gamma^1_{(n-1)}$, $\Gamma^2_{(n-1)}$, $\Gamma^3_{(n-1)}$, ..., we construct the classes $\Gamma_n{}^1$, $\Gamma_n{}^2$, $\Gamma_n{}^3$, ... The union of these classes is called $\Gamma^0_{(n+1)}$ and is a maximal consistent class of the wffs of GPL-1$_n$ by the same reasoning as for $\Gamma_1{}^0$, $\Gamma_2{}^0$, $\Gamma_3{}^0$, ...

We now have a method for constructing the classes $\Gamma_0{}^0$, $\Gamma_1{}^0$, $\Gamma_2{}^0$, $\Gamma_3{}^0$, ... each of which, first, is a maximal consistent class of GPL-1, GPL-1$_1$, GPL-1$_2$, GPL-1$_3$, ..., respectively, and each of which, second, contains the result of substituting individual constants u_{ij} (i, j = 1, 2, ...) for variables in wffs of GPL-1$_n$ of the form $\sum_\alpha \psi(\alpha)$. These classes are all consistent. We show this by induction.

Basis: $\Gamma_0{}^0$ is consistent by the method of construction of Section 11.4.
Induction Step: Assume $\Gamma_n{}^0$ is consistent. $\Gamma^0_{(n+1)}$ is the union of $\Gamma_n{}^0$, $\Gamma_n{}^1$, $\Gamma_n{}^2$, ... But if $\Gamma_n{}^0$ is consistent, so is Γ_n^{k+1} by the same reasoning as for $\Gamma_1{}^0$. Hence, $\Gamma_n{}^m$ is consistent for every m and so $\Gamma^0_{(n+1)}$ is consistent. Therefore, $\Gamma_n{}^0$ is consistent for every n.

Let Γ_ω be the union of the classes $\Gamma_1{}^0$, $\Gamma_2{}^0$, $\Gamma_3{}^0$, ... Γ_ω is a maximal consistent class of all the wffs of GPL-1, GPL-1$_1$, GPL-1$_2$, ...; and Γ_ω contains the result of substituting u_{ij} (i, j take integral values) for variables in all wffs of these systems of the form $\sum_\alpha \psi(\alpha)$. We show, first, that Γ_ω is consistent. Assume Γ_ω to be inconsistent. This is possible only if some $\Gamma_n{}^0$ is inconsistent; but we have just shown that $\Gamma_n{}^0$ is consistent for every n. We show, second, that Γ_ω is maximal. Let ψ be a wff of GPL-1$_n$ for some n. Assume that ψ is consistent with the wffs of Γ_ω. Then ψ is consistent with the wffs of Γ^0_{n+1} and so (by the method of construction) a member of $\Gamma^0_{(n+1)}$. Hence, ψ is a member of Γ_ω, since this is the union of $\Gamma_0{}^0$, $\Gamma_1{}^0$, $\Gamma_2{}^0$, ...

II. *The wffs of Γ_ω are simultaneously satisfiable in an enumerably infinite domain.*

To show this we assign values in an enumerably infinite domain to the wffs of GPL-1$_\omega$ in such a way that the wffs of Γ_ω are simultaneously satisfied. The enumerably infinite domain we select is the domain of the positive integers.

The procedure in the assignment of values to wffs of GPL-1$_\omega$ is as follows:

(a) If a statement, p, occurs in a wff of GPL-1, it is assigned, as usual, the value 1 or 0. It possesses 1 if p is a member of Γ_ω; otherwise it possesses 0.

(b) Each of the individual constants u_{ij} (i, j take integral values) corresponds to the ordered pair ⟨i j⟩ composed of its subscripts. Since these can be enumerated by the methods of Section 11.4, a positive integer, I_{ij}, corresponds to each constant. As the symbolism shows, we note this correspondence by the use of the same subscripts.

(c) No free variables occur in the wffs of GPL-1_ω. If a predicate symbol, $F(u_{i_1 j_1} u_{i_2 j_2} \ldots u_{i_m j_m})$, occurs in a wff of GPL-1_ω it is assigned as its value the ordered m-tuple of integers ⟨$I_{i_1 j_1}, I_{i_2 j_2}, \ldots, I_{i_m j_m}$⟩. This ordered m-tuple possesses 1 if $F(u_{i_1 j_1} u_{i_2 j_2} \ldots u_{i_m j_m})$ is in Γ_ω; otherwise it possesses 0.

(d) Wffs of GPL-1_ω including the symbols &, $\sim$, and $\prod_\alpha$ possess 1 or 0, depending upon assignment of values as above and by the usual matrices for evaluation. The symbols **v**, ⊃, ≡, and $\sum_\alpha$ can be replaced in any wff by the first three symbols by suitable definition.

We next show by induction that any wff without free variables of GPL-1_ω possesses 1 if it is a member of Γ_ω, on the assignment of values in the enumerably infinite domain of the positive integers. We show this by induction on the number of standard symbols in the wff, that is, on the number of occurrences of &, $\sim$, $\prod_\alpha$, p, and $F(u_{i_1 j_1}, u_{i_2 j_2}, \ldots, u_{i_n j_n})$.

Basis: The wff is one standard symbol in length. There are two cases: the wff is a statement symbol, p, or an n-adic predicate symbol with constants $F(u_{i_1 j_1}, u_{i_2 j_2}, \ldots u_{i_n j_n})$.

Case (1): The wff is a statement symbol, p. By the assignment of values in (a) above, it possesses 1 if it is in Γ_ω; otherwise it possesses 0.

Case (2): The wff is a predicate symbol followed by n constants (since there are no free variables); that is, $F(u_{i_1 j_1}, u_{i_2 j_2}, \ldots, u_{i_n j_n})$. By the assignment of values in (c) above, it possesses 1 if it is in Γ_ω; otherwise it possesses 0.

Induction Step: We assume that a wff which is n standard symbols in length or less evaluates to 1 if it is in Γ_ω; otherwise to 0. We show that the wff then has this property when it is $n + 1$ symbols in length. There are three cases. The wff is of the form $\sim\varphi$, φ & ψ, or $\prod_\alpha\varphi(\alpha)$.

Case (1): The wff is of the form $\sim\varphi$ where φ has n symbols or less. If $\sim\varphi$ is in Γ_ω then φ is not in Γ_ω since Γ_ω is a maximal consistent set, and thus is consistent. Since φ contains no more than n symbols and is not in Γ_ω, it evaluates to 0; hence, $\sim\varphi$ evaluates to 1. So, if $\sim\varphi$ is in Γ_ω it evaluates to 1. Similarly, if $\sim\varphi$ is not in Γ_ω then it evaluates to 0.

Case (2): The wff is of the form φ & ψ where φ and ψ have n symbols or less. If φ & ψ is in Γ_ω then φ is in Γ_ω and ψ is in Γ_ω—since φ and ψ

can each be deduced from φ & ψ and so are consistent with φ & ψ, and Γ_ω is a maximal consistent class. Since φ and ψ contain no more than n symbols and are in Γ_ω, each evaluates to 1, and, thus, so does φ & ψ, by the meaning of & and the usual evaluation procedure.

On the other hand, if φ & ψ is not in Γ_ω, then φ and ψ cannot both be in Γ_ω; for, supposing they were, then they could serve as premises from which φ & ψ would follow. Since φ and ψ contain no more than n symbols and one of them is not in Γ_ω, that one will evaluate to 0; hence, φ & ψ evaluates to 0, by the meaning of & and the usual evaluation procedure.

Case (3): The wff is of the form $\prod_\alpha \varphi(\alpha)$. If $\prod_\alpha \varphi(\alpha)$ is in Γ_ω, then by use of the rule $\prod$E we get $\varphi(u_{ij})$, where free α in φ is replaced by some u_{ij}. Since Γ_ω is a maximal consistent class and $\varphi(u_{ij})$ is consistent with $\prod_\alpha \varphi(\alpha)$ (being deduced from it), $\varphi(u_{ij})$ is in Γ_ω. In fact, every $\varphi(u_{ij})$ obtained by replacing free α by u_{ij} will be contained in Γ_ω. And since any $\varphi(u_{ij})$ contains no more than n symbols it will evaluate to 1. Hence, $\prod_\alpha \varphi(\alpha)$ will evaluate to 1, since all instances of it do so.

On the other hand, if $\prod_\alpha \varphi(\alpha)$ is not in Γ_ω then its negation, $\sim\prod_\alpha \varphi(\alpha)$, will be in Γ_ω, for it is possible to deduce $\sim\prod_\alpha \varphi(\alpha)$ from formulas in Γ_ω. This deduction shows $\sim\prod_\alpha \varphi(\alpha)$ to be consistent with the formulas in Γ_ω and so contained in it, since Γ_ω is a maximal consistent class. $\sim\prod_\alpha \varphi(\alpha)$ is equivalent to $\sum_\alpha \sim\varphi(\alpha)$. By the second property of Γ_ω, Γ_ω contains $\sim\varphi(u_{ij})$ since it contains $\sum_\alpha \sim\varphi(\alpha)$. Therefore, Γ_ω, being consistent, does not contain $\varphi(u_{ij})$. $\varphi(u_{ij})$ contains no more than n symbols and hence evaluates to 0. Since $\varphi(u_{ij})$ is obtained from $\varphi(\alpha)$ by substituting some u_{ij} for the free α, there is by use of $\prod$E at least one instance of $\prod_\alpha \varphi(\alpha)$ which is 0, so that $\prod_\alpha \varphi(\alpha)$ is 0.

III. *The arbitrary consistent class of wffs, Λ, without free variables selected from GPL-1 is simultaneously satisfiable in an enumerably infinite domain.*

The members of this class are members of Γ_ω and we have shown that all wffs of Γ_ω are so satisfiable. Since the class Λ is arbitrary, we have shown that any consistent wffs of GPL-1 without free variables are so satisfiable. Indeed, if a consistent class of wffs with free variables should be given, substitution of different individual constants for different free variables permits extension of the conclusion to these cases. This completes the proof of Metatheorem 11.4.

We now make use of Metatheorem 11.4 to establish the completeness of GPL-1. We wish to show that every valid quantificational formula is a D+ line, for this together with Metatheorem 11.2 gives the completeness of GPL-1. We shall proceed in a way analogous to that involved in proving

Metatheorem 10.3, 10.4, and 10.5. In particular, we present the argument in the form of the next three metatheorems.

Metatheorem 11.5: If φ is any valid wff of GPL-1 then $\sim\varphi$ is not satisfiable.

Metatheorem 11.6: If φ is not satisfiable in an enumerably infinite domain then φ is not consistent.

Metatheorem 11.7: Every valid wff of GPL-1 is a D^+ line.

Proof of Metatheorem 11.5: This follows from the definition of validity and satisfiability, since if a wff, φ, is valid, it possesses I in all domains; and hence, $\sim\varphi$ is identically 0 in all domains.

Proof of Metatheorem 11.6: This is a special case of Metatheorem 11.4. If in Metatheorem 11.4 we assume the arbitrary consistent class to contain the single member φ, and contrapose, the result follows.

Proof of Metatheorem 11.7: This follows from the fact that if $\sim\varphi$ is inconsistent then φ is deducible, that is, is a D^+ line (since any line follows from an inconsistency by $\sim$E). Hence, by a chain using Metatheorem 11.5 and 11.6, the result follows.

EXERCISE 11.5

I. Work out in detail examples for Metatheorem 11.4 as follows:

1. Select an initial consistent class of wffs of GPL-1 without free variables.
2. Illustrate the induction step that shows that $\Gamma_1{}^0$ is consistent.
3. Describe GPL-1$_\omega$.
4. Evaluate a set of wffs in terms of the value assignment given.

II. Formulate the proofs of Metatheorem 11.4 for the case of PL; for the case of MPL.

III. Formulate the proof of Metatheorem 11.5 in full.

IV. Formulate the proof of Metatheorem 11.6 in full.

V. Formulate the proof of Metatheorem 11.7 in full.

11.6 Löwenheim-Skolem Theorem

We are now in a position to establish an interesting result with far-reaching significance. We proceed as follows:

Metatheorem 11.8: Every simultaneously satisfiable class of wffs of GPL-1 is consistent.

Proof: Let Λ be an inconsistent class of wffs of GPL-1. It follows that Λ includes the wffs $\varphi_1,\ \varphi_2,\ \ldots,\ \varphi_k$, so that the following deduction exists:

1. φ_1 & φ_2 & $\ldots$ & φ_k

$\vdots$

k. ψ & $\sim\psi$

$\qquad$ **(k + 1).** $\sim(\varphi_1$ & φ_2 & $\ldots\ \varphi_k)$ 1-k, $\sim$I

Since line $(k+1)$ is a D$^+$ line, $\sim(\varphi_1$ & φ_2 & $\ldots$ & $\varphi_k)$ possesses I by Metatheorem 11.2. Hence, $(\varphi_1$ & φ_2 & $\ldots$ & $\varphi_k)$ cannot possess 1, and the wffs $\varphi_1,\ \varphi_2,\ \ldots,\ \varphi_k$ are not simultaneously satisfiable.
Metatheorem 11.8 and Metatheorem 11.4 together establish

Metatheorem 11.9:   Every simultaneously satisfiable class of wffs of GPL-1 is simultaneously satisfiable in an enumerably infinite domain.

This metatheorem, the Löwenheim-Skolem theorem, gains its significance from the fact that it applies to the axioms of an axiom system when these are stated in the terms of GPL-1. Such axioms constitute a satisfiable class of wffs if there is an interpretation (and so a model) of the axiom system. Hence, such axioms must be satisfiable in an enumerably infinite domain. However, some axioms stated in the terms of GPL-1, as those of set theory, are intended to apply to a model which is *nondenumerably* infinite. This result is sometimes referred to as *Skolem's Paradox.*

EXERCISE 11.6

I. Do Peano's axioms comprise a class of wffs? Are they simultaneously satisfiable? By what?

II. Give a class of wffs of GPL-1 that serve as axioms for some system. Show that they are simultaneously satisfiable in an enumerably infinite domain. (Consider, for example, the axioms for simple order.)

III. The wffs of GPL-1 are denumerable. The points on a line or the real numbers between 0 and 1 are nondenumerable. Is there any way in GPL-1 to specify the sets made up of each different point, that is, to state the conditions determining each such set? Does this mean that there are classes without conditions?

IV. Can you relate your answer to problem III to Metatheorem 11.9?

11.7   Decidability

It was once hoped (by Hilbert) that a decision procedure for all of mathematics might be developed. Since a decision procedure obviates the necessity for a search for proof, thus freeing the mathematician to deal with other problems, the search for such methods is tempting.

In 1936, however, Church showed that there is no decision procedure for GPL-1.* His proof lies beyond the scope of this book. It does not preclude the existence of decision procedures for special classes of formulas in GPL-1. MPL is, of course, an example; some decision procedures for this area in particular were presented in Chapter Ten. An even simpler example is provided by the class of all wffs of GPL-1 in which there are only existential quantifiers; *i.e.*, formulas of the form

$$\Sigma_{x_1} \ldots \Sigma_{x_k} \varphi(x_1 \ldots x_k)$$

(Here we assume that φ contains no quantifiers.)

It is easy enough to decide whether this formula is valid. We need only test it in a domain of one individual. If the formula is 1-valid, it will be valid in every larger domain, and hence valid.†

The fact that GPL-1 is known to be undecidable raises important problems about the nature of decidable logics—and about the nature of undecidable logics. Indeed, the investigation of the conditions for decidability has occupied many logicians and has resulted in *Church's Thesis*, which states that a logic is decidable if and only if it is general recursive. Both the full statement of this thesis and the proof of the undecidability of GPL-1 involve the use of the theory of recursive functions and the technique of arithmetizing symbols, which are best left to special studies in this field.

EXERCISE 11.7

I. Consider $\prod_x \prod_y F(x,y)$. Show that it is universally valid if and only if it is 2-valid. (Hint: Show that in any larger domain in which it was invalid it would possess 0 for two individuals.)

II. Generalize the example of I for m variables. Show that a wff of this form is universally valid if and only if it is m-valid.

III. Show that a wff of the form

$\prod_{\alpha_1 \ldots \alpha_m} \Sigma_{\beta_1 \ldots \beta_m} \varphi(\alpha_1, \ldots, \alpha_m; \beta_1, \ldots, \beta_n)$ is universally valid if and only if it is m-valid. Begin by working out a particular simple case.

SUGGESTED READINGS

1. W. Ackermann, *Solvable Cases of the Decision Problem* (Amsterdam: North Holland Pub. Co., 1954).

---

* A. Church, "A Note on the Entscheidungsproblem", *Journal of Symbolic Logic*, Vol. 1 (1936), pp. 40–41, 101–102.

† For other examples of such decidable systems, see W. Ackermann, *Solvable Cases of the Decision Problem* (Amsterdam: North Holland Pub. Co., 1954).

2. A. Church, *Introduction to Mathematical Logic* (Princeton, N.J.: Princeton Univ. Press, 1956), Chs. IV, V.

3. I. Copi, *Symbolic Logic* (New York: The Macmillan Co., 1954), Ch. IX.

4. Leon Henkin, "The Completeness of First-Order Functional Calculus", *J. of Symb. Logic*, Vol. 14 (1949), pp. 159–166.

5. David Hilbert and W. Ackermann, *Principles of Mathematical Logic* (New York: Chelsea Pub. Co., 1950), Ch. III.

Chapter 12

Intuitive Set Theory

12.1 Introduction

We began this book with a discussion of axiom systems and the kind of reasoning that is used in drawing conclusions from axioms. Throughout Part One we stressed the importance of an explicit and precise understanding of such rules of inference. Certainly ignorance concerning them must lead to trouble. It may be true that mathematicians generally have sound intuitions of these rules of inference; yet occasionally such intuitions fail and radical disagreements concerning admissible rules of inference emerge. The arguments between the Intuitionists and Classical mathematicians over the law of excluded middle is a case in point. When such arguments arise, we clearly need an open discussion and a program of study of the area of difficulty. One of the reasons for including the section on intuitionist logic in Chapter Four was to introduce this problem, which concerns the very nature of negation in propositional logic. A second point at which there are problems in connection with rules of inference is the point where inference involving n-adic predicates is required. That these rules of inference differ from those of propositional logic is made clear by differences in the conception of completeness and in the lack of a decision procedure in GPL-1. A third point at which problems concerning rules of inference arise—and these are very serious problems indeed—is the point at which inferences involving infinite sets (or the rules of higher order logics) are needed. Here it is not true that the mathematician (or anyone else) has sound intuitions of correct rules of inference, for the commonly accepted rules have been shown to lead to inconsistencies.

The problems these inconsistencies present are so serious that we shall restrict our efforts in this book to illustrating them and to suggesting some of the directions in which solutions have been sought. We begin by introducing the idea of a set and some of its ramifications, without trying to deal with the problem of inferences involving sets, which we reserve for Chapter Thirteen. This kind of discussion of sets is sometimes referred to as *intuitive set theory* to distinguish it from the *axiomatic set theory* to be discussed in Chapter Thirteen.*

12.2   Sets, Subsets, and Operations

The idea of a *set* is common enough. It is embodied in such ordinary words as class, collection, group, the German word *Menge* and the French word *ensemble*. Set theory in German is *Mengenlehre* and in French, *Théorie des Ensembles*. We do not define a set. Instead, we assume that its meaning is known in some sense—that is, the idea of a set of elements is a primitive one—and we shall seek to clarify this meaning in this chapter.

We understand the word "set" to refer to any kind of collection of entities of any sort. Thus, we may have a set of integers or a set of cities. A set of entities may be an aggregate of concrete objects, such as the set of chairs in this room, or it may be composed of abstract objects. We speak of the entities in the set as *elements* or *members* of the set and we presume to be able to say with respect to any entity and any set whether that entity is a member of that set or not. Thus, a horse is not a member of the set of all human beings; but the authors of this book are members of this set. The number π is not a member of the set of integers; but the number 6 is.

When we work with sets, we start with a definite class of objects to which the discussion is limited. This class is called the *universal set* V. The universal set varies from one problem to another, for sometimes we wish to discuss complex numbers and at other times we wish to discuss events, or persons, and so on. Usually, given a universal set, our task involves consideration of some of its *subsets*. A subset S of V is a set whose elements are all elements of V. Thus, the people in a room constitute a subset of the set of all people. The odd integers are a subset of the set of integers. When there are two sets S and S' such that every member of S is a member of S', we express this relation by saying that *S is included in S'*, or, in the symbols that we shall henceforth be using, $S \subseteq S'$. What we have just been saying is to the effect that whatever S we choose, it is included in V; symbolized as

$$S \subseteq V.$$

There are certain operations that may be performed on sets. As it happens these operations are analogous to certain operations that have been

---

* The reader familiar with set theory may wish to proceed to Section 12.6.

discussed in the development of Boolean Algebra in Chapter Eight. In fact, the diagrammatic interpretation of Boolean Algebra given there is, in effect, simply an interpretation in terms of sets.

UNION

The union of S and T is the set of objects that belong either to S or to T. Here S and T are subsets of some universal set V and their union, written S ∪ T, defines another subset of V.

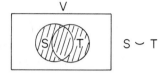

S ⌣ T

The union of S and T is analogous to the Boolean expression $a \cup b$.

INTERSECTION

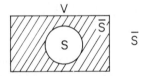

S ⌢ T

The intersection or product of S and T is the set of objects that belong to S and to T. We write the intersection S ∩ T; and this defines a subset.

The intersection of S and T is like the Boolean $a \cap b$.

COMPLEMENT

The complement of a set S consists of all the objects in V that are not in S. The complement of S is usually written S̄ and defines a subset.

The resemblance between S̄ and the Boolean $\bar{x}$ hardly needs to be made explicit.

Since the operation S ∩ T might define a set that contained no members, we shall need to define that set initially. It is called the *null set* and written Λ. Thus, the intersection of the set of odd integers and the set of even integers is null.

$$O \cap E = \Lambda$$

That we now have a Boolean algebra can be determined by noting that the axioms concerning associativity, commutativity, and distributivity hold for these operations. For example,

$$S \cup T = T \cup S$$

$$S \cap T = T \cap S.$$

The other axioms can be checked by establishing the truth of their analogous forms in the notation of set theory (see Chapter Eight, Section Three).

EXERCISE 12.2

I. Name the universal set associated with each of the following:

   1. classical mechanics
   2. objects of treatment by veterinarians
   3. astronomy
   4. political science
   5. ethics

II. List subsets of the universal sets associated with the above.

III. Form unions, intersections, and complements of these subsets, and name at least one subset which constitutes a null set.

IV. Assuming that the universal set is man, decide which of the following are subsets, unions, intersections, complements, the null set, or the universal set.

1. married men	**8.** female children
2. men	**9.** both males and females
3. unmarried men	**10.** all males and females
4. bachelors	**11.** males or females
5. married bachelors	**12.** both men and women
6. all men and all women	**13.** neither males nor females
7. women	

V. Which of the above are equivalent to one another?

VI. Draw a series of diagrams showing that the Boolean laws of distribution hold for the operations $\cup$, $\cap$.

12.3 Membership

Since a set of entities is exemplified by a set of imaginary numbers or the set of characters in Irish fairy tales, we are not likely to regard sets as tangible things. But it is well to be absolutely clear that sets are not tangible. Thus, we may note that even when the objects that belong to a set are concrete, as for example the chairs in a room, we could regard these same objects as exhaustively accounted for by another set, say the set of parts of the chairs in this room. The nails used in building the chairs are members of the latter set, but not the former, and the chairs themselves are members of the former, but not of the latter. The point is that a set may be regarded as specifying a condition or property, *e.g.*, the property of being a chair or part of a chair, or the property *human*, *prime*, or <15. Such a property is not itself tangible even when the objects to which it applies are tangible. We express the relation between any individual x that is a member of a set and the set itself, say R, by writing

$$x \in R.$$

Here the relation of membership is designated by ∈. What we have written amounts to the assertion that x has the property designated by R.

PRINCIPLE OF ABSTRACTION

We may see this important point in another way. Suppose that we assume the universal set to be all living things. We might then say

Tom is a man

or

$t \in M$.

Here we interpret the word "is" in its most common meaning, that of membership; but more significantly, we state a condition on the element t of V, namely, that it belongs to the subset of V, M. We thus *restrict* t to this subset of V. Thus, we relate an element of V to a subset M. This relation holds for those elements of V that belong to M and does not hold for those that do not. Conversely, given any condition or property that refers to some elements in V, we can define a set. Thus, we can define the set of all men in the universe of living things in the following way:

$$\{x \in V: \quad M(x)\}$$

Here we use the customary mathematical notation, which is read "the set of all elements such that they have the property M". Such a definition of a set in terms of a property is based upon the *principle of abstraction: viz., Every property defines a set*. This principle may be symbolized $\sum_R \prod_t [t \in R \equiv F(t)]$.

An alternative notation, more often used by the logician than by the mathematician, is

$$\hat{x}[M(x)]$$

which is read "the set (or class) of all x's such that x has the property M". Depending on the way in which set theory is axiomatized, sometimes the use of this notation presupposes that $x \in V$, and sometimes it does not. (The motives for choosing one axiomatization over another will be explained in the following chapter.) In any event, the notation just introduced can easily be generalized; we read

$$\hat{x}(\ldots x \ldots)$$

as "the set (or class) of all x's such that . . . .". The role of the set as a condition or restriction is once again evident.

PRINCIPLE OF EXTENSIONALITY

Since we build sets by relating properties to elements, it follows that two sets are the same when their elements are the same. If we consider the properties of *rationality* and *being a man* we argue that these define the same set if and only if the sets they define have the same members.

$$[R = M] \equiv (\{x \in V: R(x)\} = \{x \in V: M(x)\})$$

This can also be written in logical notation,

$$[R = M] \equiv \{\hat{x}[R(x)] = \hat{x}[M(x)]\}$$

or, for that matter,

$$[R = M] \equiv \prod_x (x \in R \equiv x \in M)$$

The principle that sets are identical when and only when they have the same members is called the *Principle of Extensionality*. It bears an important relation to the Principle of Leibniz discussed in Chapter Seven.

If the sets are identical when their members are the same, it is evident that we can also build sets by listing members explicitly. Thus,

$$\{1, 2, 4, 6\}$$

is the set of just these integers, while

$$\{1, 2, 4, 5\}$$

is a different set. We would be hard pressed to state the property that defines such a set, other than as whatever property it is that attaches to all and only those individuals belonging to such a set, for which no name exists in any ordinary language. It is important to note that sets can be members of sets; thus,

$$\{\{1,2\} , 3, 4\}$$

is a set. So is

$$\{\{\{\{1\}, 2\}, 3\}, 4\}$$

Here $\{1\}$ is not 1, but the set containing the element 1.

Perhaps the easiest way to obtain necessary familiarity with the idea of membership is to use it on familiar ground. The relation $\in$ can be used to restate the familiar operations $\cap$, $\cup$, and $^{-}$ as applied to sets. $S \cap T$ defines a set as follows:

$$S \cap T = \{x \in V : x \in S \ \& \ x \in T\}$$

Likewise $S \cup T$ defines a set,

$$S \cup T = \{x \in V : x \in S \ v \ x \in T\}$$

Finally, $\overline{S}$ is

$$\overline{S} = \{x \in V : x \notin S\}$$

Here the symbol $\notin$ is an abbreviation for "it is false that $x \in S$".

With this explicit use of $\in$ such truths as

$$S \cap T = T \cap S$$

are evident, for we can reason as follows:

1.	$x \in S \cap T \equiv [x \in S \ \& \ x \in T]$	Definition of $\cap$
2.	$[x \in S \ \& \ x \in T] \equiv [x \in T \ \& \ x \in S]$	CM
3.	$x \in T \cap S \equiv [x \in T \ \& \ x \in S]$	Definition of $\cap$
4.	$x \in S \cap T \equiv x \in T \cap S$	Transitivity of $\equiv$
5.	$S \cap T = T \cap S$	Principle of extensionality

Similar proofs exist for commutativity, associativity, and distributivity of $\cap$ and $\cup$. These are left to the reader as a means of becoming familiar with the relation $\in$.

Of more interest but equally useful as a device for familiarization is the proof that there is only one set Λ. We may think of Λ as any set such that

$$\prod_x \sim (x \in \Lambda)$$

i.e.,

$$\prod_x (x \notin \Lambda)$$

Suppose there are two such sets; call them Λ_1 and Λ_2. Then

$$\prod_x (x \in \Lambda_1 \supset x \in \Lambda_2)$$

since the antecedent is always false. Similarly,

$$\prod_x (x \in \Lambda_2 \supset x \in \Lambda_1)$$

whence, by $\equiv$I,

$$\prod_x (x \in \Lambda_1 \equiv x \in \Lambda_2)$$

and so, by the principle of extensionality,

$$\Lambda_1 = \Lambda_2$$

This proof should be compared with the proof of the uniqueness of the Boolean Λ in Chapter Eight. The fact that the present proof is considerably simpler is a testimony to the power of the $\in$ notation, which we did not, of course, employ when we developed Boolean algebra as such.

EXERCISE 12.3

I. You have been told that a property defines a set. Is the converse of this also true? Define a set by stipulating its members individually. What property does such a set define? What does this reveal about the statement "A set defines a property"? What does it reveal about the word "property"? (*E.g.*, consider the set which consists of a man, a chair, a star, and a labor union.)

II. How was the principle of extensionality used in the exercises for Section Two?

III. What is the relation between the principle of extensionality and that of Leibniz?

IV. Complete the proofs for commutativity, associativity, and distributivity of $\cup$ and $\cap$, as called for in the text.

V. Prove Theorems 8.4(B), 8.5(B), 8.6(B), 8.7(B) and 8.8(B) by means of $\in$ relationships.

12.4 Inclusion and Membership

Implicit in the discussion of membership in the last section is the possibility of defining inclusion by means of it. Thus,

$$S \subseteq T \equiv \prod_x (x \in S \supset x \in T)$$

There is a radical difference between $\in$ and $\subseteq$. In the first place $\subseteq$ (like $\cup$, $\cap$, and $\overline{}$) applies only *to sets*. When we write

$$S \subseteq T$$

we mean that the set S is included in the set T. Inclusion never holds between elements of sets or between elements and sets. We can say

$$\{1, 2\} \subseteq \{1, 5, 6, 2\}$$

but not

$$1 \subseteq 1$$

and not

$$1 \subseteq \{1, 2\}$$

Nor can we say

$$\{1, 2\} \subseteq \{\{1, 2\}, 2\}$$

since here the set $\{1, 2\}$ is an element of another set. This situation may be illustrated by English sentences. When we say

Men are animals

we symbolize it

$$M \subseteq A$$

since we are talking about two sets.

On the other hand, we say

Socrates is a philosopher

which we symbolize

$$s \in P$$

since Socrates is a member of a set. It would be a mistake to use $\in$ in the former case and $\subseteq$ in the latter. The sentence

Whales are a species

we symbolize as

$$W \in S$$

since we mean that the set of whales is a member of the set of species.

Some of the differences between (and hence reasons for avoiding the confusion of) $\in$ and $\subseteq$ can be formally stated in terms of the formal properties of these relations. We recall from Chapter Six that the relation $=$ is reflexive, symmetrical, and transitive. Thus, we say of any individual

$$x = x$$

and if

$$x = y$$

then

$$y = x$$

and finally,

$$[x = y \,\&\, y = z] \supset x = z$$

The relation $\in$, however, is quite different. Since it holds between an element and the set to which it belongs, we *cannot* in general say of an element x

$$x \in x$$

Similarly, if we say

$$x \in S$$

we *cannot* in general say that

$$S \in x$$

for a set does not usually belong to its elements. Finally, it does not follow that

$$x \in S \,\&\, S \in R \supset x \in R$$

To see this, consider the argument "The fish that swallowed Jonah was a whale; whales are species of animals; therefore the fish that swallowed Jonah is a species".

Although $=$ is reflexive, symmetrical, and transitive, we see that $\in$ is not reflexive (but not irreflexive, since some sets may be members of themselves), nonsymmetrical, and nontransitive.

The relation $\subseteq$ can be thought of as reflexive. We can say

$$S \subseteq S$$

Indeed, this follows from the definition of $\subseteq$, since

$$\textstyle\prod_x (x \in S \supset x \in S)$$

is a ZPC. There is, however, another relation between sets that is *not* reflexive. This is called "proper inclusion"; and when it holds between sets R and S, R is said to be a *proper subset* of S. This is symbolized $R \subset S$, and defined as

$$R \subseteq S \,\&\, R \neq S$$

If we had wished, we could have begun with proper inclusion, defining inclusion pure and simple as

$$(R \subset S) \,\mathbf{v}\, (R = S)$$

Not only is $\subset$ irreflexive, but also it is asymmetrical, since, given

$$S \subset T$$

we can conclude that $T \subset S$ is false. $\subseteq$, on the other hand, is nonsymmetrical, since, given $S \subseteq T$, it may or may not also be true that $T \subseteq S$. Finally, $\subset$ and $\subseteq$ are both transitive.

These differences in the properties of $\in$, $\subset$, $\subseteq$, and $=$ suggest the importance of separating the various meanings of the verb *to be* and avoiding their confusion in use.

EXERCISE 12.4

I. Which of the following are true? Why?

1. $\prod_x (x \in x)$

2. $\prod_x \prod_S (x \in S \supset S \in x)$

3. $\prod_x \prod_S \prod_R [(x \in S \ \& \ S \in R) \supset x \in R]$

4. $\prod_S (S \in S)$

5. $\prod_S (S \subseteq S)$

6. $\prod_S (S \subset S)$

7. $\prod_S \prod_T (S \subseteq T \supset T \subseteq S)$

8. $\prod_S \prod_T (S \subset T \supset T \subset S)$

9. $\prod_S \prod_T \prod_R [(S \subseteq T \ \& \ T \subseteq R) \supset S \subseteq R]$

10. $\prod_S \prod_T \prod_R [(S \subset T \ \& \ T \subset R) \supset S \subset R]$

II. How do the symbols $\in$, $\subseteq$, $\subset$, and $=$ symbolize different meanings of the verb *to be*? Cite English sentences exemplifying the various meanings.

12.5 Unit Sets

Λ has been defined as the set with no members. The possibility of a set with just one member has also been mentioned. We distinguished, for example, between the element 1 and the set $\{1\}$. The latter is called the *unit set* of the number 1; *i.e.*, the set whose sole member is that number. In general, given any individual a, we can define ιa, the unit set of a, as follows:

$\iota a = \hat{x}(x = a)$, or in the more usual mathematical notation,

$$\iota a = \{(x \in V) : x = a\}.$$

The notion of unit set provides us with a method of defining membership in terms of inclusion, if we care to do so. For although no element is included in any set of which it is a member, its unit set is included in just those sets of which it is a member. Thus instead of writing

$$a \in S,$$

we could always write instead

$$\iota a \subseteq S.$$

For example, although it is not true that $1 \subseteq \{1, 2, 3, 4\}$, it is true that $\{1\} \subseteq \{1, 2, 3, 4\}$. In our new notation this becomes: $\iota 1 \subseteq \{1, 2, 3, 4\}$.

The operation ι may be iterated. In general,

$$a \neq \iota a \neq \iota\iota a \neq \iota\iota\iota a$$

and so on. From this it follows that without presupposing anything about what exists in the real world, we can construct models for systems that are satisfiable in a denumerably infinite domain but not in any smaller domain. For this purpose, all that we need is Λ, from which we proceed as follows:

$$\Lambda, \iota\Lambda, \iota\iota\Lambda, \iota\iota\iota\Lambda, \ldots$$

Nor does this exhaust the possibilities, since we shall also be able to write

$$\Lambda \cup \iota\Lambda, \iota(\Lambda \cup \iota\Lambda), \Lambda \cup \iota(\Lambda \cup \iota\Lambda)$$

etc. All the requirements of the completeness proof for GPL-1 given in Chapter Eleven, for example, could be met by individual constants fabricated in this way.

From the considerations so far adduced, it follows that

$$\iota x \cup \iota(\iota x \cup \iota y) \neq \iota y \cup \iota(\iota y \cup \iota x)$$

unless, of course, $x = y$; and that

$$\{[\iota w \cup \iota(\iota w \cup \iota x)] = [\iota y \cup \iota(\iota y \cup \iota z)]\} \equiv [(w = y) \,\&\, (x = z)]$$

The proof of this latter statement depends upon the principle of extensionality, as well as the observation that $(x = y) \equiv (x \in \iota y)$. The two statements together serve as the basis for a definition of *ordered pairs* in terms of sets:

$$\langle \mathbf{x,y} \rangle: \; \iota x \cup \iota(\iota x \cup \iota y)$$

The notation $\langle x,y \rangle$ and the conception that it symbolizes will be discussed further in the next section.

12.6 Sets and Predicates

Our purpose in studying sets is to prepare for a discussion of set theory in relation to rules of inference. As the next step, let us show that predicate logic can be presented simply in terms of sets. This will illustrate something of the power of set theory as a tool and at the same time keep our attention focused on logic.

We have already indicated that a condition or property determines a set. Thus, given a property F, we determine the set of individuals having this property as

$$S = \{x \in V : F(x)\}$$

or

$$S = \hat{x}F(x)$$

Since we can do this for any property φ, we may rewrite any monadic predicate in terms of the set it determines. Thus, if F in F(x) determines S, we rewrite F(x) as $x \in S$.

It is then possible to write $\prod_x F(x)$ as $\prod_x (x \in S)$ and $\sum_x F(x)$ as $\sum_x (x \in S)$. Such compounds as

$$\prod_x F(x) \supset \sum_x G(x)$$

become

$$\prod_x (x \in S) \supset \sum_x (x \in T)$$

and so on. We may thus rewrite any formula of MPL in terms in which sets replace predicates.

In order to go on now to express all of GPL-1 in terms of set theory, we need to find the set-theoretic analogue of expressions such as F(x,y), G(x,y), H(y,z,w), and so on. Once we have developed the notion of an *ordered pair*, this analogue will be clear enough.

ORDERED PAIRS

An ordered pair consists of two elements taken in a certain order. When we think of a pair of dice or of shoes, it makes no difference which die or which shoe (the right or left) is considered first and which second. In general, when $\{a,b\} = \{b,a\}$ there is nothing essentially ordered about the two elements in the set. There are many occasions, however, when we do order elements. We speak of going from Philadelphia to New York—something which is quite different from going from New York to Philadelphia.

Similarly, if we say that $\langle x,y \rangle$ is an ordered pair, we mean that we take x first and y second—that $\langle x,y \rangle \neq \langle y,x \rangle$. In fact,

$$\langle x,y \rangle = \langle z,w \rangle$$

only when

$$x = z \text{ and } y = w$$

so that order is essentially involved here. Thus,

$$\langle 1, 2 \rangle \neq \langle 2, 1 \rangle$$
$$\langle 3, 4 \rangle \neq \langle 3, 2 \rangle$$

and

$$\langle 4, 6 \rangle \neq \langle 6, 4 \rangle$$

Now, a dyadic relation is one that holds between two elements, a pair. Thus "Tom is the father of George" involves the pair Tom and George. "Robert is taller than Joe" involves the pair Robert and Joe. Further, as we see in these relations, order is necessarily involved in the occurrence of the elements, for in "George is the father of Tom" we have quite a different situation. In fact, Tom and George form an ordered pair, so that

$$\langle t,g \rangle \neq \langle g,t \rangle.$$

The same point applies in the case of Robert and Joe—as related they form an ordered pair, $\langle r,j \rangle$.

If we think of the universal set V for some problem, then a relation connects pairs of the elements of V in a certain order. For example, if V is the set of all people, the relation of *being older than* selects exactly those pairs of individuals so related that the first is older than the second. This situation is easier to understand if we think of all possible pairs of elements of the set V. These pairs themselves form a set and a relation is a subset of this set of pairs. Suppose that we begin with a set S of three elements, $\{1, 2, 3\}$. This set generates nine pairs, as we can see from the following table:

3	$\langle 3, 1 \rangle$	$\langle 3, 2 \rangle$	$\langle 3, 3 \rangle$
2	$\langle 2, 1 \rangle$	$\langle 2, 2 \rangle$	$\langle 2, 3 \rangle$
1	$\langle 1, 1 \rangle$	$\langle 1, 2 \rangle$	$\langle 1, 3 \rangle$
	1	2	3

These nine pairs constitute a set of pairs called a Cartesian Cross Product, written S × S. Similarly, the points on a plane in analytic geometry constitute a Cartesian Cross Product of the set of real numbers N × N, that is, the set of all possible pairs of reals. The set of pairs that can be generated from any finite set by taking the cross product can be written as a table similar to the one above. If the original set is infinite, we can still write the first few pairs as illustrations. And, of course, we can form ordered pairs from two different sets, that is, take the cross product S × T. S might be the set of all parents and T the set of all children. Then the ordered pairs are all possible pairs of a parent and a child (not necessarily the parent of the child), and the relation called *being the child of* holds of a subset of these pairs.

A dyadic relation is a subset of the ordered pairs obtained by taking a cross product of a set on itself, S × S, or of two sets, S × T. A relation distinguishes some pairs from others. In the case of the set $\{1, 2, 3\}$ and the relation *greater than*, we can write

$$G = \{\langle x,y \rangle \in (S \times S): x > y\}$$

In this case, by referring to the table we can list these pairs

$$\langle 3, 1 \rangle, \langle 3, 2 \rangle, \langle 2, 1 \rangle$$

N-ADIC RELATIONS

These methods can be extended to the treatment of triadic relations and, more generally, *n*-adic ones. A triadic relation R may be expressed as a set of ordered triples of the form

$$\langle x,y,z \rangle$$

We understand this notation to mean that

$$\langle x,y,z \rangle = \langle \langle x,y \rangle,z \rangle$$

Hence it follows that (as in the case of ordered pairs)

$$\langle x,y,z \rangle = \langle u,v,w \rangle$$

if and only if

$$x = u, \quad y = v, \quad \text{and} \quad z = w$$

This follows by Substitution,

$$\langle x,y,z \rangle = \langle \langle x,y \rangle,z \rangle$$
$$\langle u,v,w \rangle = \langle \langle u,v \rangle,w \rangle$$

Hence, by the equality of the right sides,

$$\langle x,y \rangle = \langle u,v \rangle$$
$$z = w$$

But by the equality of the ordered pairs,

$$x = u \quad \text{and} \quad y = v$$

In a similar way we can define ordered quadruples,

$$\langle x,y,z,w \rangle = \langle \langle x,y,z \rangle,w \rangle$$

and ordered *n*-ads,

$$\langle x_1, x_2, \ldots, x_n \rangle = \langle \langle x_1, x_2, \ldots, x_{n-1} \rangle,x_n \rangle$$

The task of translating any statement of GPL-1 into set-theoretical notation can now be readily performed. As we have seen, any monadic formula like $F(x)$ can be rephrased as $x \in S$. In view of the developments just introduced, we can determine a set by any polyadic predicate. Thus, if G in $G(x_1, \ldots, x_n)$ determines T we rewrite $G(x_1, \ldots, x_n)$ as $\langle x_1, \ldots, x_n \rangle \in$ T. It is thus possible to rewrite any formula of GPL-1 in terms in which sets replace predicates.

It is interesting to note that if we wish, we can carry out the reduction to set theory in an additional way; namely, by defining ordered pairs—and thus ordered *n*-tuples—in terms of sets. There are, in fact, several ways of defining ordered pairs in terms of sets. One of these was anticipated in Section 12.5; namely, that $\langle x,y \rangle$ can be defined as

$$\iota x \cup \iota(\iota x \cup \iota y)$$

That this is an adequate definition follows from the fact that the definiens not only preserves the distinction between $\langle x,y \rangle$ and $\langle y,x \rangle$ (unless $x = y$), but also permits us to deduce that $w = y$ and $x = z$ in case $\langle w,x \rangle = \langle y,z \rangle$. This is all that we could appropriately demand of a definition of $\langle x,y \rangle$, because the properties just mentioned are the only properties of ordered pairs that are of any use to us in logic or mathematics.*

12.7 Uses of Sets

There is often an advantage in intuitive clarity and economy of notation in expressing even logical concepts in terms of set theory. This is clear enough when one compares Boolean algebra as stated in Chapter Eight and PL as developed in Chapter Two. The advantage of our version of PL is the light it throws upon inference in mathematical reasoning, not its intuitive obviousness or its notational simplicity. The advantages of set theory in these respects are even more marked in dealing with dyadic relations and the formulas of higher order logics. Traditionally, the calculus of relations and the formulas of GPL-2 and higher order logics have been expressed in mathematical literature in terms of sets. On this account, it seems desirable to discuss the problems of inference in higher order logics in terms of sets. It is for this reason that we have stated the relation of the concepts of PL and GPL-1 to set theory.

CALCULUS OF RELATIONS

We may illustrate the advantages of set notation further by restating in terms of sets some of the formulas of the calculus of relations presented in Chapter Six. To do this we shall find the concepts of the domain, range, and field of a dyadic relation useful. The domain of a dyadic relation, written $\mathscr{D}$, is the set of all things x such that $\langle x,y \rangle \in R$. That is, let R be the set of ordered pairs determined by the dyadic relation $R(x,y)$; then

$$\mathscr{D}R = \{x: \langle x,y \rangle \in R\}$$

The range of a dyadic relation, written $\mathscr{R}$, is the set of all things y such that $\langle x,y \rangle \in R$. That is,

$$\mathscr{R}R = \{y: \langle x,y \rangle \in R\}$$

---

* See W. V. Quine, *Mathematical Logic*, rev. ed. (Cambridge, Mass.: Harvard University Press, 1951), pp. 198–202.

The field of a dyadic relation is the union of the domain and range; that is,

$$\mathscr{F}R = \mathscr{D}R \cup \mathscr{R}R$$

Turning to some notions that were discussed in Chapter Six, we can also define $\check{R}$ and $\bar{R}$, as follows:

$$\check{R} = \{\langle y,x\rangle: \langle x,y\rangle \in R\}$$

and

$$\bar{R} = \{\langle x,y\rangle: \langle x,y\rangle \notin R\}$$

We have previously called a relation totally reflexive when $\prod_x R(x,x)$. That is,

$$\textbf{Totrx(R)} \equiv \prod_x R(x,x)$$

However, we might have defined the identity relation as the set

$$\textbf{I} = \{\langle x,y\rangle \in R: x = y\}$$

and expressed reflexivity in terms of this relation. The set I comprises a subset of the ordered pairs which comprise R (the set determined by $R(x,y)$). Thus, if we use a table to designate the ordered pairs of $R(x,y)$, I appears as the diagonal:

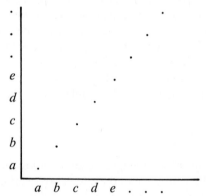

Accordingly, we can write

$$\textbf{Totrx(R)} \equiv I \subseteq R$$

Similarly, irreflexivity is simply and intuitively stated as

$$\textbf{Irrx(R)} \equiv I \cap R = \Lambda$$

Intuitively, this means that the set comprising the ordered pairs $\langle x,x\rangle$ and the ordered pairs comprising the field of R have no pairs in common.

We may understand symmetry as

$$\textbf{Sym(R)} \equiv R = \check{R}$$

Intuitively, we see that this means that the ordered pairs constituting the set

R determined by $R(x,y)$ are the same as the ordered pairs constituting the set $\check{R}$ determined by $R(y,x)$. $R(y,x)$ determines the set

$$\check{R} = \{\langle y,x \rangle : R(x,y)\}$$

while $R(x,y)$ determines

$$R = \{\langle x,y \rangle : R(x,y)\}$$

We may now express asymmetry as

$$\textbf{Asym(R)} \equiv R \cap \check{R} = \Lambda$$

Intuitively, we see that a relation is asymmetrical when no ordered pairs of the sets determined by it and its converse are the same.

Nonsymmetry is also simply expressed as

$$\textbf{Nonsym(R)} \equiv R \cap \check{R} \neq V$$

The concept of a relative product of two relations $R_1(x,y)$ and $R_2(x,y)$ can be expressed as

$$R_1/R_2 = \{\langle x,y \rangle : \sum_z(\langle x,z \rangle \in R_1 \ \& \ \langle z,y \rangle \in R_2)\}$$

In these terms the idea of transitivity becomes

$$\textbf{Tr(R)} \equiv R/R \subseteq R$$

The relative product of R with R, that is, the ordered pairs so determined, is included in R in the case of transitivity. As a final example we express connectedness,

$$\textbf{Con(R)} \equiv (R \cup \check{R} = \mathscr{F}R \times \mathscr{F}R)$$

Intuitively, we see that this means that all ordered pairs in R make up the union of R and its converse.

FUNCTIONS

Something further of the great power of the ideas of set theory can be suggested by showing how the idea of a function can be treated in these terms. Functions are used and studied in many branches of mathematics. There are books on the functions of a complex variable and the functions of a real variable, for example. Hence, we turn briefly to understanding functions as sets before considering, in the next chapter, some of the complications that arise when the rules of logic are applied to axiom systems involving sets.

We speak of a dyadic relation R on $S \times T$. In saying this, we refer to a subset of ordered pairs the first of whose elements comes from S and the second from T. If we represent R as a table of ordered pairs, letting $S = \{1, 2, 3\}$ and $\{T = 5, 6\}$

$$
\begin{array}{c|ccc}
6 & \cdot & \cdot & \cdot \\
5 & \cdot & \cdot & \cdot \\
\hline
 & 1 & 2 & 3
\end{array}
$$

we see that R could be the relation of *less than*. The domain of R is $\{1, 2, 3\}$ while the range of R is $\{5, 6\}$. 1 is not an element in the range because it is not a second member of any ordered pair constituting the relation.

We may now define a dyadic function as a relation in which each element in the domain has exactly one element in the range. (Triadic and, in general, *n*-adic functions have corresponding definitions.) In a table, this means that if we plot the set containing the domain on the abscissa, then there will be no more than one dot in each vertical column above these elements. Thus, the relation $<$, as we see immediately from the table, is not a function. On the other hand, the following table represents a function:

Here $S = \{1, 2, 3\}$ and $T = \{1, 5, 6\}$. The domain of R is S and the range of R is T. What is different about this relation is that for every x that is a member of the domain of R there exists exactly one y such that $y \in T$ and such that $R(x,y)$. We can see this by listing the ordered pairs from the table

$$\{\langle 1, 5\rangle, \langle 2, 6\rangle, \langle 3, 1\rangle\}$$

The following set of ordered pairs is a relation but not a function:

$$\{\langle 1, 5\rangle, \langle 1, 6\rangle, \langle 2, 6\rangle\}$$

whereas

$$\{\langle 1, 5\rangle, \langle 2, 5\rangle, \langle 3, 6\rangle\}$$

is a function. Hereafter, when a relation R is a function, we shall refer to it as f.

Any function can be represented on a table of a simpler sort than that required by a relation. For example, the table above can be simplified as follows:

x	1	2	3
f(x)	5	6	1

since we need only associate with each value of x in the ordered pair $\langle x,y\rangle$ one value of $y = f(x)$. That is, we can define a function by giving

(1) the sets S and T
(2) the domain of f (a subset of S)
(3) for each x in the domain, the corresponding y in T.

Note that according to the usual notation for functions, the element of T corresponding to each x in the domain is referred to as f(x).

When we write

$$f(x) = x^2 + 3$$

in ordinary algebra, we define a function. The sets S and T are the real numbers and S = T. The domain of f is S and the equation gives *the* corresponding number for each number in the domain. Of course, we often write the equation as

$$y = x^2 + 3$$

thus in effect giving the sets of ordered pairs

$$\langle x,y \rangle$$

which define the function; that is,

$$f = \{\langle x,y \rangle \in (S \times S): y = x^2 + 3\}$$

HIGHER ORDER APPLICATIONS

The examples of set notation so far given show its use in dealing with concepts we have previously expressed in GPL-1. Actually, in the history of mathematics, these concepts were first expressed in the terms of sets and only later, with the development of logic, in the terms of GPL-1. Perhaps the real strength of set theory, however, lies in its ability to express concepts of higher order logics. We noted in Chapter Six that the predicates used in stating concepts need not be restricted to those having individuals as values; that, in fact, one could introduce predicates having other predicates as values. Many of the properties of dyadic relations illustrate this point, and their expression in set notation illustrates the possibility of having sets of sets as well as sets of individuals. Thus

$$\mathbf{Totrx(R)} \equiv I \subseteq R$$

expresses a set that comprises those sets R that include I.

In the case of higher order logics, this introduction of sets of sets may be more complex than these examples. We may illustrate the more complex cases by means of the idea of simple order discussed in Chapter One.

The axioms of Chapter One formulate this concept as involving transitivity, irreflexivity, and connectedness. It is thus a relation between a set P and a relation R. We can write "P is simply ordered by R" in the notation of GPL as

$$\mathscr{SO}(P,R) \equiv \prod_x \prod_y \prod_z [[P(x) \,\&\, P(y) \,\&\, P(z)]$$
$$\supset (\sim R(x,x) \,\&\, \{x \neq y \supset [R(x,y) \vee R(y,x)]\} \,\&\, \{[R(x,y) \,\&\, R(y,z)] \supset R(x,z)\})]$$

It is intuitively clearer and simpler to observe that a set P is simply ordered when a dyadic relation exists such that $R \subseteq P$ where

     (1) $I \cap R = \Lambda$

     (2) $x \neq y \supset (R \cup \check{R} = \mathscr{F}R \times \mathscr{F}R)$

     (3) $R/R \subseteq R$

However, we are not intending to plead the cause of set notation. Rather, our purpose is to observe that the terms of set theory are widely used in mathematics, and to prepare for a discussion of the problems involved in inference in mathematics when concepts beyond the level of GPL-1 with identity are introduced. Mathematical concepts that are even more complex than simple order may be stated in terms of sets, provided we permit the introduction of sets of sets, sets of sets of sets, and, indeed, sets of sets of . . . of sets. Such formulations are the equivalents of GPL-2, GPL-3, and GPL-*n*. When we do this we might suppose that the rules of inference used so far could be carried along without modification, as was the case when we went from PL to GPL-1 and then to GPL-1 with identity in Part One. This is not the case, however, for the rules of inference we have so far used lead to paradox and contradiction when applied to set theory without restriction.

EXERCISE 12.7

I. Define the operations $R \cup R'$ and $R \cap R'$.

II. Construct two Cartesian Cross Products that satisfy the relation $R \subseteq R'$.

III. Given the following Cartesian Cross Products, construct the cross product that represents the intersection of R and R'.

3	(3, 2)	(3, 3)	(3, 4)		4	(4, 3)	(4, 4)	(4, 5)
2	(2, 2)	(2, 3)	(2, 4)		3	(3, 3)	(3, 4)	(3, 5)
1	(1, 2)	(1, 3)	(1, 4)		2	(2, 3)	(2, 4)	(2, 5)
	2	3	4			3	4	5

IV. Define the concepts *image* and *complement*.

V. From the Cartesian Cross Product below, pick out a symmetrical relation.

4	(4, 2)	(4, 3)	(4, 4)	(4, 5)
3	(3, 2)	(3, 3)	(3, 4)	(3, 5)
2	(2, 2)	(2, 3)	(2, 4)	(2, 5)
1	(1, 2)	(1, 3)	(1, 4)	(1, 5)
	2	3	4	5

VI. Which of the following sequences of ordered pairs constitute functions?

1. $(1, 1), (2, 2), (3, 3), \ldots, (n,n), \ldots$

2. $(1, 1), (1, 2), (2, 2), (2, 3), \ldots, (m,m), (m,m + 1), \ldots$

3. $(1, 2), (2, 3), (3, 4), \ldots, (m,m + 1), \ldots$

4. $(1, 2), (2, 2), (2, 3), (3, 3), \ldots, (m - 1,m), (m,m), (m,m + 1), \ldots$

VII. Which of the following relations are functions?

    1. identity

    2. is married to

    3. is a son of

    4. is the wife of

    5. is a friend of

SUGGESTED READINGS

1. G. Birkhoff and S. MacLane, *A Survey of Modern Algebra* (New York: The Macmillan Co., 1953), Ch. XI.

2. A. A. Fraenkel, *Abstract Set Theory* (Amsterdam: North Holland Pub. Co., 1953).

3. P. R. Halmos, *Naive Set Theory* (New York: Van Nostrand & Co., 1960).

4. E. Kamke, *Theory of Sets* (New York: Dover Pub., 1950).

5. R. B. Kershner and L. R. Wilcox, *The Anatomy of Mathematics* (New York: The Ronald Press Co., 1950), Ch. IV.

6. W. V. Quine, *Mathematical Logic*, rev. ed. (Cambridge, Mass.: Harvard Univ. Press, 1951), Ch. V.

7. R. L. Wilder, *Introduction to the Foundations of Mathematics* (New York: John Wiley & Sons, 1952), Ch. III.

Chapter 13

Logic and Set Theory

13.1 Contradictions and Paradoxes

If we permit the formulation of axioms involving sets of any kind at all (or, equivalently, permit the introduction of axioms requiring n^{th} order predicate logic) and if we proceed to use extensions of the rules of inference for GPL-1, the result will be inconsistency. For under these conditions it is quite easy to show that various contradictions can be derived. The contradictions existing in set theory have been known since 1895; yet no one has succeeded in producing much more than makeshift repairs. It is the purpose of this chapter to suggest the nature of the difficulties and to provide an introduction to some of the ways in which contemporary mathematicians and logicians have sought to deal with them.

RUSSELL'S CONTRADICTION

It seems quite likely that the creator of the modern theory of sets, Georg Cantor, was aware of some of the contradictions inherent in it as early as 1895. In 1902 Bertrand Russell formulated one of these contradictions in a very simple form. We begin with *Russell's Contradiction*.

When we think of a set, we consider it as comprising certain elements that belong to it. Thus we say $x \in S$. In speaking of a set and its elements we may intuitively conceive of the elements as individuals. However, as we have seen in Chapter Twelve, there is no reason for restricting the elements of sets to individuals; in fact, there is every reason for not doing so. If we speak of a library we may think of the elements belonging to this set as individual books.

But we need not think of these books as individuals, for each of them is a collection of pages. For that matter, each of the pages might be considered as a collection of sentences—and so on. In these terms, the library is a set of sets of sets—and so on. As well as being common enough in ordinary discourse, the conception of a set whose elements are sets is an essential part of mathematics. Thus, a relation, which is a set of ordered pairs each of which is a set, is a set of sets.

Not only may the elements of sets be themselves sets, but also sets may even be elements of themselves. Thus, the set of abstract ideas is itself an abstract idea. Again, we may observe that the set of all sets is itself a set, and so a member of itself. Such examples are rather rare, for in general sets are not members of themselves. Thus, the set of all cats is not a cat, nor is the set of all natural numbers a natural number. There thus seems to be a partition of sets into (1) all of those that are members of themselves and (2) those that are not members of themselves. Suppose that we form a set of the latter, that is,

$$\mathcal{O} = \{x : x \notin x\}$$

We use $\mathcal{O}$ as the first letter of "ordinary", since these sets are of the usual sort.

The set $\mathcal{O}$ is itself an ordinary set, as we can prove. Suppose it is not ordinary; then it is a member of itself. But all members of $\mathcal{O}$ are such that they are not members of themselves; therefore $\mathcal{O}$ is not a member of itself and so is ordinary.

On the other hand, the set $\mathcal{O}$ is not ordinary, as we can prove. Suppose it is ordinary; then it is not a member of itself. But all ordinary sets are members of $\mathcal{O}$; hence, (as $\mathcal{O}$ is not a member of $\mathcal{O}$) $\mathcal{O}$ is not ordinary.

The result of these two lines of reasoning is a clear contradiction. In the first we argue: if $\mathcal{O}$ is not ordinary then it is ordinary. In the second we argue: if $\mathcal{O}$ is ordinary then it is not ordinary. We must conclude that $\mathcal{O}$ is ordinary if and only if it is not ordinary. Evidently something is wrong—but equally evidently the error is not in our proofs! Perhaps the rigor of the proofs is more apparent in symbolic form.

We can argue:

1. $\prod_x [x \in \mathcal{O} \supset x \notin x]$ By definition of $\mathcal{O}$
2. $(\mathcal{O} \in \mathcal{O}) \supset (\mathcal{O} \notin \mathcal{O})$ 1, $\prod$E

Thus, if $\mathcal{O}$ is a member of $\mathcal{O}$, *i.e.*, not ordinary, then $\mathcal{O}$ is not a member of $\mathcal{O}$, *i.e.*, ordinary. This is *not* a contradiction. However,

1'. $\prod_x [x \notin x \supset x \in \mathcal{O}]$ By definition of $\mathcal{O}$
2'. $(\mathcal{O} \notin \mathcal{O}) \supset (\mathcal{O} \in \mathcal{O})$ 1, $\prod$E

Lines 2 and 2' give us

3. $(\mathcal{O} \in \mathcal{O}) \equiv (\mathcal{O} \notin \mathcal{O})$

which is a contradiction.

The existence of this contradiction tells us that axiom systems admitting axioms referring to all kinds of sets without restriction are inconsistent, if we permit the use of the usual rules of inference. The seriousness of this fact can hardly be exaggerated. It calls for a fundamental analysis of the nature of axiom systems and rules of inference. It requires either a restriction on the use of axiom systems and rules of inference, or a modification of their nature, if contradictions are to be avoided.

THE BURALI-FORTI CONTRADICTION

In 1897, the mathematician Césare Burali-Forti published an article that called attention to a contradiction in set theory. The *Burali-Forti Contradiction* is more complicated than that of Russell, but it suggests that the avoidance of contradiction is not to be attained by merely eliminating reference to the set of all sets not members of themselves.

Consider the axioms for the relation $<$ given in Section One of Chapter One. Slightly modified, these are:

Ax. 1. $\prod_x\prod_y[x \neq y \supset (x < y \lor y < x)]$

Ax. 2. $\prod_x\prod_y(x < y \supset x \neq y)$

Ax. 3. $\prod_x\prod_y\prod_z[(x < y \ \& \ y < z) \supset x < z]$

Any set of elements for which these axioms and the properties of identity hold is said to be *simply ordered*. An example of a simply ordered set is any subset of natural numbers—for example, {2, 107, 15, 34}, as ordered by $<$.

Not all sets are simply ordered. Consider a set of sets ordered by the relation $\subseteq$, as, for instance, the set of elements satisfying the axioms of Boolean algebra. It is true that if $x \subseteq y$ and $y \subseteq z$, then $x \subseteq z$, so that Ax. 3 is satisfied. But it is not necessarily the case that if $x \neq y$ then $x \subseteq y$ or $y \subseteq x$ since x and y might overlap one another. Thus Ax. 1 is not satisfied. Nor is Ax. 2, owing to the fact that $x \subseteq x$ is always true. The set of elements of Boolean algebra is accordingly said to be *partially ordered* rather than simply ordered.

In addition to satisfying all the axioms listed above, the subset of natural numbers under discussion also satisfies the following:

Ax. 4. $\prod_x\sum_y((x < y) \ \& \ \prod_z\{(x < z) \supset [(z = y) \lor (y < z)]\})$
(*i.e.*, each element has an immediate successor).

Ax. 5. Every non-empty subset has a first element. It follows from this axiom that the set as a whole has a first element:

$$\sum_x\prod_y[(y \neq x) \supset (x < y)]$$

Sets that satisfy Axioms 1–5 are said to be *well ordered.* Not only any set of natural numbers but also the set of *all* natural numbers is well ordered. So is the set of all rational numbers:

$$\langle 1, 2, 3, \ldots ; \tfrac{1}{2}, \tfrac{3}{2}, \tfrac{5}{2}, \ldots ; \tfrac{1}{3}, \tfrac{2}{3}, \tfrac{4}{3}, \ldots ; \ldots \rangle$$

Notice that two or more well-ordered sets can be combined to form a well-ordered set, although not every such combination will be well ordered. Thus, suppose that $a_1, a_2, a_3, \ldots$ and $b_1, b_2, b_3, \ldots$ are well-ordered sets of constants. Then

$$\langle a_1, a_2, a_3, \ldots ; b_1, b_2, b_3, \ldots \rangle$$

will be well ordered, too; for all the postulates, including 5, are satisfied. On the other hand,

$$\langle a_1, a_2, a_3, \ldots ; \ldots b_i, \ldots, b_3, b_2, b_1 \rangle$$

is not well ordered, since the subset comprising the b's has no first element.

Next, consider the following ordered triples which are, at the same time, well-ordered sets:

$$\langle 0, 1, 2 \rangle$$
$$\langle 1, 2, 3 \rangle$$
$$\langle 6, 17, 103 \rangle$$

These three well-ordered sets are said to be *ordinally similar*; this means that to every member of either set there corresponds one and only one member of the other, and the order of any two elements in one set is the same as the order of the corresponding elements in the other. We can now form the set of *all* well-ordered sets that are ordinally similar to some one of these given well-ordered sets. This set is called the *ordinal number* of each of these well-ordered sets.

Not all well-ordered sets, of course, are ordinally similar. Consider the following two sets, for example:

$$S_1 = \langle 0, 1, 2 \rangle$$
$$S_2 = \langle 0, 1, 2, 3 \rangle$$

Since there is no element of S_1 that corresponds to the element 3 of S_2, the sets are not ordinally similar. In fact, S_1 is ordinally similar to the segment of S_2 that comprises its first three members. So we say that $S_1 < S_2$. In general, when T and U are well-ordered sets, $T < U$ if and only if T is ordinally similar to some definite initial segment of U. (We shall make no effort here to define *initial segment*, but will suppose the idea to be intuitively clear.)

When two well-ordered sets T and U are such that $T < U$, we can also say that the ordinal number of T precedes the ordinal number of U. Thus, let α and β be ordinal numbers. Then $\alpha < \beta$ if and only if every member of the set α precedes every member of the set β; *i.e.*, if any given member of α is ordinally similar to a definite initial segment of each member of β. Thus, the ordinal numbers are themselves ordered by the relation $<$.

Now let us consider what ordinal numbers there are. So far, our examples have been well-ordered sets whose ordinal numbers are finite. It is evident, however, that there can be infinite ordinal numbers. Consider, for instance, the ordinal number of the set of all the natural numbers. Let us refer to this infinite ordinal number as ω. Accordingly, ω is the ordinal number of the well-ordered set

$$\langle 1, 2, 3, \ldots \rangle$$

Now consider the set

$$\langle 1, 2, 3, \ldots ; 1 \rangle$$

Since any member of ω is ordinally similar to a definite initial segment of this set, ω is smaller than the ordinal number of this set, which is referred to as $\omega + 1$. Similarly, there is $\omega + 2$ such that $\omega + 1 < \omega + 2$, and so on up to $\omega + \omega$, or 2ω; *i.e.*,

$$\langle 1, 2, 3, \ldots ; 1, 2, 3, \ldots \rangle$$

Nor is 2ω by any means the last ordinal number. Beyond it, there is $2\omega + 1, \ldots 3\omega, \ldots \omega \cdot \omega, \ldots \omega^\omega, \ldots \omega^{\omega+1}, \ldots \omega^{\omega+2}, \ldots \omega^{\omega^\omega}, \ldots$ and so on. Let ε be the ordinal number $\omega^{\omega^{\omega^{\cdots}}}$. Then $\varepsilon + 1$ will be an ordinal number greater than ε.

It is intuitively clear, although we have not proved this, that the set of all ordinal numbers, as ordered by the relation $<$, is itself well ordered. All of the Axioms 1–5 above are satisfied by the set of ordinal numbers arranged in the indicated order. One important consequence of the fact that the set of all ordinal numbers is itself well ordered is that this set will have an ordinal number. It is on this ordinal number, called Ω, that the Burali-Forti Contradiction rests. Since Ω is the ordinal number of the set of all ordinal numbers, any ordinal x must be smaller than Ω or equal to it. Let us illustrate this point. Ω is the ordinal number of the set

$$\langle 1, 2, \ldots ; \omega, \omega + 1, \ldots ; 2\omega, \ldots, \omega^2; \ldots, \omega^\omega; \ldots ; \varepsilon, \ldots \rangle$$

Now consider, for example, the ordinal number $\omega + 2$. This is the ordinal number of the set

$$\langle 1, 2, 3, \ldots ; 1, 2 \rangle$$

which is ordinally similar to

$$\langle 1, 2, 3, \ldots ; \omega, \omega + 1 \rangle$$

But this last set is a definite initial segment of Ω. It follows from the definition of $<$ given above that $(\omega + 2) < \Omega$. But exactly the same argument would apply to any ordinal number whatever, excepting only Ω itself. Thus, for any x that is an ordinal number, $x < \Omega$, or at best $x = \Omega$. Now let x be $\Omega + 1$. Then $(\Omega + 1) < \Omega$. This result might be acceptable but for the fact that for any ordinal number x, $x < (x + 1)$, whence $\Omega < (\Omega + 1)$. We have here an outright contradiction.*

---

* This way of formulating the contradiction owes something to Irving M. Copi, "The Burali-Forti Paradox", *Philosophy of Science*, Vol. 25 (1958), pp. 281–286.

THE RICHARD PARADOX

Consider the set of all the numbers that can be defined by means of a finite number of symbols of, say, the English language. Such numbers will include fractions which, like $\frac{1}{3}$ and $\frac{1}{7}$, are expressible as repeating decimals. Let us enumerate all the nonrepeating decimals. Thus if a_1, a_2, ... ; b_1, b_2, ... ; c_1, c_2, ... are all specific digits, the set of all nonrepeating decimals can be represented as follows:

First member: $0.\ a_1\ a_2\ a_3\ a_4\ a_5\ ...$
Second member: $0.\ b_1\ b_2\ b_3\ b_4\ b_5\ ...$
Third member: $0.\ c_1\ c_2\ c_3\ c_4\ c_5\ ...$
Fourth member: $0.\ d_1\ d_2\ d_3\ d_4\ d_5\ ...$
Fifth member: $0.\ e_1\ e_2\ e_3\ e_4\ e_5\ ...$

       ⋮   ⋮

Now consider the nonrepeating decimal v, defined as follows. After the decimal point, $a_1 + 1$ is its first digit, $b_2 + 1$ is its second, $c_3 + 1$ is its third, $d_4 + 1$ is its fourth, $e_5 + 1$ is its fifth, and in general its nth digit is one more than the nth digit of the nth member of the list. (In case the nth digit of the nth member is 9, the nth digit of v is 0.) Thus

$$v = 0.\ a_1 + 1\ b_2 + 1\ c_3 + 1\ d_4 + 1\ e_5 + 1\ ...$$

Now it is clear that for every n, v will differ from the nth member of the complete list of nonrepeating decimals; *i.e.*, it will differ from every member of the list. In other words, it will not appear on the list at all. Yet the list is composed of every number that can be defined by means of a finite number of symbols (other than fractions expressible as repeating decimals, of which v is clearly not one). It follows that v is not definable by means of a finite number of symbols. Yet in specifying how v is to be constructed, we have unambiguously defined it by means of a finite number of symbols. This is a paradox.

It is important to note the reason why we have referred to the Richard *Paradox* but to the Russell *Contradiction* and to the Burali-Forti *Contradiction*. The Contradictions are more fundamental difficulties, as we may see if we observe that the method used to form the number v fundamentally involves characterization in a language. Difficulties in formulating a concept linguistic-ally seem less central than inconsistency as such. Because of this linguistic reference, the paradoxes are often called *semantical* paradoxes. And of course some contradictions are more fundamental than others. When we are confronted with a contradiction, it is well to ask what inconsistent conditions are being imposed upon a set, and whether the difficulty could not be avoided by supposing the set to be empty. Thus while we can hardly suppose the set of all sets not members of themselves to be empty (Russell's Contradiction), some of the sets defined in Exercise II below might readily be viewed as null.

IMPREDICATIVE DEFINITIONS

A definition is said to be *impredicative* when it defines a concept in terms of a totality to which it belongs. This kind of definition seems a condition of the contradictions implicit in set theory. Thus Russell's Contradiction involves the definition of the set of all sets not members of themselves in terms of the set of all sets. That is, we consider the set of all sets and partition it into (1) the sets that are not members of themselves and (2) the sets that are members of themselves. Now the set of all sets not members of themselves belongs to the set of all sets. In order to gain a definition of this set, we ask to which of the two subsets of the set of all sets it belongs—thus seeking to define it in terms of the totality to which it belongs—and we thus generate the contradiction. Similarly, in the case of the Burali-Forti Contradiction we consider the set of all ordinal numbers. This set is itself an ordinal number, and we ask where it falls in the ordering of these numbers and thus generate the contradiction. In the case of the Richard Paradox we consider all numbers that can be defined by a finite number of symbols in the English language. This set includes the number v, which is defined by reference to the totality of such numbers. We ask whether v is a member of this set and thus generate the paradox. As it happens, this kind of reasoning, often called *self-referential*, is involved in other contradictions and paradoxes as well.

Poincaré, the important French mathematician, and Russell have both argued that the contradictions and paradoxes could be avoided by eliminating impredicative definitions of concepts from admissible axioms. Unfortunately, this cannot be done without also eliminating too much of mathematics. Impredicative definitions seem essential in stating the concept of *least upper bound*, which defines the real numbers. They are also essential to defining the cardinal numbers, as the next section will show.

EXERCISE 13.1

I. Restate Russell's Contradiction in terms of predicates; that is, by considering those predicates which are not predicable of themselves, develop a contradiction in terms of GPL.

II. Would you class the following as a contradiction or a paradox? Why? Which involve impredicative definitions? Which could be resolved by supposing the set defined to be null?

1. The Barber of Seville shaves all the men of Seville who do not shave themselves, and these are the only men he shaves. Does the Barber of Seville shave himself?

2. The sentence designated II, 2 on this page is false. (Is it?)

3. Paul, in the Epistle to Titus in the New Testament, attributes to Epimenides, a citizen of Crete, the statement "All Cretans are liars". (Are they?)

4. Suppose that a crocodile has stolen a child but promises to return the child, provided the father correctly guesses whether it will return the child or not. What will the crocodile do if the father correctly guesses that the crocodile will not return the child?

5. Suppose that an ancient king stops all persons who attempt to enter his kingdom and tells them that they can make one statement to the captain of the border patrol. He adds that if this statement is true he will have them hanged, while if it is false he will have them beheaded. What can such persons say?

6. In 1908 Grelling observed that certain words in English have the property of referring to themselves correctly. That is, "English" is an English word and "short" is a short word. On the other hand, most words do not have this property of correct self-reference, as, for example, "long" is not a long word nor is "French" a French word. If we call the words which do not refer to themselves correctly *heterological*, are we to say that *heterological* is a heterological word?

III. In stating Russell's Contradiction we assumed that $\vdash [(\mathcal{O}) \equiv (\mathcal{O})] \supset [(\mathcal{O})\ \&\ (\mathcal{O})]$. What rules of logic are involved here? Would it be possible to eliminate some of these rules and avoid the contradiction? (Hint: Could we make use of 3-valued logic?)

13.2 The Importance of Sets

The easiest way to avoid the inconsistency implicit in set theory would be to eliminate sets from mathematics. Poincaré once remarked that "Sets are a disease from which mathematics will eventually recover". Perhaps, then, following the metaphor, surgery is what is needed. Before undertaking surgery, however, let us try to get an idea of what is being amputated, for the truth is that removing sets from mathematics is pretty much like amputating the body of a man from his arm.

One of the most impressive accomplishments of the nineteenth century in mathematics was the arithmetization of analysis. This achievement is a demonstration that analysis can be based upon integers and infinite sets of integers. The point that interests us here is that an understanding of analysis requires us to assume the existence of real numbers, which are sets of sets. There would be no point in outlining this accomplishment here, for even an outline presupposes a considerable specialized acquaintance with mathematics. We can render the accomplishment plausible, however, by showing how we can use the idea of sets as a basis for an understanding of the cardinal numbers and by indicating the direction which further extension of these ideas would take. This will suggest something of the power of the concept of a set as a mathematical tool and its importance in mathematics.

Throughout the following discussion, it should be borne in mind that we are talking about cardinal numbers. These should not be confused with the ordinal numbers discussed in connection with the Burali-Forti Contradiction. The concept of a number is encountered so early in our education that it becomes a part of our tools of thought without being subjected to analysis itself. It is usually only in an advanced course in algebra or logic that the nature of the numbers we first dealt with in primary school is called into question and an account of number actually given. There are mathematicians, such as the Intuitionists, who assert that any account given of number must, in the nature of the case, be less fundamental than the idea of number itself; but this too constitutes taking number in a sophisticated way; that is, deliberately asserting it to be ultimate. Our task at the moment is to substitute an explicit statement of the nature of number for the naïve understanding of number which everyone has. The definition of cardinal number that we shall develop here we owe essentially to Frege.*

As soon as we ask what a number is, we see that it cannot be an individual. That is, no amount of analysis of individuals as such could give us more than the number 1, since each individual is exactly a unit. However, we can see something of what a number is if we note that two individuals constitute a pair, and three individuals constitute a triad. Two apples are a pair, and two-ness is a property not of apples but of a set. That is, a set of two apples has the property of being a pair. Further, a set of three apples has the property of being a triad. When we speak of the number 2, however, we do not refer to the property of being a pair as possessed by this set of two apples alone; rather, we refer to the two-ness of all pairs. This means that the number 2 is the set of all pairs, while the number 3 is the set of all triads. In general, a *cardinal number* is the set of all sets having the same number of elements.

Our definition of cardinal number, however, may appear circular, since it contains the word *number*. But there is nothing wrong in saying that a cardinal number is the set of all sets having the same number of elements, provided that we view the phrase "same number" as a kind of hyphenated word "same-number" not containing the word "number" in the usual sense. The point is that the definition given presupposes our ability to determine a one-to-one correspondence between sets, but not our ability to count the numbers. (This one-to-one correspondence may be called *cardinal similarity* by analogy with the ordinal similarity discussed in connection with the Burali-Forti Contradiction). Thus, we can easily check to see whether the

---

* See *The Foundations of Arithmetic*, translated by J. L. Austin, second ed. (Oxford: Basil Blackwell, 1953).

fingers on a right-hand and a left-hand glove are the same-number. We can do this by putting the gloves on our hands and placing our hands together palm to palm. By this method we establish the correspondence of elements in the gloves, but we do not count these elements. We can generalize this method to establish a one-to-one correspondence between the elements of any two sets (if this correspondence exists) without counting them. Thus, the definition of a cardinal number is not circular.

Let us now restate these points in a more technical way. When we say that a set of a single element has the cardinal number 1, we mean that this set is a member of the set of all sets having a single element. If we use the notation of unit classes developed in Chapter Twelve, we can express this set as

$$1 = \hat{x}[\textstyle\sum_y (x = \iota y)]$$

The number zero is even simpler. According to what has just been said, it will be the set of all sets without members. We know, however, that there is only one set without members; namely, Λ. Thus, zero is the set containing only Λ; or

$$0 = \iota \Lambda$$

We may now return to our explanation of the number 2 as the set of all pairs. Now the set whose elements are x and y may be written as $\iota x \cup \iota y$. And the set of all such pairs will be

$$2 = \hat{x}\{\textstyle\sum_y \sum_z [(y \neq z) \,\&\, (x = \iota y \cup \iota z)]\}$$

Notice that we do not insist that the pairs belonging to 2 be *ordered*; 2 is not an ordinal number. On the other hand, the members of each pair must be distinct; for if $x = y$, then $(\iota x \cup \iota y) = (\iota x \cup \iota x) = \iota x$, and our pair has vanished.

We can obviously proceed in the same way; *e.g.*,

$$5 = \hat{x}\{\textstyle\sum_{y_1} \sum_{y_2} \sum_{y_3} \sum_{y_4} \sum_{y_5} [(y_1 \neq y_2) \,\&\, (y_1 \neq y_3)$$
$$\&\, (y_1 \neq y_4) \,\&\, (y_1 \neq y_5) \,\&\, (y_2 \neq y_3) \,\&\, (y_2 \neq y_4)$$
$$\&\, (y_2 \neq y_5) \,\&\, (y_3 \neq y_4) \,\&\, (y_3 \neq y_5) \,\&\, (y_4 \neq y_5)$$
$$\&\, (x = \iota y_1 \cup \iota y_2 \cup \iota y_3 \cup \iota y_4 \cup \iota y_5)]\}$$

In omitting certain parentheses, we are assuming that the operation of set-union obeys the associative law. In fact, it does.

We now define the set of all cardinal numbers. We might try this by writing

$$C = \{1, 2, 3, \ldots\}$$

But this "definition" is defective in two ways. For one thing, it does not specify the property by virtue of which anything is entitled to membership in C. In the case of a finite set, this is no drawback, since we can make an exhaustive list of the set's members. But in the present case, the defect is serious, for the dots cannot tell us, for instance, that 76,027 is a member of C, or that V and $\iota\Lambda$ are not members. We may say that we know how to fill in the dots; but the problem here is to specify what it is that we know; *i.e.*, what property attaches to all and only those things that belong to C.

The second defect of the definition just given is that even if the dots constituted an unambiguous criterion of membership, the result of filling them in would not be an exhaustive list of cardinal numbers. For the members of the series 1, 2, 3, . . . are at best the *finite* cardinal numbers. The existence of infinite cardinal numbers has been known since the time of Cantor.

Both of these defects can be remedied if we define C in terms of same-number or cardinal similarity. As has already been suggested, two sets are cardinally similar when they can be put in one-to-one correspondence. A one-to-one correspondence between sets S_1 and S_2 is a relation R such that for each member, x, of S_1 there is exactly one member, x', of S_2 such that xRx', and for each member, y, of S_2 there is exactly one member, y', of S_1 such that yRy'. If we express the relation *is cardinally similar to* as $\approx$ we can write

$$S_1 \approx S_2 \equiv \sum_R [\prod_x (x \in S_1 \supset \sum_y \{y \in S_2 \,\&\, xRy$$
$$\&\, \prod_z [(z \in S_2 \,\&\, xRz) \supset z = y]\})$$
$$\&\, \prod_x (x \in S_2 \supset \sum_y \{y \in S_1 \,\&\, xRy$$
$$\&\, \prod_z [(z \in S_1 \,\&\, xRz) \supset z = y]\})]$$

The first half of this existentially quantified conjunction states that to every x in S_1 there corresponds one and only one y in S_2, and the second conjunct states that to every x in S_2 there corresponds one and only one y in S_1. This relation of correspondence is sometimes characterized as *bi-unique*.

We can now define C as the set of all sets of sets in one-to-one correspondence with any given set:

$$C = \hat{z}\sum_y[z = \hat{x}(x \approx y)]$$

This definition does not restrict the membership of C to finite cardinals. Indeed, it explicitly includes infinite cardinals. Infinite cardinals, such as the cardinal number of the set of all real numbers between 0 and 1, or the cardinal number of all finite cardinal numbers, are no less sets of cardinally similar sets than are their finite counterparts. Indeed, the notion of cardinal similarity enters into a celebrated definition of an infinite set as *one that is cardinally similar to at least one of its own subsets*. For example, the set F of all finite cardinals is

$$F = \{1, 2, 3, \ldots\}$$

(We can write this expression as long as we do not claim that it is a definition.) Now consider the set F_e of all even finite cardinals:

$$F_e = \{2, 4, 6, \ldots\}$$

It is fairly evident both that $F_c \approx F$ and that $F_e \subset F$. Hence, F is cardinally similar to at least one of its own subsets. So F is itself an infinite set. The cardinal number of this set is $\aleph_0$ (read "aleph-null"), the smallest of the so-called transfinite cardinals.

Beginning with the above definition of cardinals, we can define the set F of finite cardinals as follows:

$$F = \hat{z}\{\textstyle\sum_y [z = \hat{x}(x \approx y)] \& \sim(z \subset y) \& \sim(y \subset z)\}$$

This is, however, a negative definition of F—we are merely saying that F comprises the cardinals that are not infinite. A positive definition is often given in terms of the notion of *the successor of* a cardinal. We do not define that notion here, but if we say that the cardinal y' is the successor of y, we may state the following positive definition of F:

$$F = \hat{x}[x \in C \ \& \ 0 \in x \ \& \ \textstyle\prod_y(y \in x \supset y' \in x)]$$

Thus F is to consist of those cardinal numbers to which mathematical induction applies.

The cardinal numbers are the numbers we use in counting. We have succeeded in giving a definition of them using the concept of sets. The definition is elaborate and is not likely to replace our intuition in practice. However, it may be developed further to include rationals, reals, and other numbers. A result of this use of set theory is a unification of much of mathematics on the foundation of set theory. It is for these reasons that the elimination of set theory from mathematics cannot be regarded as practical.

It is also interesting to note that the definition of finite cardinals is impredicative. In expressing the property of being a finite cardinal, we presuppose the properties of being a cardinal number, that is, we give our definition in terms of the set of cardinal numbers of which the finite cardinals are members. We see from this example that impredicative definitions are close to the heart of mathematics and that their elimination is hardly practical. We must look for a solution to the problem of the contradictions in set theory along some other path.

EXERCISE 13.2

I. Show how two sets may be tested for one-to-one correspondence without counting.

II. Why is there no circularity in using numerical subscripts in the definition of the cardinal number 5?

III. What would it mean to say that the set of all finite cardinals and the set of rational numbers have the same cardinal number? Do they? (Hint: Recall the method of enumerating wffs in Chapter Eleven. Can the rational numbers be enumerated this way?)

IV. Show that each infinite subset of the natural numbers has the cardinal number aleph-null ($\aleph_0$).

V. If we begin with the conception of finite numbers, can a definition of infinite numbers be phrased in terms analogous to the negative definition of finite cardinals? What is it?

VI. Does the concept of the set of all cardinal numbers generate a contradiction?

13.3   Axiomatic Set Theory

The contradictions discussed in Section 13.1 show that the idea of a set must be modified to avoid inconsistency; but the applications of the ideas of set theory to the study of number suggest the power of this tool and its fundamental importance in mathematics. In order to be consistent in retaining the results obtainable in set theory, it is necessary to formulate the nature of sets with care. This may be done in various ways: (1) by setting up an axiomatically restricted set theory; (2) by arranging sets in an order of types beginning with sets containing individuals and proceeding to sets having just these as elements and so on; or, (3) by trying to rebuild mathematical reasoning so that it will be able to deal with sets containing infinities of members without inconsistency. Each of these approaches is aimed at avoiding the contradictions; and each has its own enthusiastic advocates. We shall say something about each, beginning in this section with the attempt to remove the contradictions by a suitable choice of axioms.

It seems clear that the problem of avoiding the contradictions might be solved by placing some sort of restrictions on sets and their use. Zermelo, a mathematician prominent in the development of set theory, conceived the idea of placing this restriction upon sets by developing an axiom system in which the undefined terms in addition to those of logic were *set* and $\in$. He then sought to introduce only those axioms governing the use of set and $\in$ that would yield all of mathematics short of the contradictions. In particular, he thought, it would be possible to introduce an axiom governing the existence of sets, thus avoiding the dangerously large set of all sets.

Let us examine briefly a version of Zermelo's axioms as illustrative of his approach and of that of his followers.* We begin with the terms *set* and $\in$, which is a dyadic relation between sets. In these terms, we can define the relation $=$ between sets. This we do as follows:

> If s and t are sets, and every member of s is a member of t, and every member of t is a member of s, we say that $s = t$.

---

* The formulation of the axioms presented here is due to A. A. Fraenkel. See, for example, his *Abstract Set Theory* (Amsterdam: North Holland Pub. Co., 1953).

In symbols

$$s = t \equiv_{\text{df}} \prod_x (x \in s \equiv x \in t)$$

The reader will recognize this as a version of the principle of extensionality given in Chapter Twelve.

We now state the first of Zermelo's axioms:

Ax. 1.   If s, t, and u are sets, and $s \in u$ and $s = t$, then $t \in u$.

In symbols, this becomes

$$\prod_s \prod_t \prod_u [(s \in u \ \& \ s = t) \supset t \in u]$$

Notice that this axiom cannot be deduced from the definition of $=$ between sets. From the premises that $s \in u$ and $\prod_x (x \in s \equiv x \in t)$ it does not necessarily follow that $t \in u$.

Since our purpose is just to suggest the way in which axioms can be introduced to ground set theory safely, rather than to deduce the theory, it will be more helpful to comment on the axioms than to use them in proving theorems. With regard to Ax. 1 we observe that it makes use of familiar ideas, such as those expressed by $\prod$ and $\supset$. Axiomatic set theory, like any other axiomatic theory, presupposes an underlying logic. In particular, the rules required will be those of GPL-1 as they have been developed in preceding chapters. If we add the rules of $=$I and $=$E to GPL-1, Ax. 1 would be unnecessary.

We turn now to the *axiom of pairing*:

Ax. 2.   If s and t are different sets, then there is a set $\{s, t\}$ such that $s \in \{s, t\}$ and $t \in \{s, t\}$. Further, if $x \in \{s, t\}$ then $(x = s) \lor (x = t)$.

This axiom may be expressed in terms of logical symbolism as

$$\prod_s \prod_t \{s \neq t \supset \sum_u \prod_v [v \in u = (v = s \lor v = t)]\}$$

This reveals a good deal about Zermelo's approach, for it is an axiom telling us how to construct sets *if we have some sets to begin with*. Thus, all that Ax. 2 says is that *if* we have sets s, t, u . . . that are different from one another, we may construct such sets as

$$\{s, t\}, \ \{s, u\}, \ \{\{s, t\}, \ \{s, u\}\}, \ \text{etc.}$$

Since we shall need sets having more than two members, we need a stronger axiom, such as

Ax. 3.   If there is a set s which contains at least one member, then there is a set which has as members all members of the members of s and only the members of the members of s.

Symbolically,

$$\prod_s \sum_t \prod_x [x \in t \equiv \sum_y (x \in y \ \& \ y \in s)]$$

This is known as the *axiom of summation*.

Suppose that Ax. 2 has given us $\{s, t\}$. Ax. 3 then gives us $s \cup t$, that is, the set made up of the elements of the elements of $\{s,t\}$. Notice that Ax. 3 presupposes that if s has any members, then these members will themselves have members. An alternative to this presupposition is the assumption that some members of sets are individuals that are not themselves sets, and consequently have no members of their own. We might have difficulty in specifying the members of the members of the set of all apples, or of the set of all points. The Theory of Types, which we shall discuss later, does in fact assume that there are individuals which do not themselves have members. If we wish to revise Zermelo's axioms so as to incorporate this assumption, we can do so, but the result is more complicated than the present set of axioms.

Ax. 4.   If there is a set, s, then there is a set whose members are the subsets of s.

This is called *the axiom of the set of subsets*.
Symbolically,

$$\prod_s \sum_t \prod_r (r \in t \equiv r \subseteq s)$$

The function of Ax. 4 is to make possible the construction of the nondenumerable sets required for the theory of real numbers. Briefly, the rationale is this: if $\aleph_0$ is the cardinal number of any denumerably infinite set, then the smallest nondenumerably infinite set would have the cardinal number $2^{\aleph_0}$. But since any set of n members has 2^n subsets, $2^{\aleph_0}$ is exactly the number of subsets of any denumerably infinite set. However, because we are interested in the way the axioms provide for the sets needed rather than the details of development, we ignore the technical problems here.

Ax. 5.   If there is a set, s, and a property, F, there is a set that contains just those members of s which satisfy the property F in a definite way.

This is *the axiom of subset formation*.
With it, Zermelo avoids the occurrence of contradictions that result when we allow a set simply to be defined by any property. Zermelo says that sets are defined by properties only on the basis of previously existing sets, s, and not in general. Thus, if we introduce properly restricted sets in later axioms, we can avoid defining sets having the property, *e.g.*, of not being members of themselves. Notice the difference between Ax. 5, which may be symbolized as

$$\prod_s \sum_r \prod_t \{t \in r \equiv [t \in s \ \& \ F(t)]\}$$

and the Principle of Abstraction of intuitive set theory stated in Chapter
Twelve, Section Three:

$$\sum_r \prod_t [t \in r \equiv F(t)]$$

This difference gives significance to the phrase "in a definite way" used in the
axiom, for it relates membership to specific sets. Thus, if we consider the set
s of integers, there is no definite way in which we can select integers having the
property, F, of being round. The gain is precision in selecting the subsets of
a set determined by a predicate.

Other subsets may be obtained by

Ax. 6.   *The axiom of choice.*

Essentially, the axiom of choice assures us that if we have a set, *s*, of
mutually exclusive sets, $T_1, T_2 \ldots$, and $\Lambda \neq s$, then there is a subset of *s* made
up of one element from each of $T_1, T_2, \ldots$ that is not Λ. The axiom of choice
is used in other formulations of set theory as well as Zermelo's. Because of its
role in the definition of multiplication, it is sometimes spoken of as the
multiplicative axiom.

Zermelo's seventh axiom asserts the existence of an infinite set. This
assertion, together with the preceding axioms for building sets out of sets,
provides the basis for set theory.

We turn now to this *axiom of infinity.*

Ax. 7.   There exists at least one set *s*, such that $\Lambda \in s$ and if $x \in s$ then
$\{x\} \in s$.

We might, of course, assert less than this. However, we need an infinite
set if we are to formulate the concept of number, since the natural numbers are
infinite. The present Ax. 7 provides for the development of the natural
numbers. For example, if Λ is a member of *s*, then *s* contains all of the
following:

$$\Lambda, \{\Lambda\}, \{\{\Lambda\}\}, \{\{\{\Lambda\}\}\}, \ldots$$

This corresponds to the familiar sequence

$$1, 2, 3, 4, \ldots$$

The last axiom we need to consider here imposes a further restriction on
sets that are permissible.

Ax. 8.   Every non-empty set *s*, contains a member *u* such that *u* and *s* have
no common member.

Symbolically, this is to say

$$\prod_s \{\sum_x (x \in s) \supset \sum_u [(u \in s) \,\&\, \prod_y \sim (y \in s \,\&\, y \in u)]\}$$

Clearly, the function of Ax. 8 is to render impossible the construction of such sets as are members of themselves, that is, $s \in s$; or such conjunctions as $s \in t$ & $t \in s$, etc., which lead to contradictions.

Fundamentally, then, Zermelo's approach permits the introduction of just those sets required to develop an adequate part of classical mathematics, but *not* those sets that lead to contradictions. There are many other ways as well in which axiomatic set theory may be formulated and many problems in its formulation as may be seen by examining recent developments in the work of Von Neumann, Bernays, Gödel and others. Perhaps its most objectionable characteristic is the tendency in it to avoid the inconsistencies rather than to understand their source. However, this is a relative matter, for the use of axioms does throw light on those characteristics of sets that produce inconsistency.

EXERCISE 13.3

    I. Show that Ax. 1 can be replaced by $=$I and $=$E.

    II. Assume that the set $\{1, 2, 3, 4, 5\}$ exists. Form all the sets possible according to Ax. 2.

    III. Assume that the set $\{\{1, 2\}, \{3\}, \{7, 6\}\}$ exists. Form the set determined by Ax. 3.

    IV. From the sets formed in Exercise II, form the set determined by Ax. 3.

    V. Assume the set in Exercise II. Form the subsets determined by Ax. 4.

    VI. In Ax. 5, what set is formed if F holds of no members of s? Is there only one such set? (Hint: Use the idea of extensionality.)

    VII. Using Ax. 5 and Ax. 2, prove that the null set exists.

    VIII. What are some properties F that are not satisfied by the members of $\{\frac{1}{2}, \frac{1}{4}, 1, 2\}$ in a *definite way*? What are some that are thus satisfied?

    IX. In Exercise VII we prove the existence of the null set. Why is this insufficient—that is, why is Ax. 7 necessary?

    X. One of the assumptions in the formulation of the Russell Contradiction is that $x \notin x$ determines a set. Does Ax. 8 deny this assumption?

13.4 Logical Types

In a way, Axioms 5 and 8 in Zermelo's set theory are the most important, for they restrict the predicates which can be used to define sets and so prevent the occurrence of Russell's Contradiction. But it seemed to Russell and to others that this result could be achieved more satisfactorily by introducing a rule of formation for formulas, according to which no symbol could be repeated on both sides of ∈.* Such a rule would prevent the occurrence of $s \notin s$ (*i.e.*, $\sim(s \in s)$) in the paradox-generating statement

$$\sum_s \prod_r (s \in r \equiv s \notin s)$$

Thus, in a general way, this rule of formation has the same purpose as Axioms 5 and 8.

Actually, the rule of formation for formulas that will be acceptable must be framed in a somewhat more complicated way in order to ensure the elimination of contradictions. It is necessary to arrange sets in levels. The first level is made up of individuals, the second of sets containing individuals, the third of sets of these sets, and so on. Thus, we take explicit account of the fact that, for example, a cardinal number is a set of sets that contains individuals. These individuals would be at first level, the sets containing them at second level, and the set of all sets containing the same number of individuals, that is, a cardinal number, at third level.

Having made this distinction between levels of sets, we can formulate the rule governing correct formation of expressions as follows: formulas involving ∈ must be such that the variable on the left is exactly one level lower than the variable on the right. Thus we can say that $x \in s$ where x refers to individuals and s to sets of individuals. We can say $s \in r$ where s is a set of individuals, and r is a set of sets of individuals and so on. We cannot meaningfully say $s \in s$, $r \notin r$, or $t \in s \,\&\, s \in t$, for each of these breaks our formation rule and in fact leads to a contradiction. Again, by way of example, we can say that s is the set of all sets at a level k; but we cannot say s is the set of all sets. Furthermore, if x is an individual and r a set of sets of individuals, the expression $x \in r$ is ruled out. No outright contradiction is known to arise from the use of such expressions, but there is obviously something odd about saying, for example, that the state of Pennsylvania ∈ the United Nations when, in fact, the state of Pennsylvania ∈ the United States and the United States ∈ the United Nations.

While there are certain objections to this approach, known as the *Theory of Types*, it does work in the same sense that Zermelo's axiomatic set theory works; that is, it eliminates all known contradictions and permits the development of most of mathematics. One of the usual objections to the theory is that it requires an infinity of duplications. For example, each level has associated with it an infinity of cardinal numbers. We cannot identify the cardinal number 6 for level 3 with that for level 4, and so on. This kind of situation has the rather odd effect of requiring a proof of a theorem at each level. In order to avoid this consequence, Russell asserted the *axiom of reducibility*, according to which every theorem, no matter what type-levels

---

* Bertrand Russell, "Mathematical Logic as Based on the Theory of Types", *Am. J. of Math.*, Vol. 30 (1908), pp. 222–262.

are involved in it, is formally equivalent with the version of it that can be proved at the lowest permissible type-levels. But that this should be the case is not intuitively clear.

A second objection to the theory of types is that impredicative definitions, such as that of the *least upper bound* of a set of real numbers, violate the theory of types even though there are areas of mathematics to which they are essential. Every attempt so far to adapt the theory of types to such requirements has resulted in the imposition of restrictions on mathematics for which there seems to be no obvious warrant.

These objections, however, need not be considered as fatal. The theory of types can be developed in many ways and must be regarded as containing an insight worth further investigation.*

EXERCISE 13.4

  I. Does the theory of types seek to solve the problem of the contradictions by denying that $x \in x$ is an acceptable statement? Compare your answer with Exercise 13.3, problem X.

  II. Formulate the concept of a cardinal number according to the theory of types; that is, show how each level has cardinals.

  III. The theory of types is associated with Frege's and the Russell-Whitehead attempt to ground mathematics on logic. Discuss the relation of mathematics to axiom systems and of axiom systems to logic.

13.5 Intuitionism

The Intuitionists' response to the contradictions of set theory may be characterized as a demand that the fundamental nature of inference in mathematical reasoning be reexamined and a new and sounder approach made to its use. Basically, the Intuitionist program calls for an insistence upon completely constructive rules of inference. Constructive rules of reasoning are those we employ when we demonstrate the existence of a mathematical entity by showing step by step how to construct it. These are opposed to nonconstructive rules, such as those governing the use of the law of excluded middle and proofs by contradiction, by which we argue the existence of a mathematical entity without actually showing how to construct it. It is fairly evident that the entities that give rise to the contradictions of set theory—the set of all sets that are not members of themselves, for instance, or the ordinal number Ω—could not be shown to exist by constructive methods. But in return for this solution of the paradoxes, the Intuitionist program demands a

---

* See especially W. V. Quine, "New Foundations for Mathematical Logic", *Am. Math. Monthly*, Vol. 44 (1937), pp. 70–80.

price that not everyone is willing to pay; for it is not possible by constructive methods to develop the entire body of mathematics.

The Dutch mathematician Brouwer, who is regarded as the founder of Intuitionism in its contemporary development, claims that mathematical reasoning is a basic mental act dependent upon neither language nor logic. We may use language to express the ideas of mathematics, but the function of language in such use is merely that of communication. More fundamental than language are the intuitions of the natural numbers and the intuitively clear constructive methods used in thinking about them. Our task, he says, is to extend the constructive methods of thinking about numbers to the various areas of mathematics and thereby to build a sound mathematics. The nineteenth-century German mathematician Kronecker once said, "God made the natural numbers; all the rest is man's handiwork". The Intuitionistic program is a proposal for carrying out this handiwork. In executing this program, we may use a formally developed logic such as that of Chapter Four, but if we do we must realize that we get this logic from a systematization of mathematical reasoning, and not vice versa.

Brouwer and his followers have made efforts to develop, on the basis of its intuitive fundamentals, a set theory free of the defects inherent in the intuitive set theory of Cantor. At the present time it is not possible to say finally whether they have been successful or whether the results of their efforts would be acceptable in the sense of retaining a sufficiently large part of classical mathematics. Further, the actual account of their views involves a special background and orientation not presupposed or expressed in this book. We refer the reader to the works of Brouwer and his followers, in particular, to Heyting.*

Even if we neglect the details of the Intuitionists' program with respect to set theory, their example should emphasize an important point. The intention in developing either axiomatic set theory or the theory of logical types appears to be just the avoidance of the contradictions. No doubt this is important; but the real problem is a somewhat different one. We can appreciate this if we note that there would be a problem of the foundations of set theory even if the contradictions had not appeared. Cantor's introduction of infinite sets into mathematics involves the use of new concepts and ideas, which inevitably must be refined and studied. The occurrence of the contradictions simply provides more pointed motivation for undertaking such a study. The study needed should result in a fuller understanding of the nature of sets and the ideas associated with them, and not merely in the avoidance of contradictions by means of *ad hoc* devices.

Although the developers of axiomatic set theory and logical types cannot be accused as a whole of proposing *ad hoc* remedies, the example of the

---

* A. Heyting, *Intuitionism: An Introduction* (Amsterdam: North Holland Pub. Co., 1956).

Intuitionistic program does provide a salutary instance of an attempt to deal with the truly fundamental issues concerning the nature of mathematics. Another example of such an attempt is to be found in the thought and program of the Formalists, which we consider next, and which constitutes the basic orientation of this book.

EXERCISE 13.5

I. Would the Intuitionist agree with the contention of the theory of types that $x \notin x$ is not a statement? Why?

II. Would the Intuitionist accept all applications of Zermelo's Ax. 5? Why? If not, give an unacceptable application.

III. Give some constructive and some nonconstructive examples of the use of the law of excluded middle in mathematics.

IV. Intuitionists often define *finite sets* as cardinally similar to an initial segment of the natural numbers. What would be their definition of a finite cardinal? In what sense are such cardinals constructive?

V. How does the definition of finite cardinals given in your answer to IV differ from that of Section 13.2? Discuss the implications of this difference.

13.6 Formalism

The Formalist program, initiated by David Hilbert, was intended to provide a new tool for the study of the difficult and fundamental problems of set theory, as well as other problems in the foundations of mathematics. Faced by the contradictions in set theory, but deeply confident of the acceptability of classical mathematics, Hilbert proposed a method for establishing the consistency of axiom systems. Advocates of axiomatic set theory and a theory of types make certain proposals for avoiding contradictions. A method for deciding whether these proposals are generally successful or not is certainly desirable—the mere fact that such proposals avoid the known ways of producing the contradictions is a negative assurance at best.

Given some axiom system, for example, some version of axiomatic set theory, Hilbert proposed to formalize it and then use elementary mathematical methods to study it. A simple example of this approach is the use of arithmetical reasoning to establish the consistency and completeness of PL in Chapter Nine. Other somewhat more complex examples are found in the metatheory of Chapters Ten and Eleven. Hilbert proposed the use of elementary, and generally acceptable, mathematical methods for the study of formal systems as a means of establishing the consistency of the classical mathematics that these systems formalized. Initially, Hilbert hoped not only to establish the consistency of classical mathematics by studying its axiomatization, but also to provide a decision process that would obviate the often very difficult task of proof. As it happened, these hopes were soon shown to be impossible of fulfillment.

The metatheoretical methods used in Chapters Nine, Ten, and Eleven are in the spirit of Hilbert's program. For Hilbert proposed, first, to formalize an axiom system and, second, to use generally acceptable elementary arithmetical reasoning to study the formal system. This second part of the program is made possible by the first, the idea of a complete formalization of an axiom system. Such a formalization sometimes makes possible an analysis of the nature of an axiom system in simple terms, and thus permits conclusions to be reached about complex systems through the use of elementary (if very abstract) mathematical methods. In 1931, however, Gödel showed that it was impossible to establish the consistency of elementary arithmetic by the study of its formalization without using more powerful tools of mathematical reasoning than arithmetical ones.* He demonstrated that the study of formal systems cannot get results in all cases by means of simple and universally acceptable methods. Thus, Hilbert's hope for a quick victory was unfounded—a suggestion confirmed by another result due to Gödel. Gödel was also able to show that if an axiomatization of arithmetic is consistent, then it cannot be complete; that is, there are some unprovable but true arithmetical statements. This is to say that an adequate axiomatization of arithmetic is impossible. Since axiomatized arithmetic, if not as simple as axiom systems based on GPL-1 only, is a relatively simple mathematical subject matter, the possibility of adequate axiomatizations of more complicated areas seems slight.

In spite of the fact that Hilbert's goal has proved unattainable, the creation by him of the metatheoretical method has turned out to afford an interesting and fruitful approach to the problems of axiom systems. The use of this method established the consistency and completeness of axiom systems based on GPL-1, as we have seen. It has enabled us to build up an exact science, indeed, a mathematics of the properties of axiom systems, and it seems possible that the use of this metamathematics may uncover new facts about the nature of axiom systems, including both something of their limitations and something of their potentialities. The present importance of the metatheoretical method is that of a tool of discovery. By its means it seems possible to find out something more about the nature of mathematical truth, the meaning of mathematical statements, and the evidence upon which those statements rest. The ultimate purpose of this book has been to present an introduction to this science of metamathematics, in the hope that the students of today may contribute to the solution of some of the problems we have been discussing.

---

* "Über formal unentscheidbare Sätze der Principia Mathematica und verwandter Systeme I", *Monats. für Math. u. Phys.*, Vol. 38 (1931), pp. 173–198.

EXERCISE 13.6

I. What is meant by saying that there are true but unprovable statements of arithmetic? (Hint: Can a model establish truth?)

II. How many different versions of consistency can you state? Can you use metatheory to study their relations? What are the results of such use?

III. If a formal system is consistent in the sense that not every wff is provable, and this system includes GPL-1, what can be said about the consistency of the axioms of the system? Define the kind of consistency which the axioms have.

IV. What axiom schemata must be added to GPL-1 plus identity to obtain an axiomatization of elementary arithmetic that includes the operations $+$ and $\cdot$. (Hint: Study Peano's axioms.)

SUGGESTED READINGS

1. Georg Cantor, *Contributions to the Founding of the Theory of Transfinite Numbers* (Chicago and London: Open Court Pub. Co., 1915).

2. Richard Dedekind, *Essays on the Theory of Numbers* (Chicago: Open Court Pub. Co., 1901).

3. A. A. Fraenkel and Y. Bar-Hillel, *Foundations of Set Theory* (Amsterdam: North Holland Pub. Co., 1958).

4. A. Heyting, *Intuitionism: An Introduction* (Amsterdam: North Holland Pub. Co., 1956).

5. David Hilbert and P. Bernays, *Grundlagen der Mathematik*, 2 vols. (Berlin: J. Springer, 1934–39).

6. Edward V. Huntington, *The Continuum* (Cambridge, Mass.: Harvard Univ. Press, 1905; second ed. 1917).

7. S. Körner, *The Philosophy of Mathematics* (London: Hutchinson's, 1960).

8. E. Nagel and James R. Newman, *Gödel's Proof* (New York: New York Univ. Press, 1958).

9. W. V. Quine, *Mathematical Logic*, rev. ed. (Cambridge, Mass.: Harvard Univ. Press, 1951).

10. Patrick Suppes, *Axiomatic Set Theory* (Princeton, N. J.: Van Nostrand Co., 1960).

11. A. N. Whitehead and Bertrand Russell, *Principia Mathematica*, second ed., 3 vols. (Cambridge, England: Cambridge Univ. Press, 1925–27).

12. R. L. Wilder, *Introduction to the Foundations of Mathematics* (New York: John Wiley & Sons, 1952), Chs. VIII, IX, X, XI.

General Index

411

Index of Proper Names

Index of Symbols